This is an authorized facsimile
printed by microfilm/xerography on acid-free paper
in 1982 by
UNIVERSITY MICROFILMS INTERNATIONAL
Ann Arbor, Michigan, U.S.A.
London, England

Plackett, R. L.
      Principles of regression analysis /
by R.L. Plackett. -- Oxford [Eng.] :
Clarendon Press, 1960.
      ix, 173 p.
      Includes bibliographical references
and index.
      Photocopy. Ann Arbor, Mich. :
University Microfilms International,
1981.

      1. Mathematical statistics.   I. Title
  1I. Title: Regression analysis.

PRINCIPLES OF
REGRESSION ANALYSIS

PRINCIPLES OF
REGRESSION
ANALYSIS

BY

R. L. PLACKETT

OXFORD
AT THE CLARENDON PRESS
1960

Oxford University Press, Amen House, London E.C.4

GLASGOW NEW YORK TORONTO MELBOURNE WELLINGTON
BOMBAY CALCUTTA MADRAS KARACHI KUALA LUMPUR
CAPE TOWN IBADAN NAIROBI ACCRA

PRINTED IN GREAT BRITAIN

PREFACE

THE field of regression analysis is here supposed to consist of the algebraic theory and numerical methods associated with the principle of least squares, its applications in the analysis of experimental data, and the construction of experimental designs. My purpose in writing this book has been to isolate the main features of regression analysis and illustrate them from the considerable amount of published work, but not to present a comprehensive survey of all possible details. The emphasis throughout is on the assumptions which are made and on the properties of relevant estimates or test criteria, whereas the questions which arise when planning an inquiry or interpreting the results of statistical analyses are omitted. There will naturally be differing views as to what features are important and what subsidiary, and my selection is a personal choice. All the numerical methods have now been adapted for electronic computors, but only layouts for desk calculators are given, since most regression computations can be done on such machines in reasonable time.

A prerequisite for reading this book is some familiarity with the basic elements in the theories of statistics, matrices, complex variables, and groups. The class of readers envisaged thus consists primarily of mathematicians, either graduates or in the final stages of their undergraduate career. In each chapter the subject-matter is developed continuously, as far as possible, and consequently the scheme of connexions between individual topics has the following structure. Chapter 3 (Least squares) contains results of central importance, to which reference is often made, particularly in Chapter 4 (Linear hypotheses). Numerical techniques for these chapters are discussed in Chapter 1 (Linear equations), and the limitations of the test criteria in Chapter 5 (Departures from standard test conditions). All the distribution theory for Chapters 4 and 5 is contained in Chapter 2 (Quadratic forms in normal variables). Special classes of regression problems are considered in Chapter 6 (Polynomial regression) and Chapter 7 (Stationary error processes). The book concludes with some aspects of experimental design: genesis and construction (Chapter 8, Symmetrical factorial experiments), and statistical inference (Chapter 9, Randomization). Each chapter contains a set of exercises and a list of references, which together give further information on the text material.

Sections are numbered within each chapter and equations within each section. Reference to either is made with the minimum of notation: thus Section 4 of Chapter 3 is referred to as such within Chapter 3, but as Section 3.4 elsewhere; equation (2) in this section is referred to as (2) throughout the section, as (4.2) in other sections of Chapter 3, and as (3.4.2) in other chapters.

I am grateful to Professor L. Rosenhead, C.B.E., F.R.S., for his constant interest and active encouragement; to Mr. M. C. K. Tweedie, for useful comments on the final typescript; to Mr. A. M. Wood, for much patience and advice on publication matters; to Dr. A. K. Gayen, Dr. A. B. L. Srivastava, the authors, and Professor E. S. Pearson, on behalf of the Trustees of *Biometrika*, for kindly permitting the reproduction of tables from that journal; to Professor G. E. P. Box, the author, and Professor W. H. Kruskal, the editor, for kindly permitting the reproduction of a table from the *Annals of Mathematical Statistics*; to Miss J. Crail, Mrs. E. G. Cottrell, and Mrs. P. Raeder, for typing various drafts; and to the staff of the Clarendon Press for their scrupulous care in printing.

R. L. P.

University of Liverpool, 1960

CONTENTS

LINEAR EQUATIONS

1.1. Introduction

CONSIDER the system of linear equations

$$Cu = b,$$

in which C is a positive definite matrix, and u and b are column vectors. By a positive definite matrix we mean a symmetric matrix such that $x'Cx > 0$ for all vectors x. We are given the numerical values of C and b, and require to find the first few decimal places in the decimal expansions of u and C^{-1}. These numerical approximations can be calculated either directly, by a single set of operations; or indirectly, through a series of approximations of increasing accuracy, all obtained by iterating a particular numerical process. Both methods are illustrated below. We have made no attempt to summarize the vast amount of work which has been done in this field. (See, however, Forsythe, 1953.) Instead, we have selected the techniques which appear to be most convenient for a computer who uses a desk calculating machine.

1.2. Direct solution of simultaneous linear equations

In the system of simultaneous linear equations $Cu = b$, let C have order $s \times s$. The elements of u can be expressed as determinantal ratios but this is not a practical method of solution except when s is small. All other direct methods of solving $Cu = b$ consist essentially in successive elimination of the unknowns. Using the first equation, eliminate u_1 from the others, which then become a set of $(s-1)$ equations in $(s-1)$ unknowns. Using the first equation of the new set, eliminate u_2 from the others, which then become a set of $(s-2)$ equations in $(s-2)$ unknowns. Continue the process until eventually an equation is reached which contains u_s only. The system which contains the first equation of each set can be represented by

$$T_1 u = T_2' b, \tag{1}$$

where T_1 and T_2 are upper triangular matrices. Successive elimination is thus effectively the same process as that of expressing C in the form $(T_2^{-1})'T_1$. Denote the common value of $T_1 u$ and $T_2' b$ by f. The

B

solution u is therefore determined in two stages by constructing $f = T_2' b$ and then solving $T_1 u = f$ for u. As the matrices in both sets of equations are triangular, these operations are effected by repeated substitution.

There are several ways in which these calculations can be set out, but the only one which we shall describe in detail is the square-root method (Cholesky, 1924; Dwyer, 1945), so named because the numerical operations hinge on finding the real upper triangular matrix T, with positive elements in the main diagonal, such that

$$C = T'T. \tag{2}$$

We now prove the theorem that this representation is always possible when C is positive definite.

The theorem is certainly true for $s = 1$. Suppose that it is true for $s = 2, 3, ..., (j-1)$. Denote by C_{j-1} the matrix formed by the first $(j-1)$ rows and columns of C. Since C_{j-1} is a principal minor of C, it is positive definite. By hypothesis, there exists an upper triangular matrix T_{j-1} with positive diagonal elements, and such that

$$T_{j-1}' T_{j-1} = C_{j-1}. \tag{3}$$

T_{j-1} is non-singular. Define

$$\begin{bmatrix} t_{1j} \\ t_{2j} \\ \cdot \\ \cdot \\ \cdot \\ t_{j-1,j} \end{bmatrix} = (T_{j-1}')^{-1} \begin{bmatrix} c_{1j} \\ c_{2j} \\ \cdot \\ \cdot \\ \cdot \\ c_{j-1,j} \end{bmatrix}, \tag{4}$$

$$t_{jj}^2 = c_{jj} - t_{1j}^2 - t_{2j}^2 - ... - t_{j-1,j}^2, \tag{5}$$

and

$$T_j = \begin{bmatrix} T_{j-1} & \begin{matrix} t_{1j} \\ t_{2j} \\ \cdot \\ \cdot \\ \cdot \\ t_{j-1,j} \end{matrix} \\ \hline 0 & t_{jj} \end{bmatrix}. \tag{6}$$

Then

$$T_j' T_j = C_j. \tag{7}$$

Taking determinants in (3), (6), and (7),

$$t_{jj}^2 = |C_j|/|C_{j-1}| > 0. \tag{8}$$

Hence t_{jj} is real and we adopt the convention that $t_{jj} > 0$. By induction, the proof is complete.

We begin the calculations by solving the system of equations

$$T'[T : h] = [C : b] \qquad (9)$$

for $[T : h]$. The elements of $[T : h]$ are computed row by row, moving from left to right in each row. Thus

$$t_{11} = \sqrt{c_{11}}, \qquad t_{1k} = c_{1k}/t_{11} \quad (k = 2, 3, ..., s),$$
$$h_1 = b_1/t_{11};$$
$$t_{22} = \sqrt{(c_{22} - t_{12}^2)}, \qquad t_{2k} = (c_{2k} - t_{12}t_{1k})/t_{22} \quad (k = 3, 4, ..., s),$$
$$h_2 = (b_2 - t_{12}h_1)/t_{22};$$
$$t_{33} = \sqrt{(c_{33} - t_{13}^2 - t_{23}^2)}, \qquad t_{3k} = (c_{3k} - t_{13}t_{1k} - t_{23}t_{2k})/t_{33} \quad (k = 4, 5, ..., s),$$
$$h_3 = (b_3 - t_{13}h_1 - t_{23}h_2)/t_{33};$$

. . . .

To check the working, write down an extra column, the elements of which are the sums of rows so far obtained, and evaluate both sides of the equation

$$t_{1k}\left(\sum_{j=1}^{s} t_{1j} + h_1\right) + t_{2k}\left(\sum_{j=2}^{s} t_{2j} + h_2\right) + ... + t_{kk}\left(\sum_{j=k}^{s} t_{kj} + h_k\right) = \sum_{j=1}^{s} c_{kj} + b_k \qquad (10)$$

immediately after the kth row of $[T : h]$ has been computed. When $[T : h]$ is known, the system of equations

$$Tu = h$$

is solved by repeated back-substitution, which gives $u_s, u_{s-1}, ..., u_1$ in turn. We now have the solution required, because

$$b = T'h = T'(Tu) = Cu.$$

TABLE 1. *Direct solution of simultaneous linear equations*

		C					b	Sum
39	3	−11	17	29	14		201·8	292·8
3	32	15	−9	0	−7		239·2	273·2
−11	15	45	−28	1	−25		62·8	59·8
17	−9	−28	24	12	15		20·7	51·7
29	0	1	12	46	4		149·0	241·0
14	−7	−25	15	4	38		2·6	41·6
Sum 91	34	−3	31	92	39		676·1	

		T				h	Sum
6·24500	0·48038	−1·76141	2·72218	4·64371	2·24179	32·31385	46·88550
	5·63642	2·81138	−1·82876	−0·39577	−1·43299	39·68424	44·47452
		5·83040	−3·09821	1·76525	−2·91963	1·39792	2·97573
			1·90957	2·14935	−1·44995	5·04819	7·65716
				4·06737	0·31789	0·32741	4·71267
					4·49369	−0·37314	4·12055
u' 3·93268	7·08744	1·49110*	2·48265*	0·08699	−0·08304*		

All the divisions which occur in the square-root method are by diagonal elements of T, and are therefore permissible, since such elements are necessarily positive.

The layout in Table 1 is based on Fox (1950).

The accuracy of this method can be judged from the fact that each of the elements of u marked with an asterisk is in error by one unit in the last place, while the others are correct to five decimal places.

1.3. Direct computation of an inverse matrix

The following method of inverting a positive definite matrix C was given by Waugh (1935), and can conveniently be combined with the operations detailed in the previous Section. As before, the first stage consists in finding the upper triangular matrix T such that $C = T'T$. We now solve the system of equations

$$TC^{-1} = (T^{-1})', \tag{1}$$

where the unknowns are the $\frac{1}{2}s(s+1)$ different elements of the symmetric matrix C^{-1}, and the known quantities are $\frac{1}{2}s(s-1)$ zero elements in T^{-1}, together with the diagonal elements of T^{-1}, each of which is the reciprocal of the corresponding diagonal element of T. The numbers of known and unknown quantities are thus equal.

The last column of $C^{-1} = \{c^{ij}\}$ is computed first, and we determine its elements in the order

$$c^{ss}, c^{s-1,s}, ..., c^{2s}, c^{1s}.$$

This gives $c^{s,s-1} (= c^{s-1,s})$ in the penultimate column, and we compute the remainder of that column in the order

$$c^{s-1,s-1}, c^{s-2,s-1}, ..., c^{2,s-1}, c^{1,s-1}.$$

The last element to be computed is c^{11}. As each column of C^{-1} is completed, we check it by evaluating its product, theoretically unity, with the vector of column totals of C:

$$\Big(\sum_{j=1}^{s} c_{j1}\Big)c^{1k} + \Big(\sum_{j=1}^{s} c_{j2}\Big)c^{2k} + ... + \Big(\sum_{j=1}^{s} c_{js}\Big)c^{sk} = 1. \tag{2}$$

The layout in Table 2 is based on Fox and Hayes (1951). Further calculations show that each of the elements of C^{-1} marked with an asterisk is in error by one unit in the last place, while all the others are correct to five decimal places.

T ABLE 2. *Direct computation of inverse matrix*

T

$$\begin{bmatrix} 6\text{·}24500 & 0\text{·}48038 & -1\text{·}76141 & 2\text{·}72218 & 4\text{·}64371 & 2\text{·}24179 \\ & 5\text{·}63642 & 2\text{·}81138 & -1\text{·}82876 & -0\text{·}39577 & -1\text{·}43299 \\ & & 5\text{·}83040 & -3\text{·}09821 & 1\text{·}76525 & -2\text{·}91963 \\ & & & 1\text{·}90957 & 2\text{·}14935 & -1\text{·}44995 \\ & & & & 4\text{·}06737 & 0\text{·}31789 \\ & & & & & 4\text{·}49369 \end{bmatrix}$$

t^{jj} 0·160128   0·177418   0·171515   0·523678   0·245859   0·222534

Column sums of C

C^{-1}

						Column sums of C
0·07614*	−0·01744	−0·02388	−0·06109	−0·02983	−0·01972	91
−0·01744	0·04127	−0·01261	0·00736	0·00919	0·00186	34
−0·02388	−0·01261	0·20296*	0·24792*	−0·05823	0·04827	−3
−0·06109	0·00736	0·24792*	0·38637*	−0·07132	0·04196	31
−0·02983	0·00919	−0·05823	−0·07132	0·06075	−0·00387	92
−0·01972	0·00186	0·04827	0·04196	−0·00387	0·04952	39

1.4. Indirect solution of simultaneous linear equations

When an indirect method is used to solve the system of linear equations $Cu = b$, the calculations proper are preceded by the selection of an initial approximation $u_{(1)}$ to u. If the diagonal elements of C are large compared with non-diagonal elements, a condition often satisfied in statistical problems, we take b_j/c_{jj} as the jth element of $u_{(1)}$; if an examination of the equations fails to reveal a convenient $u_{(1)}$, we take $u_{(1)} = 0$. Any approximation can be considered as representing the coordinates of a point in a euclidean space of s dimensions, and we choose the metric in this space so that the distance of $u_{(a)}$ from u is $(u_{(a)}-u)'C(u_{(a)}-u)$. With this definition of distance, the inequality

$$(u_{(1)}-u)'C(u_{(1)}-u) > (u_{(2)}-u)'C(u_{(2)}-u)$$

will imply that $u_{(2)}$ is a closer approximation to the solution u than is the approximation $u_{(1)}$. A sequence of approximations $u_{(1)}, u_{(2)}, u_{(3)}, \ldots$ is said to converge towards u if their distances from u steadily decrease. However, convergence may be so slow that iteration is an impracticable means of solving the equations.

In order to calculate a converging sequence of approximations, we proceed as follows (Householder, 1950). Denote the ath approximation to u by $u_{(a)}$ ($a = 1, 2, \ldots$), and let $v_{(1)}, v_{(2)}, \ldots$ be a specified sequence of vectors. Put

$$r_{(a)} = b - Cu_{(a)}. \tag{1}$$

The next approximation is given by

$$u_{(a+1)} = u_{(a)} + m_a v_{(a)} \tag{2}$$

where m_a is a scalar as yet undetermined. From (1) and (2),

$$r_{(a)} = r_{(a+1)} + m_a \, C v_{(a)}. \tag{3}$$

We shall suppose that $\qquad v'_{(a)} \, r_{(a+1)} = 0, \tag{4}$

whence $\qquad\qquad m_a = v'_{(a)} \, r_{(a)} / v'_{(a)} \, C v_{(a)}. \tag{5}$

The iterative process is now completely defined. From (3) and (4),

$$r'_{(a)} \, C^{-1} r_{(a)} = (r_{(a+1)} + m_a \, C v_{(a)})' C^{-1} (r_{(a+1)} + m_a \, C v_{(a)})$$

$$= r'_{(a+1)} C^{-1} r_{(a+1)} + m_a^2 \, v'_{(a)} \, C v_{(a)}. \tag{6}$$

Hence, if $m_a \neq 0$,

$$(u - u_{(a)})' C(u - u_{(a)}) > (u - u_{(a+1)})' C(u - u_{(a+1)}),$$

so that $u_{(a+1)}$ is an improvement on $u_{(a)}$.

The only method of successive approximation which we shall illustrate is known as *relaxation* (Fox, 1948). It consists of taking $v_{(1)}, v_{(2)}, \ldots$ as the coordinate vectors in the order which leads most rapidly to the solution. According to (5) and (6), we choose $v_{(a)}$ so as to maximize $(v'_{(a)} \, r_{(a)})^2 / v'_{(a)} \, C v_{(a)}$, and therefore select the coordinate vector corresponding to the maximum value of $(r_{(a)j})^2 / c_{jj}$, where $r_{(a)j}$ is the jth element of $r_{(a)}$. When the diagonal elements of C are the same, this is equivalent to selecting the coordinate vector corresponding to the maximum $r_{(a)j}$.

Example. Suppose that the equations to be solved are

$$\begin{bmatrix} 40 & -1 & 7 & -2 \\ -1 & 40 & -2 & -1 \\ 7 & -2 & 50 & -2 \\ -2 & -1 & -2 & 39 \end{bmatrix} \begin{bmatrix} u_1 \\ u_2 \\ u_3 \\ u_4 \end{bmatrix} = \begin{bmatrix} -31 \cdot 3798 \\ -35 \cdot 6998 \\ -20 \cdot 4298 \\ 43 \cdot 1802 \end{bmatrix}.$$

Denote by R_1 the residual when arbitrary values of u_1, u_2, u_3, u_4 are inserted in

$$40u_1 - u_2 + 7u_3 - 2u_4 + 31 \cdot 3798$$

and similarly define R_2, R_3, and R_4. We want to reduce R_1, R_2, R_3, and R_4 as near to zero as possible. The details are in Table 3. We omit the decimal point and begin by entering the residuals corresponding to

$$u_1 = u_2 = u_3 = u_4 = 0.$$

The largest is R_4 and it is almost reduced to zero by a change of 11071 in u_4. We modify the residuals, and the largest of the new values is then seen to be R_2, which is nearly removed by a change of -8648 in u_2. When each of the residuals is less than the corresponding diagonal coefficient, the totals of the first four columns give an approxi-

TABLE 3. *Indirect solution of simultaneous linear equations*

u_1	u_2	u_3	u_4	R_1	R_2	R_3	R_4
0	0	0	0	313798	356998	204298	−431802
			11071	291656	345927	182156	−33
	−8648			300304	7	199452	8615
−7507				24	7514	146903	23629
		−2938		−20542	13390	3	29505
			−756	−19030	14146	1515	21
475				−30	13671	4840	−929
	−341			311	31	5522	−588
		−110		−459	251	22	−368
11				−19	240	99	−390
			10	−39	230	79	0
	−6			−33	−10	91	6
		−2		−47	−6	−9	10
1				−7	−7	−2	8
−7020	−8995	−3050	10325				

mation to the solution. Residuals should certainly be checked at this stage and, if incorrect, they should be adjusted and relaxed further. As in most iterative processes, mistakes are not serious, but their effect will be made still smaller by occasional checking of the residuals. The method is very flexible and there is no need, for example, to begin with six significant figures in the residuals (we can bring in extra figures later), or to reduce a residual as near to zero as possible (other residuals may then be greatly increased).

In general, an indirect method should be used to solve the system $Cu = b$ only if the two following conditions are satisfied:

   (i) C^{-1} is not required;

   (ii) C has some feature which renders it likely that the process will converge fairly rapidly—this will occur, for example, if the elements in the main diagonal are large compared with non-diagonal elements.

When C^{-1} is required, in addition to u, the methods of Sections 2 and 3 form the best available combination.

1.5. Indirect computation of an inverse matrix

Suppose that $C_{(1)}^{-1}$ is an approximate inverse of the known matrix C, in which case the elements of

$$E = I - C_{(1)}^{-1} C \tag{1}$$

are small in magnitude. Since

$$\{C^{-1} - C_{(1)}^{-1}\}C = \{I - C_{(1)}^{-1} C\},$$

a second approximate inverse, $C_{(2)}^{-1}$, may reasonably be defined by

$$\{C_{(2)}^{-1} - C_{(1)}^{-1}\} = \{I - C_{(1)}^{-1}C\}C_{(1)}^{-1}$$

which gives $$C_{(2)}^{-1} = \{2I - C_{(1)}^{-1}C\}C_{(1)}^{-1}. \tag{2}$$

In general, define the ath approximation, $C_{(a)}^{-1}$, by the recurrence formula (Schulz, 1933)

$$C_{(a+1)}^{-1} = \{2I - C_{(a)}^{-1}C\}C_{(a)}^{-1}. \tag{3}$$

From (3), we obtain

$$\{I - C_{(a+1)}^{-1}C\} = \{I - C_{(a)}^{-1}C\}^2 = \ldots = E^{2^a}. \tag{4}$$

Therefore

$$C_{(a+1)}^{-1} = \{I + E^{2^{a-1}}\}\{I + E^{2^{a-2}}\}\ldots\{I + E\}C_{(1)}^{-1} \tag{5}$$

and $$\{C^{-1} - C_{(a+1)}^{-1}\} = E^{2^a}C^{-1}. \tag{6}$$

The process converges when the latent roots of E are all less than unity in absolute magnitude, but the following criterion (Hotelling, 1943) can be applied with much less difficulty. Define the norm of a matrix A by

$$N(A) = \{\text{trace}(A'A)\}^{\frac{1}{2}}. \tag{7}$$

We note that $\text{trace}(A'A)$ is the sum of squares of all elements of A. Using Schwarz's inequality on the square of each element of AB, we obtain

$$N(AB) \leqslant N(A)\,N(B). \tag{8}$$

If, therefore, $C_{(1)}^{-1}$ is such that $N(E) < 1$, then

$$N\{C^{-1} - C_{(a+1)}^{-1}\} \to 0 \text{ as } a \to \infty.$$

Consequently $C^{-1} - C_{(a+1)}^{-1}$ tends steadily to the $s \times s$ zero matrix, and the closer $C_{(1)}^{-1}$ is to C^{-1}, the more rapidly will the process converge.

In practice, this indirect method can be used to improve an approximate C^{-1}, obtained directly; or to calculate an inverse when C is so nearly diagonal that

$$C_{(1)}^{-1} = \text{diag}(1/c_{11},\ 1/c_{22}, \ldots,\ 1/c_{ss})$$

satisfies the requirement on $N(E)$.

Example. Let C have the value assigned in Section 2, and $C_{(1)}^{-1}$ the value determined in Section 3. In units of the fifth decimal place,

$$E = \begin{bmatrix} -14 & +1 & +5 & -6 & -4 & -1 \\ -3 & +9 & -5 & +1 & -13 & -4 \\ -4 & -7 & +1 & -2 & +2 & -9 \\ +10 & 0 & -11 & +9 & +13 & +3 \\ +14 & -11 & -9 & +11 & +12 & +6 \\ +10 & -13 & -22 & +14 & +3 & +17 \end{bmatrix}.$$

Using equation (5) with $a = 1$,

$$C_{(2)}^{-1} = \begin{bmatrix} 0.07613303 & -0.01743860 & -0.02387966 & -0.06108973 & -0.02982676 & -0.01971767 \\ & 0.04127367 & -0.01261245 & 0.00736156 & 0.00918618 & 0.00185729 \\ & & 0.20295340 & 0.24791148 & -0.05822704 & 0.04826577 \\ & & & 0.38636338 & -0.07131522 & 0.04195748 \\ & & & & 0.06074927 & -0.00387019 \\ & & & & & 0.04952134 \end{bmatrix}.$$

Further calculations show that 14 of these numbers are correct to eight decimal places, 4 are in error by one unit in the last place, 2 in error by two units, and 1 in error by three units.

We can use successive matrices $C_{(a)}^{-1}$ to increase the accuracy with which u has been determined, for the equation

$$C(u-u_{(a)}) = b - Cu_{(a)}$$

suggests a recurrence formula

$$\{u_{(a+1)} - u_{(a)}\} = C_{(a)}^{-1}\{b - Cu_{(a)}\}. \tag{9}$$

From (9), $\qquad \{u - u_{(a+1)}\} = \{I - C_{(a)}^{-1}C\}\{u - u_{(a)}\}.$

Hence, using (5),

$$\{u - u_{(a+1)}\} = E^{2^{a-1}} E^{2^{a-2}} \dots E\{u - u_{(1)}\} = E^{2^a - 1}\{u - u_{(1)}\}. \tag{10}$$

Under the stated condition on E, the right-hand side of (10) tends steadily to the s-rowed zero vector as $a \to \infty$.

Example. $C, b,$ and $u_{(1)}$ are taken from Section 2, and $C_{(1)}^{-1}$ from Section 3. In units of the fifth decimal place,

$$\{b - Cu_{(1)}\}' = (+6, -5, -41, +32, 0, -13).$$

Using (9) with $a = 1$,

$$u_{(2)} = \begin{bmatrix} 3.93267825 \\ 7.08744417 \\ 1.49108904 \\ 2.48266250 \\ 0.08698931 \\ -0.08305408 \end{bmatrix}.$$

None of these numbers is in error by more than three units in the last decimal place.

1.6. Errors of matrix computations

The different sources of error and their effect in matrix computations have been carefully examined by von Neumann and Goldstine (1947) and Turing (1948), and the following remarks are based on their analysis.

We have supposed hitherto that the values of C and b are known exactly, and in many statistical problems this is true as far as C is concerned. In general, however, C and b are constructed from measurements made on a continuous scale, and cannot usually be represented by finite decimal expansions; they are therefore liable— exclusive of blunders—to be incorrect by as much as half a unit in the last decimal place recorded. The deviations of the recorded values from the true values are known as *truncation* errors. Since the trunca- tion errors are carried through any system of numerical operations on the recorded values of C and b, they are responsible for errors in u and C^{-1}. In order to calculate the effect of truncation errors we can proceed in two ways. We can construct deterministic limits, obtained by considering which combination of truncation errors gives rise to the maximum possible errors in elements of u or C^{-1}. Alternatively, we can find a probable range of variation for these elements by assum- ing some joint probability distribution for the truncation errors—in the simplest case, that they are independently and uniformly distri- buted over the interval $(-\frac{1}{2}, \frac{1}{2})$ in units of the last decimal place.

By differentiating both sides of the identity $CC^{-1} \equiv I$,

$$C.dC^{-1}+dC.C^{-1} = 0.$$

Thus the error in C^{-1} caused by an infinitesimal error of dC in C is

$$dC^{-1} = -C^{-1}.dC.C^{-1}. \tag{1}$$

Similarly, the error in $u = C^{-1}b$ caused by errors in C and b is

$$du = C^{-1}.db+dC^{-1}.b.$$

Hence, from (1), $\qquad du = C^{-1}(db-dC.u). \tag{2}$

We proceed to give some illustrative examples.

Example 1. C is free from error.

Suppose that each element of b is recorded to the same number of decimal places. In units of the last place

$$|du_1| \leqslant (|c^{11}|+|c^{12}|+...+|c^{1s}|)/2. \tag{3}$$

On the other hand, when the errors are independent and uniform, each element of db has mean zero and variance $1/12$, so that

$$\mathrm{var}(du_1) = \{(c^{11})^2+(c^{12})^2+...+(c^{1s})^2\}/12. \tag{4}$$

By the central limit theorem, the probability is about 0·95 that

$$|du_1| \leqslant \sqrt{[\{(c^{11})^2+(c^{12})^2+...+(c^{1s})^2\}/3]}. \tag{5}$$

Example 2. b is free from error.

Suppose that the errors in the elements of C form a set of un-correlated random variables, each with mean zero and variance σ^2.

From (2),
$$du = -C^{-1}.dC.u. \qquad (6)$$

Taking the average over all dC,
$$\mathrm{av}(du'\ du) = \mathrm{av}\ u'(dC)'C^{-2}(dC)u = \sigma^2(u'u)N^2(C^{-1}). \qquad (7)$$

This equation can be rewritten as
$$\left\{\overline{\frac{\text{r.m.s. error of elements of } u}{\text{r.m.s. element of } u}}\right\} \Big/ \left\{\overline{\frac{\text{r.m.s. error of elements of } C}{\text{r.m.s. element of } C}}\right\}$$
$$= N(C)N(C^{-1})/s. \quad (7\ bis)$$

If a relatively slight variation in C causes a relatively large variation in u, the system of equations $Cu = b$ is said to be *ill-conditioned*. Equation (7 *bis*) suggests that the *norm condition-number*, $N(C)N(C^{-1})/s$, can reasonably be taken as a measure of the degree of ill-conditioning in a matrix, for it indicates how errors in u are affected, on the average, by errors in C.

Example 3. $C = A'A$ and $b = A'y$ where A and y have truncation errors.

By differentiating both sides of $A'Au = A'y$, we obtain
$$du = (A'A)^{-1}\{A'.dy + dA'.y - (A'.dA + dA'.A)u\}. \qquad (8)$$

If, for instance, A is free from error and the elements of dy are independently and uniformly distributed over $(-\tfrac{1}{2}, \tfrac{1}{2})$, then
$$\mathrm{var}(du_1) = c^{11}/12. \qquad (9)$$

We can do nothing to remove truncation errors from b and C, although such errors may be diminished by further experimentation. Even when b and C are exact, however, there exists an additional group of errors caused by rounding off at intermediate stages in the numerical process of computing u or C^{-1}. In principle this group lies within our control. By carrying enough extra figures throughout the calculations, and removing them at the end, the accuracy which is attained in the final results is limited only by time and the size of the calculating machine. The higher the order of C, the greater is the extent to which rounding-off errors accumulate, and a study of their accumulation is important when we require to invert a matrix of high order using an automatic digital computing machine. For the matrices likely to be met in statistical problems outside the field of geodesy and econometrics, s is not usually larger than 10; the results for large s are inapplicable, and two extra guarding figures throughout the calculations will nearly always suffice to provide the accuracy desired.

1.7. Exercises

1. The mth condensation of C, order $s \times s$, is a matrix $C_{(m)}$, order $(s-m) \times (s-m)$, with elements defined by the recurrence relation

$$c_{jk}^{(m)} = c_{jk}^{(m-1)} - c_{mj}^{(m-1)} c_{mk}^{(m-1)} / c_{mm}^{(m-1)} \quad (m = 1, 2,..., s-1; j, k = m+1, m+2,..., s)$$

and the boundary conditions $c_{jk}^{(0)} = c_{jk}$. The mth condensation of the $s \times 1$ vector b, with respect to C, is the $(s-m) \times 1$ vector $b^{(m)}$, of which the $(j-m)$th element is

$$b_j^{(m)} = b_j - c_{j1} b_1/c_{11} - c_{j2}^{(1)} b_2/c_{22}^{(1)} - ... - c_{jm}^{(m-1)} b_m/c_{mm}^{(m-1)}$$

$$(m = 1, 2,..., s-1; j = m+1, m+2,..., s),$$

the boundary conditions being $b_j^{(0)} = b_j$.

Successive elimination is employed to solve the system of linear equations $Cu = b$. Show that the equations which result are

$$c_{jj}^{(j-1)} u_j + c_{j,j+1}^{(j-1)} u_{j+1} + ... + c_{js}^{(j-1)} u_s = b_j^{(j-1)} \quad (j = 1, 2,..., s).$$

2. By successive condensations applied to the identity $C \equiv T'T$, show that

$$t_{jk} = c_{jk}^{(j-1)} / \sqrt{c_{jj}^{(j-1)}} \quad (j = 1, 2,..., s; k = j, j+1,..., s).$$

3. In the numerical example of Section 2, show that

$$T^{-1} = \begin{bmatrix} 0\cdot160128 & -0\cdot013647 & 0\cdot054957 & -0\cdot152174 & -0\cdot127583 & -0\cdot088606 \\ & 0\cdot177418 & -0\cdot085550 & 0\cdot031108 & 0\cdot037953 & 0\cdot008346 \\ & & 0\cdot171515 & 0\cdot278277 & -0\cdot221490 & 0\cdot216894 \\ & & & 0\cdot523678 & -0\cdot276731 & 0\cdot188548 \\ & & & & 0\cdot245859 & -0\cdot017392 \\ & & & & & 0\cdot222534 \end{bmatrix}$$

and hence compare $C^{-1} = (T^{-1})(T^{-1})'$ with the inverse given.

4. Two matrices, C_1 and C_2, are formed from C as follows. All elements in C_1 on or below the main diagonal are zero; the remaining elements of C_1 are the corresponding elements of C. $C_2 = C - C_1$. The system of equations $Cu = b$ is solved indirectly, taking successive vectors v as coordinate axes in the cyclic order $1, 2,..., s, 1, 2,...$.

If $u_{(a)}$ is the ath approximation to u when this method is employed, $u_{(1)}$ being a column of zeros, show that

$$C_1 u_{(a)} + C_{(2)} u_{(a+1)} = b,$$

and derive the explicit formula

$$u_{(a+1)} = C_2^{-1}\{I - (C_1 C_2^{-1}) + (C_1 C_2^{-1})^2 - ... + (-C_1 C_2^{-1})^{a-1}\}b.$$

5. Suppose that $u_{(1)}$ is a first approximation to the solution of the system $Cu = b$. Put $b_{(1)} = Cu_{(1)}, x = b'u_{(1)}/b'_{(1)}u_{(1)}, u_{(2)} = xu_{(1)}$, and $b_{(2)} = xb_{(1)}$.

Show that $b'u - b'u_{(2)} = \{u - u_{(2)}\}'C\{u - u_{(2)}\}$.

Hence prove that if the process is continued by approximating to the solution of

$$C\{u - u_{(2)}\} = b - b_{(2)},$$

a series of successive approximations to $b'u$ can be found, which approach it from below. (Quenouille, 1950.)

6. Prove that the error in C^{-1}, caused by an error of D in C, is

$$-(C^{-1}D)C^{-1} + (C^{-1}D)^2C^{-1} - (C^{-1}D)^3C^{-1} + \dots .$$

7.
$$C = \begin{bmatrix} 5 & 7 & 6 & 5 \\ 7 & 10 & 8 & 7 \\ 6 & 8 & 10 & 9 \\ 5 & 7 & 9 & 10 \end{bmatrix}.$$

Show that the norm condition-number of C is 752. (Todd, 1949.)

8. A is a real non-singular matrix, order $n \times n$. The latent roots of $A'A$ are $\lambda_1, \lambda_2, \dots, \lambda_n$. Prove that

$$N(A) = (\textstyle\sum \lambda_r)^{\frac{1}{2}}; \qquad N(A^{-1}) = (\textstyle\sum \lambda_r^{-1})^{\frac{1}{2}};$$
$$N(A'A) = (\textstyle\sum \lambda_r^2)^{\frac{1}{2}}; \qquad N\{(A'A)^{-1}\} = (\textstyle\sum \lambda_r^{-2})^{\frac{1}{2}}.$$

Deduce that the norm condition number is greater for $A'A$ than it is for A, unless

$$\lambda_1 = \lambda_2 = \dots = \lambda_n,$$

when the two condition numbers are equal. (Taussky, 1950.)

9. In a system of equations $Cu = b$,

$$C = \begin{bmatrix} 0.9824 & 0.1269 & -0.2476 & 0.0472 & 0.3712 & -0.0567 \\ 0.3726 & 0.8499 & 0.1872 & -0.2490 & -0.1648 & 0.2345 \\ 0.0672 & -0.2359 & 0.7684 & 0.0062 & -0.2100 & 0.1672 \\ 0.1234 & 0.2345 & -0.1109 & 0.9904 & 0.2341 & -0.0798 \\ -0.0529 & 0.0456 & 0.2312 & -0.1765 & 0.8079 & 0.2491 \\ -0.1575 & -0.4126 & 0.1240 & 0.0561 & 0.1901 & 0.8950 \end{bmatrix}$$

and

$$b' = [\ 0.1234 \quad 0.2345 \quad 0.3456 \quad 0.4567 \quad 0.5678 \quad 0.6789].$$

The method of relaxation converges rapidly here if unit changes in each of $u_1, u_2, \dots, u_6$ are accompanied by changes in the other variables according to the rows of the following table

u_1	u_2	u_3	u_4	u_5	u_6
1	−0·4	.	.	.	.
.	1	.	.	.	0·5
0·2	−0·3	1	.	.	−0·2
.	0·3	.	1	.	.
−0·4	0·3	0·3	−0·2	1	−0·2
0·2	−0·4	−0·4	.	−0·3	1

Hence show that

$$u' = [0.0710 \quad 0.1688 \quad 0.4703 \quad 0.4125 \quad 0.4496 \quad 0.6614]. \text{ (Fox, 1950.)}$$

1.8. References

BENOIT, Commandant (1924). Note sur une méthode de résolution des équations normales (procédé du Commandant Cholesky). *Bull. Géod. (Toulouse)*, No. 2, 67–77.

CHOLESKY, Commandant (1924). *See* Benoit (1924).

DWYER, P. S. (1945). The square root method and its use in correlation and regression. *J. Amer. Statist. Ass.* **40**, 493–503.

FORSYTHE, G. E. (1953). Tentative classification of methods and bibliography on solving systems of linear equations. Pp. 1–28 of Taussky, O. and Paige, L. J. (editors), *Simultaneous Linear Equations and the Determination of Eigenvalues*, National Bureau of Standards. Applied Mathematics Series 29. U.S. Govt. Printing Office.

FOX, L. (1948). A short account of relaxation methods. *Quart. J. Mech. Appl. Math.* **1**, 253–80.

—— (1950). Practical methods for the solution of linear equations and the inversion of matrices. *J. R. Statist. Soc.* B, **12**, 120–36.

—— and HAYES, J. G. (1951). More practical methods for the inversion of matrices. *J. R. Statist. Soc.* B, **13**, 83–91.

HOTELLING, H. (1943). Some new methods in matrix calculation. *Ann. Math. Statist.* **14**, 1–34 and 440–1.

HOUSEHOLDER, A. S. (1950). Some numerical methods for solving systems of linear equations. *Amer. Math. Monthly*, **57**, 453–9.

QUENOUILLE, M. H. (1950). Computational devices in the application of least squares. *J. R. Statist. Soc.* B, **12**, 256–72.

SCHULZ, G. (1933). Iterative Berechnung der reziproken Matrix. *Zeitschr. f. angew. Math. u. Mech.* **13**, 57–59.

TAUSSKY, O. (1950). Note on the condition of matrices. *M.T.A.C.* **4**, 111–12.

TODD, J. (1949). The condition of a certain matrix. *Proc. Camb. Phil. Soc.* **46**, 116–18.

TURING, A. M. (1948). Rounding-off errors in matrix processes. *Quart. J. Mech. Appl. Math.* **1**, 287–308.

VON NEUMANN, J., and GOLDSTINE, H. H. (1947). Numerical inverting of matrices of high order. *Bull. Amer. Math. Soc.* **53**, 1021–99.

WAUGH, F. V. (1935). A simplified method of determining multiple regression constants. *J. Amer. Statist. Ass.* **30**, 694–700.

QUADRATIC FORMS IN NORMAL VARIABLES

2.1. Introduction

SUPPOSE that y is a column vector of n real random variables $y_1, y_2, ..., y_n$. After preliminary remarks on notation and the moments of a quadratic form $y'Ay$, we make the assumption that y has a non-singular multivariate normal distribution, defined by the density function

$$f(y_1, y_2, ..., y_n) = (2\pi)^{-\frac{1}{2}n}|V|^{-\frac{1}{2}}\exp\{-\tfrac{1}{2}(y-\eta)'V^{-1}(y-\eta)\}.$$

Here V is a positive definite matrix, η is a column vector, and each variable has the range $(-\infty, \infty)$. We then discuss the probability distribution of $y'Ay$, mainly when $\eta = 0$, and derive results concerning the ratio of two such forms.

2.2. Moments of a quadratic form

We begin by describing the notation to be followed for matrix functions of several random variables.

The expectation of y_r is written $\mathscr{E}y_r$, and the column vector whose elements are $\mathscr{E}y_1, \mathscr{E}y_2, ..., \mathscr{E}y_n$ is denoted by $\mathscr{E}y$. Generally, if $Y = \{y_{ij}\}$ is a matrix of random variables, we write $\mathscr{E}Y$ for the matrix $\{\mathscr{E}y_{ij}\}$.

The covariance of y_r and y_s is

$$\mathscr{C}(y_r, y_s) = \mathscr{E}\{(y_r - \mathscr{E}y_r)(y_s - \mathscr{E}y_s)\} = \mathscr{C}(y_s, y_r).$$

In particular, the variance of y_r is

$$\mathscr{V}y_r = \mathscr{C}(y_r, y_r).$$

The matrix with $\mathscr{C}(y_r, y_s)$ in its rth row and sth column is denoted by $\mathscr{D}y$, and is termed the *dispersion* matrix of the random vector variable y. From the definitions

$$\mathscr{D}y = \mathscr{E}\{(y - \mathscr{E}y)(y - \mathscr{E}y)'\}.$$

It is a symmetric matrix, whose diagonal elements are

$$\mathscr{V}y_1, \mathscr{V}y_2, ..., \mathscr{V}y_n.$$

Consider the linear form

$$c'y = c_1 y_1 + c_2 y_2 + ... + c_n y_n$$

where $c_1, c_2, ..., c_n$ are fixed coefficients. Then

$$\mathscr{E}(c'y) = c'\mathscr{E}y$$

and $$\mathscr{V}(c'y) = \mathscr{E}\{c'(y-\mathscr{E}y)\}^2 = c'.\mathscr{D}y.c.$$

Since $\mathscr{V}(c'y)$ is non-negative, $\mathscr{D}y$ is non-negative definite; and if no set of coefficients exists such that $c'y = \mathscr{E}(c'y)$ with unit probability, we have $\mathscr{V}(c'y) > 0$ for all c, in which case $\mathscr{D}y$ is positive definite.

Consider next the quadratic form

$$y'Ay = \sum_{r=1}^{n} \sum_{s=1}^{n} a_{rs} y_r y_s,$$

where A is a fixed matrix. Then

$$\mathscr{E}(y'Ay) = \sum \sum a_{rs}\{\mathscr{C}(y_r, y_s) + \mathscr{E}y_r \mathscr{E}y_s\}$$
$$= \text{trace}(A.\mathscr{D}y) + \mathscr{E}y'.A.\mathscr{E}y. \qquad (1)$$

In deriving $\mathscr{V}(y'Ay)$, we suppose that $y_1, y_2, ..., y_n$ are statistically independent, and such that

$$\mathscr{E}y_r = 0, \qquad \mathscr{E}y_r^2 = \sigma^2, \qquad \mathscr{E}y_r^4 = \beta\sigma^4 \quad (r = 1, 2, ..., n).$$

With this notation, β is a pure number, while σ is measured in the same units as y_r. Then

$$\mathscr{E}y_r y_s y_t y_u = \begin{cases} \beta\sigma^4 & \text{(all suffixes equal)} \\ \sigma^4 & \text{(suffixes equal in pairs, but not all equal)} \\ 0 & \text{(otherwise).} \end{cases}$$

Since $$(y'Ay)^2 = \sum_{r=1}^{n} \sum_{s=1}^{n} \sum_{t=1}^{n} \sum_{u=1}^{n} a_{rs} a_{tu} y_r y_s y_t y_u,$$

$$\mathscr{E}(y'Ay)^2 = \beta\sigma^4 \sum_{r=1}^{n} a_{rr}^2 + \sigma^4 \left(\sum_{r\neq t} a_{rr} a_{tt} + \sum_{r\neq s} a_{rs} a_{rs} + \sum_{r\neq s} a_{rs} a_{sr} \right)$$

$$= \sigma^4 \left\{ (\beta-3) \sum_{r=1}^{n} a_{rr}^2 + 2 \sum_{r=1}^{n} \sum_{s=1}^{n} a_{rs}^2 + \left(\sum_{r=1}^{n} a_{rr} \right)^2 \right\}.$$

Hence $$\mathscr{V}(y'Ay) = \sigma^4 \left\{ (\beta-3) \sum_{r=1}^{n} a_{rr}^2 + 2 \sum_{r=1}^{n} \sum_{s=1}^{n} a_{rs}^2 \right\}. \qquad (2)$$

2.3. Characteristic function of a quadratic form

Let the joint probability density function of $y_1, y_2, ..., y_n$ be

$$f(y_1, y_2, ..., y_n) = (2\pi)^{-\frac{1}{2}n} |V|^{-\frac{1}{2}} \exp\{-\tfrac{1}{2}(y-\eta)'V^{-1}(y-\eta)\}, \qquad (1)$$

where V is positive definite. The characteristic function of the quadratic form $y'Ay$ is

$$\phi(t) = \int_{-\infty}^{\infty} \int_{-\infty}^{\infty} ... \int_{-\infty}^{\infty} (2\pi)^{-\frac{1}{2}n} |V|^{-\frac{1}{2}} \exp\{it\, y'Ay - \tfrac{1}{2}(y-\eta)'V^{-1}(y-\eta)\} \prod dy_r.$$

Completing the square inside the exponential brackets,

$$(y-\eta)'V^{-1}(y-\eta)-2it\,y'Ay = \eta'V^{-1}\eta-\eta'V^{-1}(V^{-1}-2itA)^{-1}V^{-1}\eta+$$

$$+\{y-(V^{-1}-2itA)^{-1}V^{-1}\eta\}'(V^{-1}-2itA)\{y-(V^{-1}-2itA)^{-1}V^{-1}\eta\}.$$

Since V^{-1} is positive definite, there exists a real non-singular transformation $y = Nz$, such that

$$N'V^{-1}N = I$$

and

$$N'AN = J,$$

where J is a diagonal matrix with real diagonal elements $j_1, j_2, ..., j_n$. Put

$$\zeta = N^{-1}(V^{-1}-2itA)^{-1}V^{-1}\eta.$$

Noting that

$$|V|^{-\frac{1}{2}} = |N|^{-1}$$

and

$$\prod dy_r = |N|\prod dz_r,$$

we obtain

$$\phi(t) = \exp\{-\tfrac{1}{2}\eta'V^{-1}\eta+\tfrac{1}{2}\eta'V^{-1}(V^{-1}-2itA)^{-1}V^{-1}\eta\}\times$$

$$\times \int_{-\infty}^{\infty}\int_{-\infty}^{\infty}...\int_{-\infty}^{\infty}(2\pi)^{-\frac{1}{2}n}\exp\{-\tfrac{1}{2}(z-\zeta)'(I-2itJ)(z-\zeta)\}\prod dz_r.$$

The multiple integral is the product of n single integrals like

$$L = \int_{-\infty}^{\infty}(2\pi)^{-\frac{1}{2}}\exp\{-\tfrac{1}{2}(1-2itj)(z-\zeta)^2\}\,dz.$$

Put $w = (1-2itj)^{\frac{1}{2}}(z-\zeta)$ and L becomes

$$(1-2itj)^{-\frac{1}{2}}\int_M (2\pi)^{-\frac{1}{2}}\exp(-\tfrac{1}{2}w^2)\,dw,$$

where the path of integration, M, is a straight line in the w-plane. If we integrate $(2\pi)^{-\frac{1}{2}}\exp(-\tfrac{1}{2}w^2)$ round the closed contour consisting of M, the real axis and suitable infinite arcs, the result is zero by Cauchy's theorem, and therefore

$$L = (1-2itj)^{-\frac{1}{2}}.$$

Consequently

$$\int_{-\infty}^{\infty}\int_{-\infty}^{\infty}...\int_{-\infty}^{\infty}(2\pi)^{-\frac{1}{2}n}\exp\{-\tfrac{1}{2}(z-\zeta)'(I-2itJ)(z-\zeta)\}\prod dz_r$$

$$= |I-2itJ|^{-\frac{1}{2}}.$$

Substituting $J = N'AV(N^{-1})'$, we finally have

$$\phi(t) = |I - 2itAV|^{-\frac{1}{2}} \exp\{-\tfrac{1}{2}\eta'V^{-1}\eta + \tfrac{1}{2}\eta'V^{-1}(V^{-1} - 2itA)^{-1}V^{-1}\eta\}. \quad (2)$$

The corresponding result for $\eta = 0$ was given by Cochran (1934).

Example 1. When $\eta = 0$, the characteristic function of $y'V^{-1}y$ is

$$\phi(t) = (1 - 2it)^{-\frac{1}{2}n}.$$

The corresponding density function is

$$p(u) = \frac{1}{2\pi} \int_{-\infty}^{\infty} e^{-itu}(1 - 2it)^{-\frac{1}{2}n}\, dt.$$

Substitute $\qquad\qquad u(1 - 2it) = 2z$

and obtain

$$p(u) = u^{\frac{1}{2}n-1}e^{-\frac{1}{2}u}2^{-\frac{1}{2}n}\left(\frac{1}{2\pi i} \int_{\frac{1}{4}u-i\infty}^{\frac{1}{4}u+i\infty} z^{-\frac{1}{2}n}e^z\, dz\right).$$

When $u > 0$, the term in curly brackets has the value $1/\Gamma(\tfrac{1}{2}n)$, as is shown, for example, by Jeffreys and Jeffreys (1956), § 12.126. When $u < 0$, it is zero, as also appears from the consideration that $y'V^{-1}y$ is positive except when y is zero. Hence

$$p(u) = u^{\frac{1}{2}n-1}e^{-\frac{1}{2}u}/2^{\frac{1}{2}n}\Gamma(\tfrac{1}{2}n) \quad (u > 0). \quad (3)$$

We shall describe the probability distribution defined by (3) as the χ^2 distribution with n degrees of freedom, and denote the corresponding random variable by $\chi^2(n)$.

Example 2. The variables $y_1, y_2, ..., y_n$ are normally and independently distributed with means $\eta_1, \eta_2, ..., \eta_n$ respectively and the same variance σ^2. We shall find the probability density for

$$x^2 = \sum_{r=1}^{n} y_r^2.$$

As in the previous example, it is zero when $x^2 < 0$.

Denote $\sum_{r=1}^{n} \eta_r^2$ by ξ^2. Here $V = \sigma^2 I$ and $A = I$.

The characteristic function of x^2 is therefore

$$\phi(t) = (1 - 2it\sigma^2)^{-\frac{1}{2}n} \exp\{-\xi^2/2\sigma^2 + \xi^2/2\sigma^2(1 - 2it\sigma^2)\}.$$

The corresponding density function is

$$g(x^2) = \frac{1}{2\pi} \int_{-\infty}^{\infty} (1 - 2it\sigma^2)^{-\frac{1}{2}n} \exp\{-itx^2 - \xi^2/2\sigma^2 + \xi^2/2\sigma^2(1 - 2it\sigma^2)\}\, dt.$$

Substitute
$$x^2(1-2it\sigma^2) = z$$
and obtain

$$g(x^2) = (1/2\sigma^2)x^{n-2}\exp\{-(x^2+\xi^2)/2\sigma^2\} \times$$

$$\times \frac{1}{2\pi i}\int_{x^2-i\infty}^{x^2+i\infty} z^{-\frac{1}{2}n}\exp(z/2\sigma^2+\xi^2 x^2/2\sigma^2 z)\,dz.$$

From a complex integral for the Bessel function of imaginary argument, given by Jeffreys and Jeffreys (1956), § 21.011, we deduce that

$$g(x^2) = (1/2\sigma^2)(x/\xi)^{\frac{1}{2}n-1}\exp\{-(x^2+\xi^2)/2\sigma^2\}I_{\frac{1}{2}n-1}(x\xi/\sigma^2) \quad (x^2 > 0). \quad (4)$$

When $\sigma = 1$, we say that x^2 has a non-central χ^2-distribution with n degrees of freedom and parameter ξ^2.

2.4. Density function of $y'Ay$ when $\eta = 0$

Denote the positive latent roots of AV by $\lambda_1, \lambda_2,..., \lambda_a$, with multiplicities $\zeta_1, \zeta_2,..., \zeta_a$ respectively; and the negative roots by $\mu_1, \mu_2,..., \mu_b$, with multiplicities $\theta_1, \theta_2,..., \theta_b$ respectively. The roots of $I-2itAV$ are then $(1-2it\lambda_r)$ with multiplicity ζ_r $(r = 1, 2,..., a)$; $(1-2it\mu_s)$ with multiplicity θ_s $(s = 1, 2,..., b)$; and 1 with multiplicity

$$n-\sum_{r=1}^{a}\zeta_r-\sum_{s=1}^{b}\theta_s.$$

Thus, when η is zero, the characteristic function of $y'Ay$ is

$$\phi(t) = \prod_{r=1}^{a}(1-2it\lambda_r)^{-\frac{1}{2}\zeta_r}\prod_{s=1}^{b}(1-2it\mu_s)^{-\frac{1}{2}\theta_s}. \quad (1)$$

Corresponding to this is the density function

$$p(u) = \frac{1}{2\pi}\int_{-\infty}^{\infty}e^{-itu}\prod_{r=1}^{a}(1-2it\lambda_r)^{-\frac{1}{2}\zeta_r}\prod_{s=1}^{b}(1-2it\mu_s)^{-\frac{1}{2}\theta_s}\,dt. \quad (2)$$

The evaluation of $p(u)$ varies considerably in difficulty depending on the values taken by $\{\zeta_r\}$ and $\{\theta_s\}$. When AV has a single root, whose value is unity, and whose multiplicity is n, Example 1 above shows that

$$p(u) = u^{\frac{1}{2}n-1}e^{-\frac{1}{2}u}/2^{\frac{1}{2}n}\Gamma(\tfrac{1}{2}n) \quad (u > 0).$$

We shall give here some results of greater complexity, all of which are adapted to computation and have been applied in numerical problems.

Case 1. *The roots have even multiplicity.* When the $\{\zeta_r\}$ and $\{\theta_s\}$ are all even, the distribution function of $y'Ay$ can be expressed as a finite series of incomplete gamma integrals. (Box, 1954.) Consider the function

$$h(z) = e^{-izu} \prod_{r=1}^{a} (1-2iz\lambda_r)^{-\frac{1}{2}\zeta_r} \prod_{s=1}^{b} (1-2iz\mu_s)^{-\frac{1}{2}\theta_s}, \qquad (3)$$

which has poles of order $\frac{1}{2}\zeta_r$ at $z = -i/2\lambda_r$, $(r = 1, 2,..., a)$, and poles of order $\frac{1}{2}\theta_s$ at $z = -i/2\mu_s$ $(s = 1, 2,..., b)$.

Firstly, take $u > 0$. Let C be the contour formed by the real axis from $+R$ to $-R$, and by a semicircular arc of $|z| = R$ below the real axis. As $R \to \infty$,

$$\int_C h(z)\, dz = \int_R^{-R} h(x)\, dx + O(e^{-R}) \to -2\pi p(u).$$

Put $q = 1-2iz\lambda_j$, and obtain

$$h(z) = e^{-u/2\lambda_j} e^{qu/2\lambda_j} q^{-\frac{1}{2}\zeta_j} \prod_{r \neq j} (1-\lambda_r/\lambda_j + \lambda_r q/\lambda_j)^{-\frac{1}{2}\zeta_r} \prod_s (1-\mu_s/\lambda_j + \mu_s q/\lambda_j)^{-\frac{1}{2}\theta_s}.$$

Let c_{jk} denote the coefficient of q^k in

$$\prod_{r \neq j} (1-\lambda_r/\lambda_j + \lambda_r q/\lambda_j)^{-\frac{1}{2}\zeta_r} \prod_s (1-\mu_s/\lambda_j + \mu_s q/\lambda_j)^{-\frac{1}{2}\theta_s}.$$

Since $dq = -2i\lambda_j\, dz$, the residue of $h(z)$ at $z = -i/2\lambda_j$ is

$$(-1/2i\lambda_j) \sum_{k=0}^{\frac{1}{2}\zeta_j-1} c_{jk}\, u^{\frac{1}{2}\zeta_j-1-k} e^{-u/2\lambda_j} / (2\lambda_j)^{\frac{1}{2}\zeta_j-1-k} (\tfrac{1}{2}\zeta_j - 1 - k)!.$$

Hence, by Cauchy's theorem,

$$p(u) = \sum_{j=1}^{a} \sum_{k=0}^{\frac{1}{2}\zeta_j-1} c_{jk}\, u^{\frac{1}{2}\zeta_j-1-k} e^{-u/2\lambda_j} / (2\lambda_j)^{\frac{1}{2}\zeta_j-k} (\tfrac{1}{2}\zeta_j - 1 - k)! \quad (u > 0). \quad (4)$$

Secondly, take $u < 0$. Let C' be the contour formed by the real axis from $-R$ to $+R$, and by a semicircular arc of $|z| = R$ above the real axis. As $R \to \infty$

$$\int_{C'} h(z)\, dz \to 2\pi p(u).$$

Let c'_{jk} denote the coefficient of q^k in

$$\prod_r (1-\lambda_r/\mu_j + \lambda_r q/\mu_j)^{-\frac{1}{2}\zeta_r} \prod_{s \neq j} (1-\mu_s/\mu_j + \mu_s q/\mu_j)^{-\frac{1}{2}\theta_s}.$$

In the same way as when $u > 0$, we find that

$$p(u) = \sum_{j=1}^{b} \sum_{k=0}^{\frac{1}{2}\theta_j-1} c'_{jk}(-u)^{\frac{1}{2}\theta_j-1-k} e^{-u/2\mu_j} / (-2\mu_j)^{\frac{1}{2}\theta_j-k} (\tfrac{1}{2}\theta_j - 1 - k)!$$
$$(u < 0). \quad (5)$$

The probability distribution of $y'Ay$ is now completely defined.

Case 2. The roots are distinct. When all the non-zero roots of AV are distinct, $p(u)$ can be expressed as a finite series of integrals. This was shown by Grad and Solomon (1955), but their derivation is somewhat condensed, and an expanded version now follows. Denote the positive roots of AV by $\lambda_1, \lambda_2, ..., \lambda_a$ where

$$\lambda_1 < \lambda_2 < ... < \lambda_a;$$

and the negative roots by $\mu_1, \mu_2, ..., \mu_b$, where

$$\mu_1 > \mu_2 > ... > \mu_b.$$

The function

$$h(z) = e^{-izu} \prod_{r=1}^{a} (1 - 2iz\lambda_r)^{-\frac{1}{2}} \prod_{s=1}^{b} (1 - 2iz\mu_s)^{-\frac{1}{2}}$$

has branch-points at $-i/2\lambda_r$ for $r = 1, 2, ..., a$; and at $-i/2\mu_s$ for $s = 1, 2, ..., b$. However, any branch of $h(z)$ is regular in the z-plane cut along the imaginary axis from $-i/2\lambda_a$ to $-i\infty$ and from $-i/2\mu_b$ to $+i\infty$. The branch which we use has zero argument on the imaginary axis between $-i/2\lambda_a$ and $-i/2\mu_b$.

Take $u > 0$. Let G be the contour formed by the real axis from $+R$ to $-R$, an arc of $|z| = R$ from $-R$ to $-iR$, thence along the negative side of the imaginary axis from $-iR$ to $-i/2\lambda_a$, with small clockwise semicircular indentations of radius ρ to avoid the singularities at $z = -i/2\lambda_r$, back similarly along the positive side of the imaginary axis, and from $-iR$ to $+R$ along an arc of $|z| = R$. Since there are no poles inside G,

$$\int_G h(z)\, dz = 0.$$

The contributions to the integral from different sections of G are as follows.

(i) From the real axis we obtain $\int_R^{-R} h(x)\, dx$, which tends to $-2\pi p(u)$ as $R \to \infty$.

(ii) The contribution from the sections of G where $|z| = R$ is $O(e^{-R})$ and so tends to zero as $R \to \infty$.

(iii) Let g_r be the path on the negative side of the imaginary axis between the points $-i/2\lambda_{r-1}$ and $-i/2\lambda_r$; and let g_{2a-r+1} be the corresponding path on the positive side. Here $-i/2\lambda_0$ denotes $-i\infty$. On the imaginary axis,

$$\arg h(z) = -\tfrac{1}{2} \sum_{r=1}^{a} \arg(1 - 2iz\lambda_r).$$

As z moves along G from g_j to g_{j+1}, or from g_{2a-j} to g_{2a-j+1}, where $j \neq a$, $\arg(1 - 2iz\lambda_j)$ decreases by π, while $\arg(1 - 2iz\lambda_r)$, for $r \neq j$, remains unaltered. As z moves from g_a to g_{a+1}, $\arg(1 - 2iz\lambda_a)$ decreases by 2π, and the other arguments remain unaltered. On g_k, therefore,

$$\arg h(z) = \begin{cases} -\tfrac{1}{2}(a-k+1)\pi & (k = 1, 2,..., a) \\ \tfrac{1}{2}(k-a)\pi & (k = a+1, a+2,..., 2a). \end{cases}$$

Hence

$$\left(\int_{g_r} + \int_{g_{2a-r+1}} \right) h(z)\, dz = \{e^{-\tfrac{1}{2}\pi i(a-r+1)} - e^{\tfrac{1}{2}\pi i(a-r+1)}\} \int_{g_r} |h(z)|\, dz.$$

In the limit as $\rho \to 0$, this gives

$$\sum_{k=1}^{2a} \int_{g_k} h(z)\, dz = 2 \sum_{r=1}^{a} \sin\{\tfrac{1}{2}\pi(a-r+1)\} \int_{-1/2\lambda_{r-1}}^{-1/2\lambda_r} |h(iy)|\, dy.$$

(iv) Let G_j be the clockwise circular contour where

$$z = -i/2\lambda_j - \rho e^{i\theta}.$$

Then $\int_{G_j} h(z)\, dz$ is $O(\rho^{\frac{1}{2}})$ and tends to zero as $\rho \to 0$.

Thus, when a is even, equal to $2m$,

$$p(u) = \frac{1}{\pi} \sum_{v=1}^{m} (-1)^{m-v} \int_{-1/2\lambda_{2v-1}}^{-1/2\lambda_{2v}} |h(iy)|\, dy. \tag{6}$$

When n is odd, equal to $2m+1$,

$$p(u) = \frac{1}{\pi} \sum_{v=0}^{m} (-1)^{m-v} \int_{-1/2\lambda_{2v}}^{-1/2\lambda_{2v+1}} |h(iy)|\, dy. \tag{7}$$

Similar expressions are obtained when $u < 0$ on integrating $h(z)$ round the contour corresponding to G in the upper half of the z-plane. The calculation of the integrals which occur in (6) and (7) is described in the reference cited. A related evaluation of $p(u)$ is given by McCarthy (1939).

Case 3. *The roots are positive.* Several methods are available in which $p(u)$ takes the form of an infinite series. Thus, when all the roots of AV are positive, Robbins and Pitman (1949) express

$$\phi(t) = \prod_{r=1}^{a} (1 - 2it\lambda_r)^{-\frac{1}{2}\zeta_r}$$

as a power series in $(1-2it)^{-1}$, and hence obtain the distribution function of $y'Ay$ as an infinite series of incomplete gamma integrals.

Consider an individual term in the product forming $\phi(t)$:

$$(1 - 2it\lambda)^{-\frac{1}{2}\zeta} = \{\lambda(1-2it) - (\lambda-1)\}^{-\frac{1}{2}\zeta} = \lambda^{-\frac{1}{2}\zeta}\omega^{\frac{1}{2}\zeta}\{1 - (1-1/\lambda)\omega\}^{-\frac{1}{2}\zeta},$$

where $\omega = (1-2it)^{-1}$.

For any $\lambda > 0$, and $|\omega| < |1-1/\lambda|^{-1}$,

$$\lambda^{-\frac{1}{2}\zeta}\{1-(1-1/\lambda)\omega\}^{-\frac{1}{2}\zeta} = \sum_{m=0}^{\infty} f_m\,\omega^m, \tag{8}$$

where $\qquad f_m = \lambda^{-\frac{1}{2}\zeta}\frac{1}{2}\zeta(\frac{1}{2}\zeta+1)...(\frac{1}{2}\zeta+m-1)(1-1/\lambda)^m/m!.$

Suppose, however, that $\lambda \geqslant 1$. In this case all the f_m are non-negative. Furthermore, $|1-1/\lambda|^{-1} > 1$, so that the expansion (8) is valid for all $|\omega| \leqslant 1$; and on putting $\omega = 1$, we obtain

$$\sum_{m=0}^{\infty} f_m = 1.$$

Since $(1-2it)^{-1}$ is a permissible value of ω in the expansion,

$$(1-2it\lambda)^{-\frac{1}{2}\zeta} = \sum_{m=0}^{\infty} f_m(1-2it)^{-\frac{1}{2}\zeta-m},$$

which shows that $\lambda\chi^2(\zeta)$ has the same probability distribution as $\sum f_m\,\chi^2(\zeta+2m)$, where the $\chi^2(\zeta+2m)$ are independent χ^2 variables with the specified degrees of freedom. In order to apply this device to

$$u = \sum_{r=1}^{a} \lambda_r\,\chi^2(\zeta_r),$$

write $\qquad\qquad \lambda_r = \tau\psi_r,$

where τ is the smallest of $\lambda_1, \lambda_2, ..., \lambda_a$, and consider u/τ, which is a linear combination of independent χ^2 variables with all coefficients $\geqslant 1$. By analogy with the foregoing, define constants $\{f_m\}$ by

$$\prod_{r=1}^{a} [\psi_r^{-\frac{1}{2}\zeta_r}\{1-(1-1/\psi_r)\omega\}^{-\frac{1}{2}\zeta_r}] = \sum_{m=0}^{\infty} f_m\,\omega^m. \tag{9}$$

As before, $f_m > 0$, $\sum f_m = 1$, and

$$\phi(t) = \sum_{m=0}^{\infty} f_m(1-2it)^{-\frac{1}{2}\sum \zeta_r - m}. \tag{10}$$

Hence, if $P(v)$ is the distribution function of u/τ, and $P_m(v)$ is that of $\chi^2(\sum \zeta_r + 2m)$, then

$$P(v) = \sum_{m=0}^{\infty} f_m P_m(v). \tag{11}$$

For computational work, bounds for $P(v)$ are obtained as follows. Given integers m_1 and m_2, with $0 \leqslant m_1 \leqslant m_2$,

$$0 \leqslant P(v) - \sum_{m=m_1}^{m_2} f_m P_m(v) = \sum_{m=0}^{m_1-1} f_m P_m(v) + \sum_{m=m_2+1}^{\infty} f_m P_m(v)$$

$$\leqslant \sum_{m=0}^{m_1-1} f_m + \sum_{m=m_2+1}^{\infty} f_m = 1 - \sum_{m=m_1}^{m_2} f_m. \tag{12}$$

2.5. Independence of two quadratic forms

Suppose now that $y_1, y_2, ..., y_n$ are normally and independently distributed with zero means and unit variances. Then a necessary and sufficient condition for the statistical independence of the quadratic forms $y'Ay$ and $y'By$ is that $AB = 0$. This theorem was first published by Craig (1943), and the proof which follows is due to Matusita (1949). Independent proofs are given by Ogawa (1949) and Aitken (1950).

The joint characteristic function of $y'Ay$ and $y'By$ is

$$\mathscr{E} \exp(i\alpha y'Ay + i\beta y'By) = |I - 2i\alpha A - 2i\beta B|^{-\frac{1}{2}}. \tag{1}$$

Thus the quadratic forms are independent if and only if

$$|I - 2i\alpha A| \, |I - 2i\beta B| = |I - 2i\alpha A - 2i\beta B| \tag{2}$$

for all real values of α and β. The left-hand side is

$$|I - 2i\alpha A - 2i\beta B - 4\alpha\beta AB|,$$

and so the condition that $AB = 0$ is sufficient for the independence of $y'Ay$ and $y'By$.

We next show that this condition is also necessary. Let H be an orthogonal matrix such that $A* = H'AH$ is a diagonal matrix formed by the latent roots of A. Denote $H'BH$ by $B*$. Then

$$|I - 2i\alpha A*| \, |I - 2i\beta B*| = |I - 2i\alpha A* - 2i\beta B*|. \tag{3}$$

Equate here the coefficients of $(i\alpha)^r$, where r is the rank of A, and obtain

$$|I - 2i\beta B*| = |I - 2i\beta B_{22}^*|, \tag{4}$$

where B_{22}^* is the matrix formed by the last $(n-r)$ rows and columns of $B*$. This equation holds for all real values of β and hence, by identifying coefficients in the polynomial expansion of each side, for all complex values also. Put $\lambda = 1/2i\beta$, and (4) becomes

$$|\lambda I - B*| = \lambda^r |\lambda I - B_{22}^*|. \tag{5}$$

According to (5), the non-zero latent roots of $B*$ are those of B_{22}^*. Since, however, the sum of squares of the latent roots of a matrix is the sum of squares of all its elements, we deduce that all the elements of $B*$, other than those in B_{22}^*, are zero. The last $(n-r)$ rows and columns of $A*$ consist of zeros only, and therefore $A*B* = 0$, whence $AB = 0$ as required.

2.6. Distribution of the ratio of two quadratic forms

Let $q_1 = y'A_1y$ and $q_2 = y'A_2y$ be two quadratic forms in normal variables, the second of which is positive definite. We require the probability distribution of

$$r = q_1/q_2. \tag{1}$$

Suppose that $h(q_1, q_2)$ is the joint density function of q_1 and q_2. Put $q_1 = rq$, $q_2 = q$, and the density function of r is seen to be

$$p(r) = \int_0^\infty h(rq, q)q \, dq. \tag{2}$$

For example, let q_1 and q_2 be statistically independent, and such that the application of methods already described has led to the following expressions for their density functions:

$$b_1(q_1) = \begin{cases} \sum_{m=1}^\infty f_{1m} c_{1m}^{\frac{1}{2}m} q_1^{\frac{1}{2}m-1} \exp(-c_{1m} q_1) \big/ \Gamma(\tfrac{1}{2}m) & (c_{1m} > 0; \ q_1 > 0), \\[2mm] \sum_{m=1}^\infty f'_{1m} c_{1m}'^{\frac{1}{2}m} (-q_1)^{\frac{1}{2}m-1} \exp(c'_{1m} q_1) \big/ \Gamma(\tfrac{1}{2}m) & (c'_{1m} > 0; \ q_1 < 0), \end{cases}$$

and $b_2(q_2) = \sum_{n=1}^\infty f_{2n} c_{2n}^{\frac{1}{2}n} q_2^{\frac{1}{2}n-1} \exp(-c_{2n} q_2) \big/ \Gamma(\tfrac{1}{2}n) \quad (c_{2n} > 0; \ q_2 > 0).$

For $r > 0$, put $\qquad x_{mn} = c_{1m} r/(c_{1m} r + c_{2n}),$

and for $r < 0$, put

$$x'_{mn} = c'_{1m} r/(-c'_{1m} r + c_{2n}).$$

Using equation (2) with $h(q_1, q_2) = b_1(q_1)b_2(q_2)$, we then obtain

$$p(r)dr = \begin{cases} \sum_{m=1}^\infty \sum_{n=1}^\infty f_{1m} f_{2n} x_{mn}^{\frac{1}{2}m-1}(1-x_{mn})^{\frac{1}{2}n-1} dx_{mn} \big/ B(\tfrac{1}{2}m, \tfrac{1}{2}n) \\[2mm] \hspace{5cm} (0 \leqslant x_{mn} \leqslant 1), \\[2mm] \sum_{m=1}^\infty \sum_{n=1}^\infty f'_{1m} f_{2n}(-x'_{mn})^{\frac{1}{2}m-1}(1+x'_{mn})^{\frac{1}{2}n-1} dx'_{mn} \big/ B(\tfrac{1}{2}m, \tfrac{1}{2}n) \\[2mm] \hspace{5cm} (-1 \leqslant x'_{mn} \leqslant 0). \end{cases}$$

The distribution function of r can now be calculated from tables of the incomplete beta-function ratio (Pearson, 1934), provided that the two doubly-infinite series converge with sufficient rapidity.

We shall now reformulate equation (2) in terms of moment-generating functions and thus open the way for the use of complex variable techniques. Suppose that the joint moment-generating function of q_1 and q_2 is

$$W(T_1, T_2) = \iint e^{T_1 q_1 + T_2 q_2} h(q_1, q_2) \, dq_1 \, dq_2.$$

By the inversion theorem for two variables,

$$h(q_1, q_2) = \frac{1}{(2\pi i)^2} \iint W(T_1, T_2) e^{-T_1 q_1 - T_2 q_2} \, dT_1 \, dT_2,$$

where the integration is taken along the imaginary axes of T_1 and T_2, or any allowable deformations of them. Hence

$$h(rq, q) = \frac{1}{(2\pi i)^2} \int\int W(T, u-rT)e^{-uq} \, du \, dT,$$

where $u = rT_1 + T_2$. Inversion with respect to u gives

$$\int_0^\infty h(rq, q)e^{uq} \, dq = \frac{1}{2\pi i} \int W(T, u-rT) \, dT.$$

Differentiating, when permissible,

$$\int_0^\infty h(rq, q)q e^{uq} \, dq = \frac{1}{2\pi i} \int \frac{\partial W(T, u-rT)}{\partial u} \, dT.$$

When $u = 0$, the integral on the left is $p(r)$, and therefore

$$p(r) = \frac{1}{2\pi i} \int \left[\frac{\partial W(T, u-rT)}{\partial u}\right]_{u=0} dT. \tag{3}$$

This formula was developed by Cramér (1937) and Geary (1944). The proof above is due to Daniels (1956).

Example 1.

Take
$$q_1 = \lambda_1 y_1^2 + \lambda_2 y_2^2 + ... + \lambda_n y_n^2$$

and
$$q_2 = y_1^2 + y_2^2 + ... + y_n^2$$

where $y_1, y_2, ..., y_n$ are normally and independently distributed with zero means and unit variances. Then

$$W(T_1, T_2) = |I - 2T_1 I - 2T_2 \Lambda|^{-\frac{1}{2}},$$

in which Λ is the diagonal matrix formed by $\lambda_1, \lambda_2, ..., \lambda_n$. Hence

$$W(u-rT, T) = \prod_{j=1}^n \{1 - 2(u-rT) - 2\lambda_j T\}^{-\frac{1}{2}},$$

giving

$$p(r) = \frac{1}{2\pi i} \int \sum_{j=1}^n (1 + 2rT - 2\lambda_j T)^{-\frac{3}{2}} \prod_{k \neq j} (1 + 2rT - 2\lambda_k T)^{-\frac{1}{2}} \, dT.$$

Put $\lambda - r = 1/2T$, and integrate by parts, whence

$$p(r) = \frac{\frac{1}{2}n - 1}{2\pi i} \int_{r+i\infty}^{r-i\infty} (\lambda-r)^{\frac{1}{2}n-2} \prod_{j=1}^n (\lambda-\lambda_j)^{-\frac{1}{2}} \, d\lambda. \tag{4}$$

This result was obtained by Koopmans (1942), using a direct approach.

When the exact evaluation of $p(r)$ from (3) is difficult, we can sometimes derive an approximate density by taking the path of integration in the T-plane to be a curve of steepest descent passing through a saddlepoint of the integrand (Jeffreys and Jeffreys, 1956, § 17.04). This was pointed out by Daniels (loc. cit.), who gives several examples, of which the following is one.

Example 2. The joint density function of $y_1, y_2, ..., y_n$ is
$$(2\pi)^{-\frac{1}{2}n}(1-\rho^n)\times$$
$$\times \exp[-\tfrac{1}{2}\{(1+\rho^2)(y_1^2+...+y_n^2)-2\rho(y_1 y_2+...+y_{n-1}y_n+y_n y_1)\}].$$
Take
$$q_1 = y_1 y_2+...+y_{n-1}y_n+y_n y_1$$
and
$$q_2 = y_1^2+...+y_n^2.$$
Their joint moment-generating function is
$$W(T_1, T_2) = |V^{-1}|^{\frac{1}{2}}|V^{-1}-2T_1 A - 2T_2 I|^{-\frac{1}{2}},$$
where A is the matrix of q_1. Denote by D the circulant matrix

$$\begin{bmatrix} 1+\rho^2-2T_2 & -(\rho+T_1) & 0 & 0 & 0 & . & . & -(\rho+T_1) \\ -(\rho+T_1) & 1+\rho^2-2T_2 & -(\rho+T_1) & 0 & 0 & . & . & 0 \\ 0 & -(\rho+T_1) & 1+\rho^2-2T_2 & -(\rho+T_1) & 0 & . & . & 0 \\ . & . & . & . & . & . & . & . \\ 0 & 0 & 0 & -(\rho+T_1) & 1+\rho^2-2T_2 & . & . & -(\rho+T_1) \\ -(\rho+T_1) & 0 & 0 & 0 & -(\rho+T_1) & . & . & 1+\rho^2-2T_2 \end{bmatrix}$$

Then
$$W(T_1, T_2) = (1-\rho^n)|D|^{-\frac{1}{2}}. \tag{5}$$
The evaluation of a circulant is described by Aitken (1951, § 51). Put
$$z+z^{-1} = (1+\rho^2-2T_2)/(\rho+T_1) \tag{6}$$
and let $\omega_1, \omega_2, ..., \omega_n$ be the nth roots of 1. We find
$$|D| = (\rho+T_1)^n \prod_{j=1}^{n} (z+z^{-1}+\omega_j-\omega_j^{-1}) = (\rho+T_1)^n(1-z^n)^2/z^n. \tag{7}$$
Substitute $T_2 = u-rT$, $T_1 = T$, and (6) gives
$$\rho+T = z(1-2r\rho+\rho^2-2u)/(1-2rz+z^2). \tag{8}$$
Thus, using (5), (7), and (8),
$$W(T, u-rT) = (1-\rho^n)(1-2rz+z^2)^{\frac{1}{2}n}/(1-z^n)(1-2r\rho+\rho^2-2u)^{\frac{1}{2}n}. \tag{9}$$

The general formula (3) is now taken in the form
$$p(r) = \frac{1}{2\pi i} \int \frac{\partial}{\partial u}\left\{W(T, u-rT)\frac{\partial T}{\partial z}\right\}\bigg|_{u=0} dz. \tag{10}$$
Performing the differentiations indicated,
$$p(r) = \frac{(n-2)(1-\rho^n)}{2\pi i(1-2r\rho+\rho^2)^{\frac{1}{2}n}} \int \frac{(1-z^2)(1-2rz+z^2)^{\frac{1}{2}n-2}\, dz}{(1-z^n)}, \tag{11}$$
where
$$\rho+T = z(1-2r\rho+\rho^2)/(1-2rz+z^2). \tag{12}$$

The transformation (12) can be regarded as combining

$$z+z^{-1} = \zeta$$

with $\qquad\qquad \zeta-2r = (1-2r\rho+\rho^2)/(\rho+T).$

The first of these maps the region $|z| \leqslant 1$ on to the whole ζ-plane cut from -2 to $+2$, and the second maps it farther on to the whole T-plane cut from $-\infty$ to $-(1+\rho)^2/2(1+r)$, and from $(1-\rho)^2/2(1-r)$ to ∞. A path in the T-plane which goes from $\tau-i\infty$ to $\tau'+i\infty$ through the gap in the real axis is transformed into a path in the z-plane which goes from $r-i(1-r^2)^{\frac{1}{2}}$ to $r+i(1-r^2)^{\frac{1}{2}}$ inside $|z| \leqslant 1$.

The integrand in (11) contains a term $(1-2rz+z^2)^{\frac{1}{2}n-2}$. It has a saddlepoint at $z = r$, and the corresponding line of steepest descent is the branch of $\arg(1-2rz+z^2) = 0$ which cuts the real axis orthogonally, i.e. the straight line joining the points $r\pm i(1-r^2)^{\frac{1}{2}}$. We choose this to be the path of integration, and put $z = r+iw(1-r^2)^{\frac{1}{2}}$, where $-1 \leqslant w \leqslant 1$. The factors $(1-\rho^n)$ and $1/(1-z^n)$ in (11) can be ignored provided that neither ρ nor r is near ± 1, and hence

$$p(r) \simeq \frac{(n-2)(1-r^2)^{\frac{1}{2}(n-1)}}{2\pi(1-2r\rho+\rho^2)^{\frac{1}{2}n}} \int_{-1}^{1} (1+w^2)(1-w^2)^{\frac{1}{2}n-2}\,dw$$

$$= \frac{\Gamma(\tfrac{1}{2}n+1)(1-r^2)^{\frac{1}{2}(n-1)}}{\pi^{\frac{1}{2}}\Gamma(\tfrac{1}{2}n+\tfrac{1}{2})(1-2r\rho+\rho^2)^{\frac{1}{2}n}}.$$

2.7. Exercises

1. The variables $y_1, y_2, ..., y_n$ are normally and independently distributed with variances $1/w_1, 1/w_2, ..., 1/w_n$ respectively. Define $\bar{y} = \sum_{r=1}^{n} w_r y_r \big/ \sum_{r=1}^{n} w_r$.

Prove that $\sum_{r=1}^{n} w_r(y_r-\bar{y})^2$ has a χ^2 distribution with $(n-1)$ degrees of freedom. (Irwin, 1942.)

2. The random variables r_1 and r_2 are independently distributed as non-central χ^2 with n_1 and n_2 degrees of freedom respectively and parameters ρ_1 and ρ_2 respectively.

Prove that r_1+r_2 is distributed as non-central χ^2 with (n_1+n_2) degrees of freedom and parameter $\rho_1+\rho_2$; and that the density function of $v = r_1/r_2$ is

$$\sum_{m_1=0}^{\infty} \sum_{m_2=0}^{\infty} (\tfrac{1}{2}\rho_1)^{m_1}(\tfrac{1}{2}\rho_2)^{m_2} v^{\frac{1}{2}n_1+m_1-1}(1+v)^{-\frac{1}{2}(n_1+n_2)-m_1-m_2}\, e^{-\frac{1}{2}(\rho_1+\rho_2)} \times$$

$$\times [m_1!\,m_2!\,\mathrm{B}(\tfrac{1}{2}n_1+m_1, \tfrac{1}{2}n_2+m_2)]^{-1}.$$

$$\left[\text{Note that } I_n(x) = \sum_{m=0}^{\infty} (\tfrac{1}{2}x)^{n+2m}/m!\,\Gamma(n+m+1).\right] \quad \text{(Tang, 1938.)}$$

3. $\phi(t) = (1-2it\lambda_1)^{-\frac{1}{2}\zeta_1}(1-2it\lambda_2)^{-\frac{1}{2}\zeta_2}$.

Prove that the corresponding density function is

$$p(u) = \kappa_1^{\frac{1}{2}\zeta_1}\kappa_2^{\frac{1}{2}\zeta_2}u^{\frac{1}{2}\zeta_1+\frac{1}{2}\zeta_2-1}e^{-\kappa_1 u}M\{\tfrac{1}{2}\zeta_2;\ \tfrac{1}{2}\zeta_1+\tfrac{1}{2}\zeta_2;\ (\kappa_1-\kappa_2)u\}/\Gamma(\tfrac{1}{2}\zeta_1+\tfrac{1}{2}\zeta_2),$$

where $\kappa_1 = 1/2\lambda_1$, $\kappa_2 = 1/2\lambda_2$, and $M(a;c;z)$ is Kummer's confluent hyper-geometric series, defined by

$$M(a;c;z) = \sum_{m=0}^{\infty} \frac{a(a+1)...(a+m-1)}{c(c+1)...(c+m-1)}\frac{z^m}{m!}. \qquad \text{(Bateman Manuscript Project, 1954.)}$$

4. The latent roots of AV are all positive and $\lambda > \frac{1}{2}\max\lambda_r$ $(r = 1, 2,..., a)$. Verify that

$$(1-2it\lambda_r) = (1-2it\lambda)[1+\{(\lambda_r-\lambda)/\lambda\}\{1-(1-2it\lambda)^{-1}\}]$$

where $\qquad |\{(\lambda_r-\lambda)/\lambda\}\{1-(1-2it\lambda)^{-1}\}| < 1$.

Let f_m be the coefficient of x^m in

$$\prod_{r=1}^{a} \{1+(\lambda_r-\lambda)x/\lambda\}^{-\frac{1}{2}\zeta_r}$$

and put $\nu = \frac{1}{2}\sum_{r=1}^{a}\zeta_r$. Show that

$$\prod_{r=1}^{a}(1-2it\lambda_r)^{-\frac{1}{2}} = (1-2it\lambda)^{-\nu}\sum_{m=0}^{\infty}f_m\{1-(1-2it\lambda)^{-1}\}^m.$$

Deduce that the corresponding density function is

$$p(u) = (1/2\lambda)(u/2\lambda)^{\nu-1}e^{-u/2\lambda}\sum_{m=0}^{\infty}f_m L_m^{(\nu)}(u/2\lambda)m!/\Gamma(m+\nu),$$

where the Laguerre polynomial $L_m^{(\nu)}(x)$ is defined by

$$L_m^{(\nu)}(x) = \sum_{j=0}^{m}\binom{m+\nu-1}{m-j}\frac{(-x)^j}{j!}.$$

(Bhattacharya, 1945; Hotelling, 1948; Gurland, 1955; Grad and Solomon, 1955.)

5. The random variables $y_1, y_2,..., y_a$ are normally and independently distributed with zero means and unit variances. The constants $\lambda_1, \lambda_2,..., \lambda_a$ are all positive. Put

$$u = \frac{1}{2}\sum_{r=1}^{a}\lambda_r y_r^2,$$

and $\qquad u^* = \frac{1}{2}\sum_{r=1}^{a}\lambda_r^{-1}y_r^2.$

Prove that the distribution function of u is given by

$$P(u) = \sum_{m=0}^{\infty}p_m,$$

where $\qquad p_m = u^{\frac{1}{2}a}(-u)^m\mathscr{E}(u^*)^m/\prod_{r=1}^{a}\lambda_r^{\frac{1}{2}}m!\Gamma(\tfrac{1}{2}a+m+1).$

Show that the series is absolutely convergent and that

$$\sum_{m=0}^{2m_1}p_m > P(u) > \sum_{m=0}^{2m_2+1}p_m$$

for any two non-negative integers m_1 and m_2. (Pachares, 1955.)

6. The vector y consists of normally and independently distributed variables, each with zero mean and unit variance. Prove that the sth cumulant of $y'Ay$ is $2^{s-1}(s-1)! \times$ trace A^s. (Lancaster, 1954.)

7. The variables $y_1, y_2, ..., y_n$ are normally and independently distributed with zero means and unit variances. Show that a necessary and sufficient condition for the statistical independence of the linear form, $c'y$, and the quadratic form, $y'Ay$, is that $Ac = 0$. (Kac, 1945.)

8. The variables $y_1, y_2, ..., y_n$ are normally and independently distributed with mean η and variance σ^2.

Put
$$\bar{y} = \sum_{r=1}^{n} y_r/n.$$

Show that $n\bar{y}^2$ and $\sum_{r=1}^{n} (y_r - \bar{y})^2$ are independently distributed. Find the distribution of the square of the coefficient of variation, namely

$$\sum_{r=1}^{n} (y_r - \bar{y})^2/n\bar{y}^2. \qquad\qquad \text{(Tang, 1938.)}$$

9. The random variables $g_1, g_2, ..., g_n$ are independently distributed, and the density function of g_k is

$$g^{a_k-1}e^{-g}/\Gamma(a_k) \quad (a_k > 0, \; g > 0).$$

Define new variables $h_1, h_2, ..., h_n$ by

$$g_1 + g_2 + ... + g_n = h_1$$
$$g_2 + ... + g_n = h_1 h_2$$
$$\cdot \quad \cdot \quad \cdot \quad \cdot \quad \cdot$$
$$g_n = h_1 h_2 ... h_n$$

Prove that $h_1, h_2, ..., h_n$ are independently distributed.

Let $\psi(g_1, g_2, ..., g_n)$ be a function satisfying

$$\psi(g_1, g_2, ..., g_n) = \psi(cg_1, cg_2, ..., cg_n)$$

for all c. Show that h_1 and $\psi(g_1, g_2, ..., g_n)$ are statistically independent.

The elements of y are normally and independently distributed with zero means and unit variances. Deduce from the foregoing results that $r = y'Ay/y'y$ and $y'y$ are statistically independent. (Pitman, 1937; von Neumann, 1941.)

10. The variables $y_1, y_2, ..., y_n$ are normally and independently distributed, each with zero mean and unit variance.

$$r = \sum_{j=1}^{n} \lambda_j y_j^2 \Big/ \sum_{j=1}^{n} y_j^2,$$

where $\lambda_1 \geqslant \lambda_2 \geqslant ... \geqslant \lambda_n$.

Use the statistical independence of r and $\sum_{j=1}^{n} y_j^2$ to evaluate the characteristic function of $\sum_{j=1}^{n} \lambda_j y_j^2$ in two different ways, and hence show that

$$\prod_{j=1}^{n} (1 - 2it\lambda_j)^{-\frac{1}{2}} = \int_{\lambda_n}^{\lambda_1} (1 - 2itr)^{-\frac{1}{2}n} h(r) \, dr,$$

in which $h(r)$ is the density function of r. (von Neumann, 1941.)

11. The elements of y are normally and independently distributed with zero means and unit variances. Let

$$A = \begin{bmatrix} B & 0 & 0 \\ 0 & \lambda I_p & 0 \\ 0 & 0 & B \end{bmatrix},$$

where B is a real symmetric matrix with distinct roots $\lambda_1 > \lambda_2 > \ldots > \lambda_l$ and I_p is a unit matrix of order $p \times p$. Denote by $\prod'$ a product over $j = 1, 2, \ldots, l$ but $j \neq k$. For $\lambda < \lambda_l$, show that

$$\Pr(y'Ay > x.y'y) = \sum_{k=1}^{s} \frac{(\lambda_k - x)^{l + \frac{1}{2}p - 1}}{(\lambda_k - \lambda)^{\frac{1}{2}p} \prod' (\lambda_k - \lambda_j)} \qquad (\lambda_{s+1} \leqslant x \leqslant \lambda_s).$$

For $\lambda > \lambda_1$, show that

$$\Pr(y'Ay > x.y'y) = 1 - \sum_{k=s+1}^{l} \frac{(x - \lambda_k)^{l + \frac{1}{2}p - 1}}{(\lambda - \lambda_k)^{\frac{1}{2}p} \prod' (\lambda_j - \lambda_k)} \qquad (\lambda_{s+1} \leqslant x \leqslant \lambda_s).$$

(Anderson, 1942; Watson and Durbin, 1951.)

2.8. References

AITKEN, A. C. (1951). *Determinants and Matrices*, seventh edition. Edinburgh: Oliver and Boyd.

—— (1950). On the statistical independence of quadratic forms in normal variates. *Biometrika*, **37**, 93–96.

ANDERSON, R. L. (1942). Distribution of the serial correlation coefficient. *Ann. Math. Statist.* **13**, 1–13.

BATEMAN MANUSCRIPT PROJECT (1954). *Tables of Integral Transforms*, vol. **1**, ed. A. Erdélyi. New York: McGraw-Hill.

BHATTACHARYA, A. (1945). A note on the distribution of the sum of chi-squares. *Sankhyā*, **7**, 27–28.

BOX, G. E. P. (1954). Some theorems on quadratic forms applied in the study of analysis of variance problems, I. Effect of inequality of variance in the one-way classification. *Ann. Math. Statist.* **25**, 290–302.

COCHRAN, W. G. (1934). The distribution of quadratic forms in a normal system, with applications to the analysis of covariance. *Proc. Camb. Phil. Soc.* **30**, 178–91.

CRAIG, A. T. (1943). Note on the independence of certain quadratic forms. *Ann. Math. Statist.* **14**, 195–7.

CRAMÉR, H. (1937). *Random Variables and Probability Distributions*. Cambridge University Press.

DANIELS, H. E. (1956). The approximate distribution of serial correlation coefficients. *Biometrika*, **43**, 169–85.

GEARY, R. C. (1944). Extension of a theorem by Harald Cramér on the frequency distribution of the quotient of two variables. *J. R. Statist. Soc.* **107**, 56–57.

GRAD, A., and SOLOMON, H. (1955). Distribution of quadratic forms and some applications. *Ann. Math. Statist.* **26**, 464–77.

GURLAND, J. (1955). Distribution of definite and of indefinite quadratic forms. *Ann. Math. Statist.* **26**, 122–7.

HOTELLING, H. (1948). *See* Grad and Solomon (1955).

IRWIN, J. O. (1942). On the distribution of a weighted estimate of variance and on analysis of variance in certain cases of unequal weighting. *J. R. Statist. Soc.* **105**, 115–18.

JEFFREYS, H., and JEFFREYS, B. S. (1956). *Methods of Mathematical Physics*, third edition. Cambridge University Press.

KAC, M. (1945). A remark on independence of linear and quadratic forms involving independent Gaussian variables. *Ann. Math. Statist.* **16**, 400–1.

KOOPMANS, T. (1942). Serial correlation and quadratic forms in normal variables. *Ann. Math. Statist.* **13**, 14–33.

LANCASTER, H. O. (1954). Traces and cumulants of quadratic forms in normal variables. *J. R. Statist. Soc.* B, **16**, 247–54.

McCARTHY, M. D. (1939). On the application of the z-test to randomized blocks. *Ann. Math. Statist.* **10**, 337–59.

MATUSITA, K. (1949). Note on the independence of certain statistics. *Ann. Inst. Statist. Math.* **1**, 79–82.

OGAWA, J. (1949). On the independence of bilinear and quadratic forms of a random sample from a normal population. *Ann. Inst. Statist. Math.* **1**, 83–108.

PACHARES, J. (1955). Note on the distribution of a definite quadratic form. *Ann. Math. Statist.* **26**, 128–31.

PEARSON, K. (1934). *Tables of the Incomplete B-function.* Cambridge University Press.

PITMAN, E. J. G. (1937). The 'closest' estimates of statistical parameters. *Proc. Camb. Phil. Soc.* **33**, 212–22.

ROBBINS, H., and PITMAN, E. J. G. (1949). Application of the method of mixtures to quadratic forms in normal variates. *Ann. Math. Statist.* **20**, 552–60.

TANG, P. C. (1938). The power function of the analysis of variance tests with tables and illustrations of their use. *Statist. Res. Mem.* **2**, 126–57.

VON NEUMANN, J. (1941). Distribution of the ratio of the mean square successive difference to the variance. *Ann. Math. Statist.* **12**, 367–95.

WATSON, G. S., and DURBIN, J. (1951). Exact tests of serial correlation using non-circular statistics. *Ann. Math. Statist.* **22**, 446–51.

LEAST SQUARES

3.1. Introduction

AN experiment results in n observations $y_1, y_2, ..., y_n$, concerning which we make the following assumptions:

(i) Their expected values are linear combinations of p unknown parameters $\theta_1, \theta_2, ..., \theta_p$. Thus

$$\mathscr{E}y_r = \sum_{j=1}^{p} a_{rj}\theta_j \quad (r = 1, 2, ..., n),$$

where the coefficients $\{a_{rj}\}$ are known and form a matrix A, of order $n \times p$, termed the *design matrix*.

(ii) Their dispersion matrix is the product of an unknown scalar σ^2 and a known positive definite matrix $V = \{v_{rs}\}$. Thus

$$\mathscr{C}(y_r, y_s) = \sigma^2 v_{rs}.$$

In the special case where $V = I$, a unit matrix, each observation has the same variance σ^2 and every pair is uncorrelated.

Let θ denote any one of the unknowns $\theta_1, \theta_2; ..., \theta_p, \sigma^2$. A random variable $\theta^\times$ which is a function of $y_1, y_2, ..., y_n$ is termed an estimate of θ. Ideally we would like $\theta^\times$ to equal θ with unit probability for all admissible values of θ, but except in trivial cases $\theta^\times$ differs from θ with positive probability, and when the joint probability distribution of $y_1, y_2, ..., y_n$ is described by a density function, $\theta^\times$ almost certainly differs from θ. This chapter deals with the estimation of $\theta_1, \theta_2, ..., \theta_p$, and σ^2 by means of the principle of least squares. Except where otherwise indicated, the main results are essentially those of Gauss (1821, collected works 1873).

3.2. Least squares when rank $A = p$ and $V = I$

We suppose until further notice that the rank of A is p $(< n)$ and V is a unit matrix. According to the principle of least squares, we estimate $\theta_1, \theta_2, ..., \theta_p$ simultaneously by selecting those functions $\theta_1^*, \theta_2^*, ..., \theta_p^*$ of $y_1, y_2, ..., y_n$ which minimize

$$W = \sum_{r=1}^{n} \left(y_r - \sum_{j=1}^{p} a_{rj}\theta_j\right)^2 \tag{1}$$

D

with respect to $\theta_1, \theta_2, ..., \theta_p$ considered as independent variables. Differentiating (1) with respect to θ_k and equating to zero,

$$\sum_{r=1}^{n} a_{rk}\left(y_r - \sum_{j=1}^{p} a_{rj}\theta_j^*\right) = 0.$$

Rearranging,
$$\sum_{r=1}^{n} a_{rk} y_r = \sum_{j=1}^{p} \theta_j^* \left(\sum_{r=1}^{n} a_{rj} a_{rk}\right). \tag{2}$$

Denote by C the symmetric matrix $A'A$, and let c_{jk} be a typical element of C. Equation (2) becomes

$$\sum_{r=1}^{n} a_{rk} y_r = \sum_{j=1}^{p} c_{jk} \theta_j^*. \tag{3}$$

When k runs over the values $1, 2, ..., p$, (3) gives the *equations of estimation* (or *normal* equations) for the parameters $\{\theta_j\}$. Since A has rank p, there is no vector x such that $Ax = 0$ and therefore $(Ax)'(Ax)$ is positive for any vector x. Consequently $x'A'Ax$, i.e. $x'Cx$, is a positive definite quadratic form. Thus C is positive definite and the equations (3) have a unique solution. Moreover, the matrix of second-order differential coefficients of W with respect to $\theta_1, \theta_2, ..., \theta_p$ is $2C$, which is positive definite, and so W has an absolute minimum when $\theta_j = \theta_j^*$ $(j = 1, 2, ..., p)$.

The foregoing results can be presented in matrix notation, as follows. Let y be the $n \times 1$ vector of observations, θ the $p \times 1$ vector of parameters, and θ^* the $p \times 1$ vector of estimates. We have assumed that

$$\mathscr{E}y = A\theta$$

and

$$\mathscr{D}y = \sigma^2 I.$$

The absolute minimum value of

$$W = (y - A\theta)'(y - A\theta),$$

with respect to variation in θ, is

$$R = (y - A\theta^*)'(y - A\theta^*),$$

where θ^* is the unique solution of

$$A'y = C\theta^*,$$

and can be written in the form

$$\theta^* = C^{-1}A'y.$$

Example 1. We shall illustrate the formation of the equations of estimation when $n = 10$, $p = 6$,

$$A = \begin{bmatrix} 0 & 0 & -1 & +1 & -2 & +1 \\ 0 & 0 & +2 & -1 & -1 & 0 \\ +3 & -1 & -3 & +2 & +1 & +3 \\ -2 & +2 & +3 & -2 & -2 & -2 \\ +2 & -3 & -2 & +2 & +1 & +1 \\ -2 & -3 & +2 & -2 & -2 & -2 \\ +1 & +2 & -1 & 0 & -3 & 0 \\ -2 & 0 & 0 & -2 & -3 & +1 \\ -2 & -1 & -2 & +1 & -2 & -3 \\ +3 & +2 & +3 & -1 & +3 & -3 \end{bmatrix} \text{ and } y = \begin{bmatrix} 2\cdot1 \\ -0\cdot5 \\ 4\cdot5 \\ 5\cdot3 \\ -11\cdot5 \\ -30\cdot9 \\ 16\cdot1 \\ -12\cdot8 \\ -15\cdot7 \\ 29\cdot0 \end{bmatrix}.$$

These values give

$$C = \begin{bmatrix} 39 & 3 & -11 & 17 & 29 & 14 \\ & 32 & 15 & -9 & 0 & -7 \\ & & 45 & -28 & 1 & -25 \\ & & & 24 & 12 & 15 \\ & & & & 46 & 4 \\ & & & & & 38 \end{bmatrix} \text{ and } A'y = \begin{bmatrix} 201\cdot8 \\ 239\cdot3 \\ 62\cdot8 \\ 20\cdot7 \\ 149\cdot0 \\ 2\cdot6 \end{bmatrix}$$

where the elements of C below the main diagonal are omitted because C is symmetric. Check as follows:

(i) Sum the elements in each row of A and add y.

$$(A.1+y)' = [1\cdot1, \ -0\cdot5, \ 9\cdot5, \ 2\cdot3, \ -10\cdot5, \ -39\cdot9,$$
$$15\cdot1, \ -18\cdot8, \ -24\cdot7, \ 36\cdot0].$$

(ii) Sum the elements in each row of C and add $A'y$.

$$(C.1+A'y)' = [292\cdot8, \ 273\cdot2, \ 59\cdot8, \ 51\cdot7, \ 241\cdot0, \ 41\cdot6].$$

(iii) Verify that $A'(A.1+y) = C.1+A'y$.

Example 2. Let $\mathcal{E}y_r = \alpha + \beta(x_r - x.)$ for $r = 1, 2,..., n$, where $x. = \Sigma x_r/n$. Thus

$$A' = \begin{bmatrix} 1 & 1 & . & . & . & 1 \\ x_1-x. & x_2-x. & . & . & . & x_n-x. \end{bmatrix}$$

and
$$C = \begin{bmatrix} n & 0 \\ 0 & X \end{bmatrix}$$

where $X = \Sigma(x_r - x.)^2$. The estimates are

$$\alpha^* = y., \quad \text{where } y. = \Sigma y_r/n,$$

and
$$\beta^* = Z/X, \text{ where } Z = \Sigma(x_r - x.)(y_r - y.).$$

3.3. Properties of least-squares estimates

The estimate θ^* is *unbiased*, in the sense that $\mathcal{E}\theta^* = \theta$. In fact,

$$\mathcal{E}\theta^* = C^{-1}A'\mathcal{E}y = C^{-1}A'A\theta = \theta. \tag{1}$$

As regards the dispersion matrix of θ^*, we have

$$\mathcal{D}\theta^* = (C^{-1}A')\mathcal{D}y(C^{-1}A')' = \sigma^2 C^{-1}A'AC^{-1} = \sigma^2 C^{-1}. \tag{2}$$

Thus, apart from a factor σ^2, $\mathcal{D}\theta^*$ is obtained by inverting the matrix of the equations of estimation.

We show next that if some elements of θ^* are eliminated from the equations of estimation, then the dispersion matrix of the elements which remain is obtained by inverting the matrix of the new system. Suppose that θ^* is partitioned in the form

$$\begin{bmatrix} \theta_1^* \\ \theta_2^* \end{bmatrix}.$$

Let $b = A'y$, C and C^{-1} be correspondingly partitioned, so that

$$b = \begin{bmatrix} b_1 \\ b_2 \end{bmatrix}, \qquad C = \begin{bmatrix} C_{11} & C_{12} \\ C_{21} & C_{22} \end{bmatrix}, \qquad \text{and} \qquad C^{-1} = \begin{bmatrix} C^{11} & C^{12} \\ C^{21} & C^{22} \end{bmatrix}.$$

Then
$$C_{11}\theta_1^* + C_{12}\theta_2^* = b_1,$$
$$C_{21}\theta_1^* + C_{22}\theta_2^* = b_2.$$

Eliminating θ_1^* from the second equation by means of the first,

$$(C_{22} - C_{21}C_{11}^{-1}C_{12})\theta_2^* = b_2 - C_{21}C_{11}^{-1}b_1. \tag{3}$$

A similar argument shows that

$$(C_{22} - C_{21}C_{11}^{-1}C_{12})C^{22} = I; \tag{4}$$

whence $(C_{22} - C_{21}C_{11}^{-1}C_{12})$ is positive definite, being the inverse of a positive definite matrix. Since, however,

$$\mathcal{D}(b_2 - C_{21}C_{11}^{-1}b_1) = \sigma^2(C_{22} - C_{21}C_{11}^{-1}C_{12}),$$

we deduce that

$$\mathcal{D}\theta_2^* = \sigma^2(C_{22} - C_{21}C_{11}^{-1}C_{12})^{-1}. \tag{5}$$

This is the result stated above.

The least-squares estimate of θ is linear in the observations. Consider an arbitrary linear estimate, say

$$\theta^\times = Ly,$$

where L is any matrix of order $p \times n$.

$$\mathcal{E}\theta^\times = L\mathcal{E}y = LA\theta,$$

and so $\theta^\times$ will be unbiased for all θ provided that

$$LA = I. \tag{6}$$

Its dispersion matrix is

$$\mathscr{D}\theta^\times = \sigma^2 LL'.$$

We now prove that the least-squares estimate θ^* is better than any other unbiased linear estimate $\theta^\times$ in the sense that, for each parameter θ_j,

$$\mathscr{V}\theta_j^* \leqslant \mathscr{V}\theta_j^\times.$$

The proof rests on the equation

$$LL' = (C^{-1}A')(C^{-1}A')' + (L - C^{-1}A')(L - C^{-1}A')' \tag{7}$$

which becomes an identity on substituting (6). Multiplying by σ^2,

$$\mathscr{D}\theta^\times = \mathscr{D}\theta^* + \sigma^2 (L - C^{-1}A')(L - C^{-1}A')'.$$

Each diagonal element of $\mathscr{D}\theta^\times$ is therefore minimized if the corresponding row of $L - C^{-1}A'$ consists entirely of zeros. Hence θ^* is the best linear unbiased estimate of θ.

A similar result holds for any set of linear combinations of $\theta_1, \theta_2, ..., \theta_p$, since the best linear unbiased estimate of $\phi = N\theta$ is $\phi^* = N\theta^*$. To prove this, suppose that $\phi^\times = Ly$ is an unbiased estimate of ϕ, whatever θ. Then $LA = N$, in which case

$$LL' = NC^{-1}N' + (L - NC^{-1}A')(L - NC^{-1}A')'.$$

Each diagonal element in $\mathscr{D}\phi^\times$ is therefore at least equal to the corresponding element in $\mathscr{D}\phi^*$, which completes the proof.

3.4. Sum of squared residuals

The best linear unbiased estimate of $\mathscr{E}y_r = \sum\limits_{j=1}^{p} a_{rj}\theta_j$ is

$$\sum_{j=1}^{p} a_{rj}\theta_j^*,$$

which is termed the *graduated* value of y_r. The difference

$$y_r - \sum_{j=1}^{p} a_{rj}\theta_j^*$$

is the rth *residual*, and

$$R = \sum_{r=1}^{n} \left(y_r - \sum_{j=1}^{p} a_{rj}\theta_j^*\right)^2$$

is the sum of squared residuals. It can be recognized as the absolute minimum value of W with respect to variation in $\theta_1, \theta_2, ..., \theta_p$; and it is a function of the observations only.

In matrix notation,

$$R = (y - A\theta^*)'(y - A\theta^*). \tag{1}$$

A useful identity is obtained by summing the squares of the elements on both sides of

$$(y-A\theta) = (y-A\theta^*)+A(\theta^*-\theta).$$

Since the product $(\theta^*-\theta)'A'(y-A\theta^*)$ vanishes by definition of θ^*,

$$(y-A\theta)'(y-A\theta) = (y-A\theta^*)'(y-A\theta^*)+(\theta^*-\theta)'A'A(\theta^*-\theta). \quad (2)$$

The second term on the right is a positive definite quadratic form, and hence this equation affords a further proof that R is the absolute minimum of W when θ varies. Substituting for θ^*,

$$(\theta^*-\theta)'C(\theta^*-\theta) = (y-A\theta)'AC^{-1}A'(y-A\theta),$$

whence (2) gives

$$R = (y-A\theta)'(I-AC^{-1}A')(y-A\theta). \quad (3)$$

Although R now appears to involve θ, actually the coefficient of θ is zero, because $A'(I-AC^{-1}A') = 0$.

We proceed to derive $\mathscr{E}R$ and $\mathscr{V}R$. As regards $\mathscr{E}R$, apply (2.2.1), noting that

$$\text{trace}(I-AC^{-1}A') = n-\text{trace } C^{-1}A'A = n-p.$$

We thus reach the fundamental result that

$$\mathscr{E}R = (n-p)\sigma^2, \quad (4)$$

with its corollary that $R/(n-p)$ is an unbiased estimate of σ^2. In evaluating $\mathscr{V}R$, we assume that the elements of $(y-A\theta)$ are statistically independent random variables, each with mean zero, variance σ^2, and fourth moment $\beta\sigma^4$. Denote $I-AC^{-1}A'$ by $H = \{h_{rs}\}$. According to (2.2.2),

$$\mathscr{V}R = \sigma^4\left\{(\beta-3)\sum_{r=1}^{n} h_{rr}^2+2\sum_{r=1}^{n}\sum_{s=1}^{n} h_{rs}^2\right\}. \quad (5)$$

Now H is an idempotent matrix, for

$$H^2 = I-2AC^{-1}A'+AC^{-1}A'.AC^{-1}A' = I-AC^{-1}A' = H.$$

Consequently $$\sum_{r=1}^{n}\sum_{s=1}^{n} h_{rs}^2 = \sum_{r=1}^{n} h_{rr} = (n-p). \quad (6)$$

Denote $AC^{-1}A'$ by $G = \{g_{rs}\}$. Then

$$\sum_{r=1}^{n} h_{rr}^2 = \sum_{r=1}^{n} (1-g_{rr})^2 = (n-2p)+\sum_{r=1}^{n} g_{rr}^2. \quad (7)$$

Substitution of (6) and (7) into (5) gives

$$\mathscr{V}R = \sigma^4\left\{(n-p)(\beta-1)+(\beta-3)\left(\sum_{r=1}^{n} g_{rr}^2-p\right)\right\}. \quad (8)$$

We turn next to the computation of R. Separate residuals may

sometimes yield useful information but in general the sum of their squares will provide a laborious and inaccurate method of calculating R. If, however, we substitute $\theta = 0$ in (2), and remember that $C\theta^* = A'y$, then
$$R = y'y - y'A\theta^*. \qquad \qquad .(9)$$

Example 3. In Example 1,
$$y'y = 2650\cdot60,$$
$$(\theta^*)' = [3\cdot93268,\, 7\cdot08744,\, 1\cdot49110,\, 2\cdot48265,\, 0\cdot08699,\, -0\cdot08304]$$
and $y'A = [201\cdot8,\, 239\cdot2,\, 62\cdot8,\, 20\cdot7,\, 149\cdot0,\, 2\cdot6]$.

Hence $y'A\theta^* = 2646\cdot71$, giving $R = 3\cdot89$. The elements of $A'y$ may be large compared with the corresponding elements of θ^*, and it will therefore often be necessary to compute θ^* to more decimal places than the data justify, in order to avoid an erroneous value of R.

In another method, R is expressed in terms of the vector h, which is obtained at an intermediate stage in the direct solution of the equations of estimation. With T as the upper triangular matrix such that $T'T = C$, h is defined by $T'h = A'y$. Since
$$y'A\theta^* = y'AC^{-1}A'y = h'TC^{-1}T'h = h'h,$$
equation (9) becomes $R = y'y - h'h.$ (10)

The equations of estimation for the example of Section 2 were solved in Section 1.2, where it was found that,
$$h' = [32\cdot31385,\, 39\cdot68424,\, 1\cdot39792,\, 5\cdot04819,\, 0\cdot32741,\, -0\cdot37314],$$
whence $h'h = 2646\cdot71$, in agreement with $y'A\theta^*$. This method is advantageous when fitting polynomials of successively higher degree, and an example appears in Section 6.2.

Example 4. In Example 2,
$$(\theta^*)' = [y_.,\, Z/X]$$
and $y'A = [ny_.,\, Z].$
Hence $R = Y - Z^2/X$, where $Y = \sum (y_r - y_.)^2.$

The sum of squared residuals is a quadratic form in the observations and can be described as an unbiased quadratic estimate of $(n-p)\sigma^2$. Consider an arbitrary quadratic form in the observations, say Q. If Q is comparable with R, it should satisfy the following requirements:

(a) $\mathscr{E}Q = (n-p)\sigma^2$ for all θ;

(b) $\mathscr{V}Q$ is independent of the value of θ.

In view of the minimum variance property of θ^*, a natural procedure is to seek conditions under which Q has minimum variance. This problem was examined by Hsu (1938), who proved that the best unbiased quadratic estimate of $(n-p)\sigma^2$ is R

(i) for any A, if and only if $\beta = 3$;

(ii) for any β, if and only if

$$(n-p) \sum_{r=1}^{n} h_{rr} h_{rs}^2 = h_{ss} \sum_{r=1}^{n} h_{rr}^2 \quad (s = 1, 2, ..., n).$$

Rao (1952) has shown that optimum properties of R can be established with less difficulty if (b) is replaced by the assumption that Q is a definite quadratic form, and his argument can be further abbreviated by confining attention to a class of estimates defined as follows. Since $I - AC^{-1}A'$ is idempotent, it can be expressed in the form $F'F$, where $FF' = I$. Define $u = Fy$ and consider the class of unbiased estimates of $(n-p)\sigma^2$ which are quadratic forms in u. We shall prove that R is the member of this class with minimum variance when $\beta = 3$.

Suppose that $u'Ju$ is an unbiased estimate of $(n-p)\sigma^2$ with minimum variance and that $u'Ku$ is an unbiased estimate of zero. Then $u'Ju + \psi u'Ku$ is an unbiased estimate of $(n-p)\sigma^2$ for any ψ and

$$\mathscr{V}(u'Ju + \psi u'Ku) = \mathscr{V}(u'Ju) + 2\psi \mathscr{C}(u'Ju, u'Ku) + \psi^2 \mathscr{V}(u'Ku).$$

If $\mathscr{C}(u'Ju, u'Ku) > 0$, we can choose ψ small and negative such that

$$\mathscr{V}(u'Ju + \psi u'Ku) < \mathscr{V}(u'Ju).$$

Similarly, if $\mathscr{C}(u'Ju, u'Ku) < 0$, we can choose ψ small and positive to achieve the same result. The result contradicts our initial assumption that $u'Ju$ has minimum variance, and therefore

$$\mathscr{C}(u'Ju, u'Ku) = 0 \tag{11}$$

for every quadratic form $u'Ku$ which is an unbiased estimate of zero. Moreover, the best estimate of $(n-p)\sigma^2$ is unique, for if there are two such estimates, $u'J_1 u$ and $u'J_2 u$, then from (11) we have

$$\mathscr{C}(u'J_1 u, u'J_1 u - u'J_2 u) = 0.$$

This implies that $u'J_1 u$ and $u'J_2 u$ are identical, since they have the same means and variances.

In terms of y, (11) becomes

$$\mathscr{C}(y'F'JFy, y'F'KFy) = 0.$$

A straightforward extension of (2.2.2) shows that when $\beta = 3$, this covariance is

$$\sigma^4 \operatorname{trace}(F'JF \cdot F'KF) = \sigma^4 \operatorname{trace}(F'JKF),$$

which must be zero for every K satisfying $\operatorname{trace}(F'KF) = 0$. A solution is $J = I$ and, by the argument given above, this solution is unique. The proof is now complete.

3.5. Least squares when rank $A < p$ and $V = I$

In certain types of experimental design, the natural specification for $\mathscr{E}y = A\theta$ involves a matrix A, whose rank is less than the number of parameters in the vector θ. The results of previous Sections have been derived on the assumption that rank $A = p$, and need to be modified when rank $A = p-m$, where $m > 0$, because $A'A$ is then singular and the equations for θ^* and $\mathscr{D}\theta^*$ are meaningless. We show here that the principle of least squares can be restated in such a way that it still leads to the best linear unbiased estimate of θ. The arguments derive from Yates and Hale (1939), Rao (1946), and Plackett (1950), where further details can be found.

The first point to establish is that $\theta^\times = Ly$ cannot now be an unbiased estimate of θ for all values of θ. When A has rank $p-m$, there are m independent linear relations between its columns; equivalently, there exists a matrix D with order $p \times m$, rank m, and such that

$$AD = 0. \tag{1}$$

If $\theta^\times$ is unbiased for all θ, then $I = LA$, which leads to the contradiction that $D = LAD = 0$.

At this stage, one approach consists in finding which linear combinations of the parameters have unbiased estimates. We can choose $p-m$ columns of A which are linearly independent, and express the remaining m columns as linear combinations of them. This implies that $A\theta$ can be written in the form $XY\theta$, where X has order $n \times (p-m)$, Y has order $(p-m) \times p$, and both have rank $(p-m)$. The ordinary theory of least squares then applies to the vector $\phi = Y\theta$, because $\mathscr{E}y = X\phi$, and the rank of X is the number of parameters in ϕ. From $AD = 0$ we deduce $YD = 0$, which limits the choice of ϕ.

The alternative approach adopted here is directed towards preserving the symmetry usually present in the original specification of A. We introduce a set of linearly independent equations $B\theta = 0$ which restrict the parameters θ to a class where unbiased estimation is possible, but impose no restrictions on $\phi = Y\theta$, and hence none on

$\mathscr{E}y$. These objects are achieved if the equations $Y\theta = \phi$ and $B\theta = 0$ have a unique solution for θ, in which case $\begin{bmatrix} Y \\ \cdots \\ B \end{bmatrix}$ has rank p. As a result, rank $B = m$. Moreover, the number of linear relations connecting the rows of Y and B is the number of linearly independent vectors $(u' \vdots v')$ such that

$$u'Y + v'B = 0.$$

On post-multiplying by D we obtain $v'BD = 0$, and any non-zero solution v of these equations leads to a corresponding vector u. The number of relations is therefore $m - \text{rank } BD$. This number is zero if $\begin{bmatrix} Y \\ \cdots \\ B \end{bmatrix}$ has rank p and therefore BD is non-singular.

The difficulty connected with the estimate $\theta^{\times} = Ly$ now disappears. If $\theta^{\times}$ is unbiased for all values of θ subject to the restriction $B\theta = 0$, then $(I - LA)\theta = 0$ whenever $B\theta = 0$ and so $I = LA + MB$. Post-multiplying by D we obtain $D = MBD$, whence

$$LA = I - D(BD)^{-1}B$$

in place of the equation $LA = I$ which holds when rank $A = p$. A more convenient expression for LA is derived as follows. The matrix $\begin{bmatrix} A \\ \cdots \\ B \end{bmatrix}$ has rank p because the only vectors x which make $Ax = 0$ are linear combinations of the columns of D and the fact that BD is non-singular then precludes $Bx = 0$. Thus $A'A + B'B$ is positive definite and its inverse exists. The equation

$$(A'A + B'B)D = B'BD$$

therefore gives

$$D(BD)^{-1} = (A'A + B'B)^{-1}B'.$$

Hence $\qquad I - D(BD)^{-1}B = (A'A + B'B)^{-1}A'A,$

so that $(A'A + B'B)^{-1}A'A$ is an alternative form for LA.

Under the conditions on A, B, and D which are stated above, the best linear unbiased estimate of θ is the value which minimizes $(y - A\theta)'(y - A\theta)$ subject to $B\theta = 0$. To prove this result, we introduce a vector λ of Lagrange multipliers, and seek the unconditional minimum of

$$(y - A\theta)'(y - A\theta) + \lambda'B\theta.$$

Differentiating with respect to θ,

$$-(y - A\theta^{*})'A + \lambda'B = 0.$$

Post-multiplying by D and noting that BD is non-singular, we obtain

$\lambda = 0$ which confirms what is implicit in the definition of B, namely that the absolute minimum of $(y-A\theta)'(y-A\theta)$ is the same as the conditional minimum subject to $B\theta = 0$. Thus the estimate to which the modified least-squares procedure leads is the solution of the equations

$$A'A\theta^* = A'y$$

and

$$B\theta^* = 0,$$

which combine to yield

$$\theta^* = (A'A + B'B)^{-1}A'y.$$

If, however, Ly is an unbiased estimate of θ when $B\theta = 0$, then we have shown that

$$LA = (A'A + B'B)^{-1}A'A$$

in which case

$$LL' = \{(A'A + B'B)^{-1}A'\}\{(A'A + B'B)^{-1}A'\}' +$$
$$+ \{L - (A'A + B'B)^{-1}A'\}\{L - (A'A + B'B)^{-1}A'\}'.$$

The left-hand side here is $\mathcal{D}(Ly)/\sigma^2$ and its diagonal elements are minimized simultaneously if $L = (A'A + B'B)^{-1}A'$. This completes the proof.

The dispersion matrix of θ^* is

$$\mathcal{D}\theta^* = \sigma^2(A'A + B'B)^{-1}A'A(A'A + B'B)^{-1}$$

which simplifies to

$$\mathcal{D}\theta^* = \sigma^2(I - D(BD)^{-1}B)(A'A + B'B)^{-1}.$$

Since $A'A\theta^* = A'y$, the sum of squared residuals is still given by the formula

$$R = y'y' - y'A\theta^*.$$

However, its expectation now becomes

$$\mathcal{E}R = (n + m - p)\sigma^2$$

because $A\theta$ can be expressed in the form $X\phi$, where X has order $n \times (p-m)$ and rank $(p-m)$. Thus $R/(n+m-p)$ is an unbiased estimate of σ^2.

We make two remarks in conclusion:

(i) The whole of the foregoing argument remains valid if D is replaced by DM and B by NB, where M and N are non-singular matrices—this corresponds to the fact that $AD = 0$ is equivalent to $ADM = 0$, and $B\theta = 0$ to $NB\theta = 0$.

(ii) Suppose that $\theta^* = \begin{bmatrix} \theta_1^* \\ \theta_2^* \end{bmatrix}$. Eliminating θ_1^* from the equations of estimation, we obtain a system of equations for θ_2^*, with matrix E. When rank $A = p$, $\mathscr{D}\theta_2^* = \sigma^2 E^{-1}$, as shown in Section 3. When rank $A < p$, we find a D of the maximum rank consistent with $D'E = 0$ and choose B such that BD is non-singular. Then

$$\mathscr{D}\theta_2^* = \sigma^2(I - D(BD)^{-1}B)(E + B'B)^{-1},$$

a result which can be proved by methods essentially the same as those given above.

Example 5. In the following data, each observation in the cell formed by the ith row and jth column has mean $\mu + \rho_i + \kappa_j$ and variance σ^2 ($i = 1, 2; j = 1, 2, 3$).

2·45	2·82	1·85			
2·89	1·89	1·52	1·79	1·28	2·24
2·48					
1·00	1·25	1·55	1·55	0·55	0·57
1·46	1·81	1·54	0·57	0·94	0·37

The table below is required in the ensuing analysis. It gives the cell, row, and column totals, with corresponding frequencies in brackets.

7·82 (3)	8·08 (4)	5·31 (3)	21·21 (10)
2·46 (2)	6·15 (4)	4·55 (6)	13·16 (12)
10·28 (5)	14·23 (8)	9·86 (9)	34·37 (22)

We shall consider two problems independently. The first problem is the simultaneous estimation of μ, ρ_1, ρ_2, κ_1, κ_2, κ_3. The equations of estimation are

$$\begin{aligned}
\text{(i)} \quad & 22\mu^* + 10\rho_1^* + 12\rho_2^* + 5\kappa_1^* + 8\kappa_2^* + 9\kappa_3^* = 34\cdot37, \\
\text{(ii)} \quad & 10\mu^* + 10\rho_1^* \qquad\quad + 3\kappa_1^* + 4\kappa_2^* + 3\kappa_3^* = 21\cdot21, \\
\text{(iii)} \quad & 12\mu^* \qquad\quad + 12\rho_2^* + 2\kappa_1^* + 4\kappa_2^* + 6\kappa_3^* = 13\cdot16, \\
\text{(iv)} \quad & 5\mu^* + 3\rho_1^* + 2\rho_2^* + 5\kappa_1^* \qquad\qquad = 10\cdot28, \\
\text{(v)} \quad & 8\mu^* + 4\rho_1^* + 4\rho_2^* \qquad + 8\kappa_2^* \qquad = 14\cdot23, \\
\text{and} \quad \text{(vi)} \quad & 9\mu^* + 3\rho_1^* \quad 6\rho_2^* \qquad\qquad\quad + 9\kappa_3^* = 9\cdot86.
\end{aligned}$$

They are not independent, for premultiplication by either row of

$$D' = \begin{bmatrix} -1 & 1 & 1 & 0 & 0 & 0 \\ -1 & 0 & 0 & 1 & 1 & 1 \end{bmatrix}$$

gives $0 = 0$. Introduce the restrictions

$$10\rho_1 + 12\rho_2 = 0,$$

and

$$5\kappa_1 + 8\kappa_2 + 9\kappa_3 = 0,$$

where the coefficients are the total row and column frequencies. Thus

$$B = \begin{bmatrix} 0 & 10 & 12 & 0 & 0 & 0 \\ 0 & 0 & 0 & 5 & 8 & 9 \end{bmatrix}$$

and BD is non-singular. Equation (i) now yields $\mu^* = 1.5623$. Insert this value in (ii), (iii),..., (vi) and divide by the diagonal elements. Then

$$\rho_1^* + (3\kappa_1^* + 4\kappa_2^* + 3\kappa_3^*)/10 = \quad 0.5587,$$
$$\rho_2^* + (2\kappa_1^* + 4\kappa_2^* + 6\kappa_3^*)/12 = -0.4656,$$
$$\kappa_1^* + (3\rho_1^* + 2\rho_2^*)/5 \qquad = \quad 0.4937,$$
$$\kappa_2^* + (4\rho_1^* + 4\rho_2^*)/8 \qquad = \quad 0.2164,$$

and
$$\kappa_3^* + (3\rho_1^* + 6\rho_2^*)/9 \qquad = -0.4667.$$

These equations can be solved fairly quickly by iteration, beginning with the approximate solution $\rho_1^* = 0.5587,..., \kappa_3^* = -0.4667$. The method was proposed and illustrated by Stevens (1948) and an appropriate scheme of calculation is given in Table 4, the arrangement being due to Yates (1949, § 5.24).

TABLE 4. *Iterative estimation procedure for row-and-column classification*

22	5	8	9					ρ_i^*
10	3	4	3	0.5587	−0.0686	−0.0032	0.0001	0.4870
12	2	4	6	−0.4656	0.0572	0.0027	0.0001	−0.4058
	0.4937	0.2164	−0.4667					
	−0.1490	−0.0465	0.1242					
	0.3447	0.1699	−0.3425					
	0.0183	0.0057	−0.0153					
	0.0008	0.0002	−0.0007					
κ_j^*	0.3638	0.1758	−0.3585					

The cell frequencies are bordered above and to the left by their marginal totals. To the right are deviations of row means from the grand mean; below are deviations of column means from the grand mean. From the row deviations, calculate

$$-\{3(0.5587) - 2(0.4656)\}/5 = -0.1490,$$
$$-\{4(0.5587) - 4(0.4656)\}/8 = -0.0465,$$

and
$$-\{3(0.5587) - 6(0.4656)\}/9 = \quad 0.1242.$$

The adjusted column deviations are $0.4937 - 0.1490 = 0.3447$, $0.2164 - 0.0465 = 0.1699$, and $-0.4667 + 0.1242 = -0.3425$. In their turn, these give row corrections. For example,

$$-\{3(0{\cdot}3447)+4(0{\cdot}1699)-3(0{\cdot}3425)\}/10 = -0{\cdot}0686.$$

The row corrections provide further column corrections and vice versa; and the process is continued in this way until it converges.

The second problem is to estimate $\kappa_1, \kappa_2, \kappa_3$, and the dispersion matrix of κ_1^*, κ_2^*, and κ_3^*. Given that two decimal places are required in the sum of squared residuals, we shall need four in the estimates because the sum of the elements of $A'y$ is about 100. In the equations of estimation, use (ii) and (iii) to eliminate $\mu^*+\rho_1^*$ and $\mu^*+\rho_2^*$ from (iv), (v), and (vi). The matrix of the new system for κ_1^*, κ_2^*, and κ_3^*, say E, is such that each column sums to zero, corresponding to

$$D' = [1 \quad 1 \quad 1].$$

Take
$$B = 22^{-\frac{1}{2}}[5 \quad 8 \quad 9],$$

and add $B'B$ to the matrix of coefficients, whence

$$\begin{bmatrix} 5-0{\cdot}0970 & -0{\cdot}0485 & 0{\cdot}1455 \\ & 8-0{\cdot}0242 & 0{\cdot}0727 \\ & & 9-0{\cdot}2182 \end{bmatrix}\begin{bmatrix} \kappa_1^* \\ \kappa_2^* \\ \kappa_3^* \end{bmatrix} = \begin{bmatrix} 1{\cdot}7237 \\ 1{\cdot}3593 \\ -3{\cdot}0830 \end{bmatrix}$$

where, e.g. $-0{\cdot}1455 = (3)(3)/10+(2)(6)/12-(5)(9)/22,$

and $1{\cdot}7237 = 10{\cdot}28-3(21{\cdot}21)/10-2(13{\cdot}16)/12.$

In general, following Quenouille (1950), B is defined as $n^{-\frac{1}{2}}$ times the row vector of column total frequencies. The factor of $n^{-\frac{1}{2}}$ is chosen because the non-diagonal elements of $E+B'B$ are usually small, and will be zero if the cell frequencies in each row are proportional to the column total frequencies. Returning to our example, an approximate inverse of $E+B'B$ is

$$\begin{bmatrix} 1/25 & 0 & 0 \\ & 1/64 & 0 \\ & & 1/81 \end{bmatrix}\begin{bmatrix} 5{\cdot}0970 & 0{\cdot}0485 & -0{\cdot}1455 \\ & 8{\cdot}0242 & -0{\cdot}0727 \\ & & 9{\cdot}2182 \end{bmatrix} = \begin{bmatrix} 0{\cdot}2039 & 0{\cdot}0019 & -0{\cdot}0058 \\ & 0{\cdot}1254 & -0{\cdot}0011 \\ & & 0{\cdot}1138 \end{bmatrix}.$$

In accordance with Section 1.5, compute

$$2I-\begin{bmatrix} 0{\cdot}2039 & 0{\cdot}0019 & -0{\cdot}0058 \\ & 0{\cdot}1254 & -0{\cdot}0011 \\ & & 0{\cdot}1138 \end{bmatrix}\begin{bmatrix} 4{\cdot}9030 & -0{\cdot}0485 & 0{\cdot}1455 \\ & 7{\cdot}9758 & 0{\cdot}0727 \\ & & 8{\cdot}7818 \end{bmatrix} = \begin{bmatrix} 1{\cdot}0012 & -0{\cdot}0048 & 0{\cdot}0211 \\ -0{\cdot}0048 & 1{\cdot}0000 & 0{\cdot}0003 \\ 0{\cdot}0211 & 0{\cdot}0003 & 1{\cdot}0016 \end{bmatrix}.$$

A second approximation to $(E+B'B)^{-1}$ is then given by

$$\begin{bmatrix} 1{\cdot}0012 & -0{\cdot}0048 & 0{\cdot}0211 \\ -0{\cdot}0048 & 1{\cdot}0000 & 0{\cdot}0003 \\ 0{\cdot}0211 & 0{\cdot}0003 & 1{\cdot}0016 \end{bmatrix}\begin{bmatrix} 0{\cdot}2039 & 0{\cdot}0019 & -0{\cdot}0058 \\ 0{\cdot}0019 & 0{\cdot}1254 & -0{\cdot}0011 \\ -0{\cdot}0058 & -0{\cdot}0011 & 0{\cdot}1138 \end{bmatrix} = \begin{bmatrix} 0{\cdot}2040 & 0{\cdot}0013 & -0{\cdot}0034 \\ 0{\cdot}0013 & 0{\cdot}1254 & -0{\cdot}0010 \\ -0{\cdot}0034 & -0{\cdot}0010 & 0{\cdot}1139 \end{bmatrix}.$$

Hence
$$\begin{bmatrix} \kappa_1^* \\ \kappa_2^* \\ \kappa_3^* \end{bmatrix} = \begin{bmatrix} 0\cdot2040 & 0\cdot0013 & -0\cdot0034 \\ & 0\cdot1254 & -0\cdot0010 \\ & & 0\cdot1139 \end{bmatrix} \begin{bmatrix} 1\cdot7237 \\ 1\cdot3593 \\ -3\cdot0830 \end{bmatrix} = \begin{bmatrix} 0\cdot3639 \\ 0\cdot1758 \\ -0\cdot3584 \end{bmatrix}.$$

Substituting this solution in the original equations,

$$\rho_1^* = 0\cdot4867$$

and
$$\rho_2^* = -0\cdot4057.$$

As before, $\mu^* = 1\cdot5623$. The other estimates agree well with the values previously obtained.

$$y'A\theta^*$$
$$= (34\cdot37)(1\cdot5623) + (21\cdot21)(0\cdot4867) + \ldots + (9\cdot86)(-0\cdot3584) = 61\cdot39.$$

The value of $y'y$ is $64\cdot74$ and thus

$$R = 64\cdot74 - 61\cdot39 = 3\cdot35.$$

Here $n = 22$, $p = 6$, and $m = 2$, so that the estimate of σ^2 is

$$(3\cdot35)/18 = 0\cdot186.$$

For the dispersion matrix of κ_1^*, κ_2^*, and κ_3^*, we need

$$I - D(BD)^{-1}B = (1/22) \begin{bmatrix} 17 & -8 & -9 \\ -5 & 14 & -9 \\ -5 & -8 & 13 \end{bmatrix}.$$

$$\mathscr{D}\begin{bmatrix} \kappa_1^* \\ \kappa_2^* \\ \kappa_3^* \end{bmatrix} = (\sigma^2/22) \begin{bmatrix} 17 & -8 & -9 \\ -5 & 14 & -9 \\ -5 & -8 & 13 \end{bmatrix} \begin{bmatrix} 0\cdot2040 & 0\cdot0013 & -0\cdot0034 \\ 0\cdot0013 & 0\cdot1254 & -0\cdot0010 \\ -0\cdot0034 & -0\cdot0010 & 0\cdot1139 \end{bmatrix}$$

$$= \sigma^2 \begin{bmatrix} 0\cdot1586 & -0\cdot0442 & -0\cdot0489 \\ -0\cdot0442 & 0\cdot0799 & -0\cdot0465 \\ -0\cdot0488 & -0\cdot0465 & 0\cdot0684 \end{bmatrix}.$$

The result is slightly asymmetrical on account of rounding-off errors but checks satisfactorily on post-multiplication by $[5\ 8\ 9]'$, which should, in theory, give a column of zeros.

3.6. Extended principle of least squares

Suppose once again that rank $A = p$. We shall derive the best linear unbiased estimate of θ when $\mathscr{D}y = \sigma^2 V$, where V is a positive definite matrix, known exactly, and σ^2 is unknown.

Denote by P the lower triangular matrix such that $V = PP'$, and define $z = P^{-1}y$. Then

$$\mathscr{E}z = P^{-1}\mathscr{E}y = P^{-1}A\theta,$$

and
$$\mathscr{D}z = P^{-1}\mathscr{D}y(P^{-1})' = \sigma^2 I.$$

:

Since P^{-1} is non-singular, $P^{-1}A$ has the same rank as A, namely p. According to Section 3, the best linear unbiased estimate of θ is

$$\theta^* = (A'(P^{-1})'P^{-1}A)^{-1}A'(P^{-1})'z = (A'V^{-1}A)^{-1}A'V^{-1}y.$$

Its dispersion matrix is

$$\mathscr{D}\theta^* = \sigma^2(A'(P^{-1})'P^{-1}A)^{-1} = \sigma^2(A'V^{-1}A)^{-1}.$$

An unbiased estimate of σ^2 is $R/(n-p)$, where

$$R = (z-P^{-1}A\theta^*)'(z-P^{-1}A\theta^*) = (y-A\theta^*)'V^{-1}(y-A\theta^*).$$

We are justified in describing θ^* as resulting from an extension of the principle of least squares because it is the value of θ at which the quadratic form $\quad W = (y-A\theta)'V^{-1}(y-A\theta)$

attains its absolute minimum. The extension was made by Aitken (1934).

Example 6. Let $y_1, y_2, ..., y_5$ be an ordered sample of five observations from a normal population with mean μ and standard deviation σ, the order being $y_1 < y_2 < y_3 < y_4 < y_5$. The problem is to find the best linear unbiased estimate of σ.

Define $x_i = (y_i-\mu)/\sigma$. Then

$$\mathscr{E}y \doteq \mu.1+\sigma.\mathscr{E}x \quad \text{and} \quad \mathscr{D}y = \sigma^2\mathscr{D}x.$$

Godwin (1949 b, and personal communication, 1951) has computed that

$$\mathscr{E}x = \begin{bmatrix} -1{\cdot}1629645 \\ -0{\cdot}4950190 \\ 0 \\ \vdots \\ \vdots \end{bmatrix} \text{ and } \mathscr{D}x = \begin{bmatrix} 0{\cdot}4475341 & 0{\cdot}2243310 & 0{\cdot}1481477 & 0{\cdot}1057720 & 0{\cdot}0742153 \\ & 0{\cdot}3115190 & 0{\cdot}2084354 & 0{\cdot}1499427 \\ & & 0{\cdot}2868337 \\ & & & \\ & & & \end{bmatrix}$$

where several elements can be omitted because $\mathscr{E}x_i = -\mathscr{E}x_{n-i}$ and $\mathscr{D}x$ is symmetrical about both diagonals. With the same convention,

$$V^{-1} = \begin{bmatrix} 3{\cdot}4970062 & -2{\cdot}5490533 & 0{\cdot}0339322 & 0{\cdot}0136506 & 0{\cdot}0044643 \\ & 8{\cdot}1066177 & -4{\cdot}6083840 & 0{\cdot}0371690 \\ & & 10{\cdot}1489036 \\ & & & \\ & & & \end{bmatrix}.$$

Next, $A'V^{-1} = \begin{bmatrix} 1{\cdot}0000000 & 1{\cdot}0000000 & 1{\cdot}0000000 & \cdot & \cdot \\ -2{\cdot}7931151 & -1{\cdot}0141968 & 0 & \cdot & \cdot \end{bmatrix}.$

The first row should, in theory, consist of units, and is calculated as a further check on V^{-1}. $A'V^{-1}A$ is a diagonal matrix whose $(2,2)$

element is $7 \cdot 5006808$. On dividing the second row of $A'V^{-1}A$ by $7 \cdot 5006808$, we obtain the coefficients in

$$\sigma^* = 0 \cdot 3723815(y_5 - y_1) + 0 \cdot 1352140(y_4 - y_2).$$

3.7. Exercises

Unless otherwise stated, $\mathscr{E}y = A\theta$, where A has full rank, and $\mathscr{D}y = \sigma^2 I$.

1. Prove that

$$(\textstyle\sum w_r)(\textstyle\sum c_r^2/w_r) - (\textstyle\sum c_r)^2 \equiv \textstyle\sum\sum_{r<s} w_r w_s (c_r/w_r - c_s/w_s)^2.$$

The observations y_r each have mean θ; y_r has variance $1/w_r$; and y_r and y_s are uncorrelated ($r \neq s$). If $\sum c_r y_r$ is an unbiased estimate of θ, use the above identity to show that its variance is a minimum when c_r/w_r is constant. Find this constant and the minimum variance. (Markoff, 1912, § 38.)

2. If $\theta^+ = Ly$ is an unbiased estimate of θ, show that $x'(LL')x \leqslant x'C^{-1}x$ for any vector x. By integrating $\exp\{-x'(LL')x\}$ over a suitable range of x, or otherwise, prove that each principal minor of $\mathscr{D}\theta^*$ is not greater than the corresponding principal minor of $\mathscr{D}\theta^+$. (Aitken, 1934.)

3. Suppose that $\mathscr{E}y = A\theta + B\phi$ and $\mathscr{D}y = \sigma^2 I$. Prove the following assertions, in which C, θ^*, R, and H have their usual meanings.

(i) The least squares estimate of ϕ is given by

$$B'HB\phi^0 = B'Hy.$$

(ii) The least squares estimate of θ is

$$\theta^0 = \theta^* - C^{-1}A'B\phi^0.$$

(iii) $\mathscr{D}\theta^0 = \sigma^2\{C^{-1} + C^{-1}A'B(B'HB)^{-1}B'AC^{-1}\}$.

(iv) The sum of squared residuals is

$$R^0 = R - y'HB\phi^0. \qquad \text{(Grundy, 1951.)}$$

4. In an experiment whose design matrix is $A = \begin{bmatrix} A_1 \\ \hline A_2 \end{bmatrix}$, the vector of observations corresponding to A_1 is y_1 and the vector of observations corresponding to A_2 is missing. $\mathscr{E}y_1 = A_1\theta$ and $\mathscr{D}y_1 = \sigma^2 I$. Prove that the least squares estimate of θ is

(i) $\theta^0 = C^{-1}(A_1'y_1 + A_2'y_2)$,

where y_2 is obtained as the solution of (i) and

(ii) $y_2 = A_2\theta^0$.

Prove further that

(iii) $\mathscr{D}\theta^0 = \sigma^2\{C^{-1} + C^{-1}A_2'(I - A_2 C^{-1}A_2')^{-1}A_2 C^{-1}\}$;

(iv) the sum of squared residuals is $(y - A\theta^0)'(y - A\theta^0)$, where y denotes $\begin{bmatrix} y_1 \\ \hline y_2 \end{bmatrix}$.

(Yates, 1933.)

5. The observations are normally and independently distributed. Show that $2R^2/(n - p + 2)$ is an unbiased estimate of $\mathscr{V}R$.

6. The observations are divisible into p groups. All those in the jth group, which contains n_j members, have expectation θ_j $(j = 1, 2, ..., p)$. If $\gamma\sigma^4$ is the fourth cumulant of each observation, prove that

$$\mathscr{V} R = \sigma^4\{2(n-p)+\gamma(n-2p+\textstyle\sum n_j^{-1})\}.$$

7. $\mathscr{D}y = \sigma^2 V$ and the columns of A are latent vectors of V. Show that the estimates $(A'A)^{-1}A'y$ and $(A'V^{-1}A)^{-1}A'V^{-1}y$ are both equal to $A'y$.

8. $\mathscr{E}y = A\theta$ and $\mathscr{D}y = \sigma^2 V$. The design matrix A contains a column of unit elements, denoted by 1. Verify that

$$(I - AC^{-1}A')1 = 0.$$

If $\qquad\qquad V = (1-\rho)I + \rho 11' \quad (0 \leqslant \rho < 1)$

prove that

    (i) $V^{-1} = I/(1-\rho) - \rho 11'/(1-\rho)\{1+(n-1)\rho\}$;

    (ii) $(A'V^{-1}A)^{-1} = (1-\rho)C^{-1} + \rho C^{-1}A'11'A C^{-1}$;

    (iii) the best linear unbiased estimate of θ is $C^{-1}A'y$;

    (iv) $R = y'(I - AC^{-1}A')y/(1-\rho)$.

9. A sample of size n is taken from the distribution whose density function is

$$f(u) = 1/\theta_2 \quad (\theta_1 - \tfrac{1}{2}\theta_2 \leqslant u \leqslant \theta_1 + \tfrac{1}{2}\theta_2).$$

The observations of the ordered sample are $y_1 < y_2 < ... < y_n$. If $x_r = (y_r - \theta_1 + \tfrac{1}{2}\theta_2)/\theta_2$, show that $\mathscr{E}x_r = r/(n+1)$ and

$$\mathscr{C}(x_r, x_s) = r(n+1-s)/(n+1)^2(n+2) \quad (r \leqslant s).$$

Prove that the inverse of the dispersion matrix of x is proportional to

$$\begin{bmatrix}
2 & -1 & 0 & 0 & 0 & . & . & 0 & 0 \\
-1 & 2 & -1 & 0 & 0 & . & . & 0 & 0 \\
0 & -1 & 2 & -1 & 0 & . & . & 0 & 0 \\
. & . & . & . & . & . & . & . & . \\
0 & 0 & 0 & 0 & 0 & . & . & -1 & 2
\end{bmatrix}$$

and hence show that the best linear estimates of θ_1 and θ_2 in terms of $y_1, y_2, ..., y_n$ are respectively

$$\theta_1^* = \tfrac{1}{2}(y_n + y_1) \qquad \text{and} \qquad \theta_2^* = (n+1)(y_n - y_1)/(n-1).$$

(Godwin, 1949 a; Lloyd, 1952.)

10. Suppose that y is symmetrically distributed about its mean μ with standard deviation σ, and let the observations of an ordered sample be $y_1 < y_2 < ... < y_n$. Put $x_r = (y_r - \mu)/\sigma$. If $\mathscr{D}x = \sigma^2 V$, where $V1 = 1$, prove that the best linear estimate of μ in terms of $y_1, y_2, ..., y_n$ is the sample mean.

(Lloyd, 1952.)

3.8. References

AITKEN, A. C. (1934). On least squares and linear combination of observations. *Proc. Roy. Soc. Edinb.* A, **55**, 42–47.

GAUSS, C. F. (1873). Theoria combinationis observationum erroribus minimis obnoxiae. *Werke*, **4**, 3–93. Göttingen.

GODWIN, H. J. (1949 a). On the estimation of dispersion by linear systematic statistics. *Biometrika*, **36**, 92–100.

GODWIN, H. J. (1949 b). Some low moments of order statistics. *Ann. Math. Statist.* **20**, 279–85.

GRUNDY, P. M. (1951). A general technique for the analysis of experiments with incorrectly treated plots. *J. R. Statist. Soc.* B, **13**, 272–83.

HSU, P. L. (1938). On the best unbiassed quadratic estimate of the variance. *Statist. Res. Mem.* **2**, 91–104.

LLOYD, E. H. (1952). Least-squares estimation of location and scale parameters using order statistics. *Biometrika*, **39**, 88–95.

MARKOFF, A. A. (1912). *Wahrscheinlichkeitsrechnung* (trans. H. Liebmann). Leipzig and Berlin : Teubner.

PLACKETT, R. L. (1950). Some theorems in least squares. *Biometrika*, **37**, 149–57.

QUENOUILLE, M. H. (1950). Computational devices in the application of least squares. *J. R. Statist. Soc.* B, **12**, 256–72.

RAO, C. R. (1946). On the linear combination of observations and the general theory of least squares. *Sankhyā*, **7**, 237–56.

—— (1952). Some theorems on minimum variance estimation. *Sankhyā*, **12**, 27–42.

STEVENS, W. L. (1948). Statistical analysis of a non-orthogonal tri-factorial experiment. *Biometrika*, **35**, 346–67.

YATES, F. (1933). The analysis of replicated experiments when the field results are incomplete. *Emp. J. Exp. Agric.* **1**, 129–42.

—— (1949). *Sampling Methods for Censuses and Surveys.* London : Griffin.

—— and HALE, R. W. (1939). The analysis of Latin squares when two or more rows, columns, or treatments are missing. *J. R. Statist. Soc. Suppl.* **6**, 67–79.

LINEAR HYPOTHESES

4.1. Introduction

THIS Chapter is a continuation of the preceding and the following assumptions are made once again. An experiment results in n observations, which form a random vector variable y. $\mathscr{E}y = A\theta$, where A is a known matrix, and θ is a vector of p unknown parameters; and $\mathscr{D}y = \sigma^2 I$, where σ^2 also is unknown.

Let $\mathfrak{h}$ be a hypothesis which asserts that the parameters $\theta_1, \theta_2,..., \theta_p$ are subject to specified linear restrictions. We shall formulate and discuss rules of procedure for testing whether $\mathfrak{h}$ is supported or contradicted by the experimental data, and indicate what conclusions can be drawn when $\mathfrak{h}$ is rejected.

4.2. Estimation under linear constraints

A linear hypothesis $\mathfrak{h}$ is a system of linear constraints on the values of $\theta_1, \theta_2,..., \theta_p$. It can be expressed in matrix form as

$$Q\theta = z, \tag{1}$$

where Q has order $b \times p$ and rank b ($\leqslant p$), z has order $b \times 1$, and both Q and z are specified.

When $\mathfrak{h}$ is true, the best linear unbiased estimate of θ is obtained by minimizing
$$W = (y - A\theta)'(y - A\theta) \tag{2}$$

with respect to variation in θ, subject to the condition (1). This can be shown by the following argument. Suppose that the first b columns of Q form a non-singular matrix. If not, relabel the elements of θ so that this is the case. One method of calculating the relative minimum of W would then be to solve the system of equations (1) for $\theta_1, \theta_2,..., \theta_b$ in terms of $\theta_{b+1}, \theta_{b+2},..., \theta_p$; express W as a function of $\theta_{b+1}, \theta_{b+2},..., \theta_p$; and minimize W with respect to these parameters. Since the minimizing values of $\theta_{b+1}, \theta_{b+2},..., \theta_p$ are derived by the principle of least squares, they are the best linear unbiased estimates of these parameters; and since $\theta_1, \theta_2,..., \theta_b$ are linear combinations of $\theta_{b+1}, \theta_{b+2},..., \theta_p$, we obtain their best linear unbiased estimates on substituting those for $\theta_{b+1}, \theta_{b+2},..., \theta_p$.

When the rank of A is p, the relative minimum of W can be found explicitly as follows. We have shown that

$$W = R + (\theta^* - \theta)'C(\theta^* - \theta) \qquad (3.4.2)$$

and the problem is therefore equivalent to minimizing $(\theta^* - \theta)'C(\theta^* - \theta)$ with respect to variation in θ, subject to (1). Introduce a vector λ of b undetermined multipliers $\lambda_1, \lambda_2, ..., \lambda_b$. Differentiating

$$\sum_{j=1}^{p} \sum_{k=1}^{p} c_{jk}(\theta_j^* - \theta_j)(\theta_k^* - \theta_k) + \sum_{i=1}^{b} \lambda_i \left(\sum_{j=1}^{p} q_{ij}\theta_j - z_i \right)$$

with respect to θ_k,

$$- \sum_{j=1}^{p} c_{jk}(\theta_j^* - \theta_j) + \sum_{i=1}^{b} \lambda_i q_{ik} = 0.$$

Accumulating the results for $k = 1, 2, ..., p$,

$$Q'\lambda = C(\theta^* - \theta). \qquad (3)$$

Now C is positive definite, whence

$$QC^{-1}Q'\lambda = Q(\theta^* - \theta) = Q\theta^* - z.$$

Again, $QC^{-1}Q'$ is positive definite, for Q has rank b, and so

$$\lambda = (QC^{-1}Q')^{-1}(Q\theta^* - z). \qquad (4)$$

The value of θ given by (3) and (4) is

$$\theta^+ = \theta^* - C^{-1}Q'(QC^{-1}Q')^{-1}(Q\theta^* - z). \qquad (5)$$

This is the value at which $(\theta^* - \theta)'C(\theta^* - \theta)$ attains its relative minimum; for consider the identity

$$(\theta^* - \theta)'C(\theta^* - \theta) \equiv (\theta^* - \theta^+)'C(\theta^* - \theta^+) + (\theta^+ - \theta)'C(\theta^+ - \theta) + $$
$$+ 2(\theta^+ - \theta)'C(\theta^* - \theta^+).$$

From (3), $\qquad (\theta^+ - \theta)'C(\theta^* - \theta^+) = (\theta^+ - \theta)'Q'\lambda,$

which is zero, because $Q\theta = Q\theta^+ = z$ and so $Q(\theta^+ - \theta) = 0$. Consequently

$$(\theta^* - \theta)'C(\theta^* - \theta) = (\theta^* - \theta^+)'C(\theta^* - \theta^+) + (\theta^+ - \theta)'C(\theta^+ - \theta), \qquad (6)$$

whence the result stated, since $(\theta^+ - \theta)'C(\theta^+ - \theta)$ is a positive definite quadratic form.

Thus θ^+ is the best linear unbiased estimate of θ when $\mathfrak{h}$ is true. Direct calculation gives

$$\mathscr{D}\theta^+ = \sigma^2 \{ C^{-1} - C^{-1}Q'(QC^{-1}Q')^{-1}QC^{-1} \}. \qquad (7)$$

From (3.4.2) and (6) we deduce that the relative minimum of W, say E, is given by

$$E = R + (\theta^* - \theta^+)'C(\theta^* - \theta^+). \qquad (8)$$

This is the sum of squared residuals which would be obtained by expressing W as a function of $\theta_{b+1}, \theta_{b+2}, ..., \theta_p$ and therefore

$$\mathscr{E}E = (n-p+b)\sigma^2. \tag{9}$$

When the rank of A is less than p, the relative minimum of W and the value of θ at which it is attained are best calculated by substituting into $A\theta$ either $Q\theta = z$, or some convenient equivalent set of constraints, and then using the appropriate technique from the previous Chapter.

Example 1. Observations are made on different parameters but are *conditioned* in the sense that the parameters are subject to linear constraints. Denote $\mathscr{E}y$ by η and suppose that $Q\eta = 0$. We require the best linear estimate of η, its dispersion matrix and the sum of squared residuals.

Here $A = I$ so that $\eta^* = y$ and $R = 0$. Since also $z = 0$, we obtain

$$\eta^+ = y - Q'(QQ')^{-1}Qy,$$
$$\mathscr{D}\eta^+ = \sigma^2\{I - Q'(QQ')^{-1}Q\},$$

and
$$E = y'Q'(QQ')^{-1}Qy.$$

Take $y' = [679{\cdot}0, 405{\cdot}2, 294{\cdot}2, 458{\cdot}3, 165{\cdot}5, 143{\cdot}5, 294{\cdot}9]$ and

$$Q = \begin{bmatrix} 1 & -1 & -1 & 0 & 0 & 0 & 0 \\ 0 & 0 & 1 & -1 & 1 & 0 & 0 \\ 0 & 0 & 0 & 0 & 1 & 1 & -1 \end{bmatrix}.$$

Then
$$(QQ')^{-1} = \tfrac{1}{21}\begin{bmatrix} 8 & 3 & -1 \\ 3 & 9 & -3 \\ -1 & -3 & 8 \end{bmatrix}$$

whence $(\eta^+)' = [687{\cdot}2, 397{\cdot}0, 290{\cdot}3, 454{\cdot}0, 163{\cdot}7, 137{\cdot}4, 301{\cdot}0]$

and $E = 248{\cdot}71.$

The estimated variance of the adjusted value $687{\cdot}2$, for instance, is $(13/21)(248{\cdot}71/3) = 51{\cdot}32$, and its standard error is $7{\cdot}16$.

4.3. The variance-ratio test

The *sum of squares* corresponding to a linear hypothesis $\mathfrak{h}$ is denoted by S and defined as $E-R$, i.e. the difference between the relative minimum of W when $\mathfrak{h}$ is true and the absolute minimum of W.

When the rank of A is p, (2.8) shows that

$$S = (\theta^* - \theta^+)'C(\theta^* - \theta^+). \tag{1}$$

Denote $Q\theta - z$ by ψ and substitute for $\theta^* - \theta^+$ from (2.5), whence also

$$S = \{Q(\theta^* - \theta) + \psi\}'(QC^{-1}Q')^{-1}\{Q(\theta^* - \theta) + \psi\}. \tag{2}$$

Using the formula (2.2.1) for the expectation of a quadratic form,

$$\mathscr{E}S = b\sigma^2 + \psi'(QC^{-1}Q')^{-1}\psi. \tag{3}$$

When $\mathfrak{h}$ is true, ψ is zero, and S/b is an unbiased estimate of σ^2. Otherwise, S/b tends to overestimate σ^2 because $\psi'(QC^{-1}Q')^{-1}\psi$ is a positive definite quadratic form. These results suggest that $\mathfrak{h}$ can be tested by comparing S/b with $R/(n-p)$, which is an unbiased estimate of σ^2 whether $\mathfrak{h}$ is true or not. A suitable test criterion is therefore the ratio of S/b to $R/(n-p)$, for $(n-p)S/bR$ is independent of the unknown σ^2. This criterion is termed the *variance-ratio* and denoted by F. Values of F will lie near unity when $\mathfrak{h}$ is true, but will tend to be larger than unity when $\mathfrak{h}$ is false. Thus large values of the variance-ratio indicate that $\mathfrak{h}$ should be rejected.

When the rank of A is less than p, say $p-m$, the argument justifying the use of the variance-ratio remains valid because $\mathscr{E}y$ can be expressed in the form $X\phi$, where X has full rank. The only modification of importance rests in the value of $\mathscr{E}S$ when $\mathfrak{h}$ is true. Let D be the matrix defined in Section 3.5. The argument given there in respect of $B\theta = 0$ shows that the number of linear restrictions which $\mathfrak{h}$ imposes on $\eta = A\theta$ is rank Q — rank QD. Hence $\mathfrak{h}$ reduces the number of independent parameters in the specification of η from $(p-m)$ to $(p-m)-(b-x)$, where x denotes rank QD. Consequently, when $\mathfrak{h}$ is true,

$$\mathscr{E}S = (b-x)\sigma^2. \tag{4}$$

Example 2. The observations are divisible into p groups. Those in the jth group have expectation θ_j and they are denoted by y_{jk} ($j = 1, 2, ..., p$; $k = 1, 2, ..., n_j$). We require the sum of squares corresponding to the hypothesis

$$\theta_1 = \theta_2 = ... = \theta_p.$$

Write y_{j0} for $\displaystyle\sum_{k=1}^{n_j} y_{jk}$ and y_{00} for $\displaystyle\sum_{j=1}^{p}\sum_{k=1}^{n_j} y_{jk}$.

$$W = \sum_{j=1}^{p}\sum_{k=1}^{n_j}(y_{jk} - \theta_j)^2.$$

Since the minimum of $\displaystyle\sum_{k=1}^{n_j}(y_{jk} - \theta_j)^2$ occurs when $\theta_j = y_{j0}/n_j$,

$$R = \sum_{j=1}^{p}\sum_{k=1}^{n_j} y_{jk}^2 - \sum_{j=1}^{p} y_{j0}^2/n_j.$$

The relative minimum of W under $\mathfrak{h}$ is the absolute minimum of

$$\sum_{j=1}^{p} \sum_{k=1}^{n_j} (y_{jk}-\theta)^2$$

with respect to variation in θ and is therefore

$$E = \sum_{j=1}^{p} \sum_{k=1}^{n_j} y_{jk}^2 - y_{00}^2/n.$$

Hence
$$S = \sum_{j=1}^{p} y_{j0}^2/n_j - y_{00}^2/n.$$

Let Q be a matrix of rank $p-1$ such that $Q1 = 0$. Then the only solution of the system
$$Q\theta = 0$$
is
$$\theta_1 = \theta_2 = \ldots = \theta_p.$$
From this alternative expression for $\mathfrak{h}$ we see that the value of b is $p-1$.

Example 3. In the following data, each observation in the cell formed by the ith row and jth column has mean $\mu+\rho_i+\kappa_j$ and variance σ^2 $(i = 1, 2; j = 1, 2, 3)$.

2·45	2·82	1·85			
2·89	1·89	1·52	1·79	1·28	2·24
2·48					
1·00	1·25	1·55	1·55	0·55	0·57
1·46	1·81	1·54	0·57	0·94	0·37

These data were discussed in Section 3.5, where we introduced the restrictions
$$10\rho_1+12\rho_2 = 0$$
and
$$5\kappa_1+8\kappa_2+9\kappa_3 = 0,$$
since the rank of the design matrix is 2 less than the number of parameters. We wish to test the hypothesis, $\mathfrak{h}_\kappa$, that
$$\kappa_1 = \kappa_2 = \kappa_3,$$
in which case their common value is evidently zero.

The sum of squared residuals for these data is $R = 3\cdot35$. Denote the observations in the ith row by $\{y_{ik}\}$ where $k = 1, 2,\ldots, n_i$ $(n_1 = 10, n_2 = 12)$. Under the hypothesis stated,
$$\mathscr{E}y_{ik} = \mu+\rho_i,$$
and the relative minimum of W is therefore
$$E_\kappa = \sum_{i=1}^{2} \sum_{k=1}^{n_i} y_{ik}^2 - \sum_{i=1}^{2} y_{i0}^2/n_i.$$
Here $E_\kappa = 5\cdot32$, giving $S_\kappa = 1\cdot97$.

Let θ' denote $[\mu, \rho_1, \rho_2, \kappa_1, \kappa_2, \kappa_3]$. Then $\mathfrak{h}_\kappa$ can be expressed as $Q\theta = 0$ where Q has the form

$$\begin{bmatrix} 0 & 0 & 0 & r_1 & r_2 & r_3 \\ 0 & 0 & 0 & s_1 & s_2 & s_3 \end{bmatrix}$$

in which $r_1+r_2+r_3 = s_1+s_2+s_3 = 0$, and the two rows are linearly independent. Since

$$D' = \begin{bmatrix} -1 & 1 & 1 & 0 & 0 & 0 \\ -1 & 0 & 0 & 1 & 1 & 1 \end{bmatrix},$$

we obtain $QD = 0$ and therefore $b_\kappa = 2$. Similarly $S_\rho = 4 \cdot 14$ and $b_\rho = 1$.

These results can be presented in tabular form as an *analysis of variance*, in which the divisors b_κ, b_ρ and $n-p$ are described as the *degrees of freedom* associated with the corresponding sums of squares, or sum of squared residuals.

Hypothesis	Sum of squares	Degrees of freedom	Mean square
$\rho_1 = \rho_2$	4·14	1	4·14
$\kappa_1 = \kappa_2 = \kappa_3$	1·97	2	0·98
Residual	3·35	18	0·186

The last column consists of the ratios S/b and $R/(n-p)$. It gives a variance-ratio of 22·3 for rows and 5·3 for columns.

The use of the variance-ratio can be placed on a more precise numerical basis by making some assumption which completely specifies the probability distribution of the observations, and then evaluating the corresponding distribution of F when $\mathfrak{h}$ is true. We proceed to do this when y is normally distributed with the specified values of $\mathscr{E}y$ and $\mathscr{D}y$.

When $\mathfrak{h}$ is true, $\psi = 0$, and (2) becomes

$$S = (y-A\theta)'AC^{-1}Q'(QC^{-1}Q')^{-1}QC^{-1}A'(y-A\theta). \tag{5}$$

The matrix of this quadratic form is idempotent so that all its latent roots are either 1 or 0. Taking expectations, we find that its trace is b, whence its rank is also b. The distribution theory of Section 2.4 now shows that S/σ^2 is distributed as χ^2 with b degrees of freedom. Similarly

$$R = (y-A\theta')'(I-AC^{-1}A')(y-A\theta) \tag{3.4.3}$$

is a quadratic form with an idempotent matrix of rank $n-p$, whence R/σ^2 is distributed as χ^2 with $(n-p)$ degrees of freedom. Moreover, R and S are statistically independent by the criterion of Section 2.5,

because
$$(I - AC^{-1}A')AC^{-1}Q'(QC^{-1}Q')^{-1}QC^{-1}A' = 0.$$

Using the formula (2.6.2) for the probability distribution of a ratio, and writing $c = n - p$, we find that the density function of cS/bR is

$$g(F; b, c) = \frac{b^{\frac{1}{2}b}c^{\frac{1}{2}c}F^{\frac{1}{2}b-1}}{B(\frac{1}{2}b, \frac{1}{2}c)(c+bF)^{\frac{1}{2}(b+c)}} \qquad (0 \leqslant F < \infty). \tag{6}$$

This density was first derived by Fisher (1922) and was incorporated in a general framework for testing linear hypotheses by Kolodziejczyk (1935). It is described as the F-distribution with b degrees of freedom in the numerator and c degrees of freedom in the denominator. The corresponding random variable is denoted by $F(b, c)$, and the constant $F_\alpha(b, c)$ is defined by

$$\Pr\{F(b, c) \geqslant F_\alpha(b, c)\} = \alpha.$$

Tables of $F_\alpha(b, c)$ are listed by Fletcher, Miller, and Rosenhead (1946).

Example 4. In Example 3 the value $F = 5\cdot3$ was observed, with $b = 2$ and $c = 18$. Assuming normality, and referring to a table of $F_\alpha(b, c)$, we find that this value of F corresponds to a probability between $2\frac{1}{2}$ per cent and 1 per cent. An experimenter who rejected the possibility that an event as rare as this had occurred in his observations would accordingly dismiss the hypothesis that $\kappa_1 = \kappa_2 = \kappa_3$.

4.4. Power of the variance-ratio test

Throughout the remainder of this Chapter we shall continue to suppose that y is normally distributed. The test illustrated at the end of the previous Section is adequate for practical situations, but not definite enough for theoretical purposes, and a formal test of $\mathfrak{h}$ is defined as follows. Select a small probability α (usually $0\cdot05$ or $0\cdot01$) and determine from tables the value of $F_\alpha(b, c)$. Then $\mathfrak{h}$ is regarded as consistent with the data (or *accepted*) if the observed value of $F(b, c)$ falls below $F_\alpha(b, c)$; otherwise, $\mathfrak{h}$ is regarded as inconsistent with the data (or *rejected*). The reason for choosing α to be small is that it represents the probability of rejecting $\mathfrak{h}$ when $\mathfrak{h}$ is true; α is termed the *significance level* of the test.

The *power* of the formal test is defined as the probability with which it rejects $\mathfrak{h}$ when the value of $\psi = Q\theta - z$ may differ from zero, which is the value when $\mathfrak{h}$ is true. In order to present the discussion of power in its simplest terms, we begin by making a canonical reduction of the problem of testing $\mathfrak{h}$ (Hsu, 1941 a). Firstly, consider S. Let U be the

upper triangular matrix such that
$$U'U = (QC^{-1}Q')^{-1}.$$

Put
$$K = AC^{-1}Q'U'$$

and
$$v = K'y - Uz. \tag{1}$$

Alternatively
$$v = K'(y - A\theta) + U\psi$$

so that (3.2) becomes
$$S = v'v. \tag{2}$$

We note that
$$K'K = UQC^{-1}A'AC^{-1}Q'U' = UQC^{-1}Q'U' = I.$$

Secondly, consider R. Let T be the upper triangular matrix such that
$$T'T = C.$$

Then $M = AT^{-1}$ is orthogonal by columns and we can therefore find N such that $[M \vdots N]$ is a square orthogonal matrix. Thus
$$MM' + NN' = I$$

whence
$$NN' = I - AC^{-1}A'.$$

Starting from $(I - AC^{-1}A')A = 0$, we deduce successively that $N'A$ and $N'K$ are also zero. Put
$$w = N'y \tag{3}$$

and obtain
$$R = w'w. \tag{4}$$

The vectors v and w have the following properties:
  (i) $\mathscr{E}v = U\psi$, which is zero if and only if $\mathfrak{h}$ is true.
  (ii) $\mathscr{E}w = 0$, since $N'A = 0$.
  (iii) The elements of v and w are normally and independently distributed with the same variance σ^2, since $K'K = I, N'N = I$, and $N'K = 0$.

In consequence of these properties
  (I) θ^* has a normal multivariate distribution and is statistically independent of R;
  (II) S/σ^2 is distributed as non-central χ^2 with b degrees of freedom and parameter
$$\zeta = (U\psi)'(U\psi)/\sigma^2 = \psi'(QC^{-1}Q')\psi/\sigma^2;$$

  (III) R/σ^2 is independently distributed as χ^2 with c degrees of freedom;
  (IV) the ratio S/R has the density function (Tang, 1938)

$$h(x; \zeta) = \sum_{a=0}^{\infty} \{(\tfrac{1}{2}\zeta)^a e^{-\tfrac{1}{2}\zeta}/a!\}\{x^{\tfrac{1}{2}b+a+1}(1+x)^{-\tfrac{1}{2}(b+c)-a}/\mathrm{B}(\tfrac{1}{2}b+a, \tfrac{1}{2}c)\}. \tag{5}$$

As ζ increases in the neighbourhood of ζ_0, the terms in the first bracket decrease for $a < \frac{1}{2}\zeta_0$, and increase for $a > \frac{1}{2}\zeta_0$. Integrating the second bracket,

$$\int_{F_\alpha}^{\infty} x^{\frac{1}{2}b+a-1}(1+x)^{-\frac{1}{2}(b+c)-a}\, dx/\mathrm{B}(\tfrac{1}{2}b+a, \tfrac{1}{2}c)$$

$$= \int_{F_\alpha/(1+F_\alpha)}^{\infty} y^{\frac{1}{2}b+a-1}(1-y)^{\frac{1}{2}c-1}\, dy/\mathrm{B}(\tfrac{1}{2}b+a, \tfrac{1}{2}c),$$

which is an increasing function of a. Thus the power of the variance-ratio test increases as ζ increases in the neighbourhood of ζ_0. Since ζ_0 is arbitrary, the power increases steadily with ζ.

We now examine the relation between the variance-ratio test and other comparable tests of $\mathfrak{h}$. A test of $\mathfrak{h}$ is defined by considering the space of $b+c$ dimensions in which $v_1, v_2, ..., v_b, w_1, w_2, ..., w_c$ are current coordinates, and specifying a set of points $\mathfrak{D}$ in the space, such that $\mathfrak{h}$ is rejected whenever the sample point falls in $\mathfrak{D}$, which is termed the *critical region* of the test. For example, the critical region of the variance-ratio test is defined by the inequality

$$c \sum_{i=1}^{b} v_i^2 \geqslant bF_\alpha(b, c) \sum_{j=1}^{c} w_j^2. \tag{6}$$

One method of justifying the choice of this critical region is as follows. The problem of testing $\mathfrak{h}$ is left invariant by any orthogonal transformation from v to v_0, or from w to w_0, or by multiplying these vectors by the same constant, because the effect of such transformations is that the elements of v_0 and w_0 remain normally and independently distributed with the same variance and we still have $\mathscr{E}v_0 = 0$ if and only if $\mathfrak{h}$ is true. Making the requirement that the test criterion must also be invariant under these transformations, we find that it is necessarily a function of $\sum_{i=1}^{b} v_i^2 \Big/ \sum_{j=1}^{c} w_j^2$. Take $\sum_{i=1}^{b} v_i^2 \Big/ \sum_{j=1}^{c} w_j^2$ as the criterion, and suppose that the critical region $\mathfrak{m}$ is defined as the set of points x where

$$h(x; \zeta_0) \geqslant kh(x; 0),$$

the value of k being chosen so that

$$\int_{\mathfrak{m}} h(x; 0)\, dx = \alpha.$$

Let $\mathfrak{n}$ be any other set of points x such that

$$\int_{\mathfrak{n}} h(x; 0)\, dx = \alpha.$$

According to the Neyman-Pearson lemma (Cramér, § 35.3)

$$\int_{\mathfrak{m}} h(x;\zeta_0)\,dx \geqslant \int_{\mathfrak{n}} h(x;\zeta_0)\,dx.$$

Thus, while the tests corresponding to $\mathfrak{m}$ and $\mathfrak{n}$ have the same significance level, $\mathfrak{m}$ has greater power than $\mathfrak{n}$ at the alternative hypothesis $\zeta = \zeta_0$. In the present application, the ratio

$$h(x;\zeta)/h(x;0) = \sum_{a=0}^{\infty} \{\tfrac{1}{2}\zeta x/(1+x)\}^a e^{-\frac{1}{2}\zeta} B(\tfrac{1}{2}b,\tfrac{1}{2}c)/a! B(\tfrac{1}{2}b+a,\tfrac{1}{2}c)$$

which is a steadily increasing function of x for any $\zeta > 0$.

Hence the test of $\mathfrak{h}$ obtained by regarding large values of

$$\sum_{i=1}^{b} v_i^2 \Big/ \sum_{j=1}^{c} w_j^2$$

as significant is uniformly more powerful than other tests using the same criterion and the same significance level but different critical regions. Combining both results, we conclude that the critical region defined by (6) gives the *uniformly most powerful invariant* test of $\mathfrak{h}$ (Lehmann, 1950).

Another optimum property of the variance-ratio test is concerned with the way in which its power increases with departures from $\mathfrak{h}$. We begin with an alternative expression of the fact that our test should be independent of σ^2. Let $\mathfrak{C}$ be the class of all tests of $\mathfrak{h}$ for which, as for the variance-ratio test, the probability of rejecting $\mathfrak{h}$ is independent of σ^2 when $\mathfrak{h}$ is true. Then any test in $\mathfrak{C}$ is such that its critical region encloses a constant proportion α of the surface area of any hypersphere

$$\sum_{i=1}^{b} v_i^2 + \sum_{j=1}^{c} w_j^2 = r^2. \tag{7}$$

The following proof is due to Wolfowitz (1949). Suppose, in fact, that $\mathfrak{D}$ encloses a proportion $\phi(r^2)$ of the surface area. Since r^2/σ^2 is distributed as χ^2 with $(b+c)$ degrees of freedom when $\mathfrak{h}$ is true,

$$\{\Gamma(\tfrac{1}{2}q)\}^{-1} \int_0^{\infty} \phi(x)\nu^{\frac{1}{2}q}x^{\frac{1}{2}q-1}e^{-\nu x}\,dx = \alpha,$$

where $\nu = 1/2\sigma^2$ and $q = b+c$. This equation is to hold for all positive values of ν. Rewrite it in the form

$$\{\alpha\Gamma(\tfrac{1}{2}q)\}^{-1} \int_0^{\infty} \phi(x)x^{\frac{1}{2}q-1}e^{-\nu x}\,dx = \nu^{-\frac{1}{2}q},$$

differentiate both sides k times with respect to ν, and put $\nu = 1$. We find that

$$j(x) = \phi(x)x^{\frac{1}{2}q-1}e^{-x}/\alpha\Gamma(\tfrac{1}{2}q)$$

is a density function whose kth moment is

$$(\tfrac{1}{2}q)(\tfrac{1}{2}q+1)\ldots(\tfrac{1}{2}q+k-1).$$

This, however, is the kth moment of the density function

$$x^{\frac{1}{2}q-1}e^{-x}/\Gamma(\tfrac{1}{2}q),$$

which, according to the criterion given by Cramér (1946, § 15.4), is the only distribution with the specified moments. Hence also

$$j(x) = x^{\frac{1}{2}q-1}e^{-x}/\Gamma(\tfrac{1}{2}q).$$

Thus, for all x, $\qquad\qquad \phi(x) = \alpha,$

a result equivalent to the completeness (Lehmann and Scheffé, 1950) of the family of probability densities obtained by varying the parameter ν in

$$\nu^{\frac{1}{2}q}x^{\frac{1}{2}q-1}e^{-\nu x}/\Gamma(\tfrac{1}{2}q).$$

Finally, we show that the variance-ratio test is such that the integral of its power over any surface

$$\psi'(QC^{-1}Q')^{-1}\psi = \xi^2 \quad (\xi > 0)$$

is greater than for any other test in $\mathfrak{C}$. This theorem was developed by Wald (1942) from a more restricted result of Hsu (1941 b), and the proof we give is again due to Wolfowitz (1949). Denote $U\psi$ by τ. The joint density function of the variables $v_1, v_2, \ldots, v_b,\ w_1, w_2, \ldots, w_c$ is

$$f(v_i, w_j) = (2\pi\sigma^2)^{-\frac{1}{2}(b+c)}\exp\Big[-\Big\{\sum_{i=1}^{b}(v_i-\tau_i)^2 + \sum_{j=1}^{c}w_j^2\Big\}\Big/2\sigma^2\Big].$$

Integrating this expression over the surface $\sum_{i=1}^{b}\tau_i^2 = \xi^2$, on which $d\rho$ represents an element of area, we obtain

$$(2\pi\sigma^2)^{-\frac{1}{2}c}\exp\Big\{-\sum_{j=1}^{c}w_j^2/2\sigma^2\Big\}\int_{\substack{\sum_{i=1}^{b}\tau_i^2 = \xi^2}}\cdots\int(2\pi\sigma^2)^{-\frac{1}{2}b}\times$$

$$\times\exp\Big\{-\sum_{i=1}^{b}(v_i-\tau_i)^2/2\sigma^2\Big\}d\rho.$$

The integral here can be evaluated by interchanging x and ξ in the density function for $x = \Big(\sum_{i=1}^{b}v_i^2\Big)^{\frac{1}{2}}$, namely

$$\sigma^{-2}x^{\frac{1}{2}b}\xi^{1-\frac{1}{2}b}\exp\{-(x^2+\xi^2)/2\sigma^2\}I_{\frac{1}{2}b-1}(x\xi/\sigma^2).$$

Consequently

$$\int_b \cdots \int f(v_i, w_j)\, d\rho$$
$$\sum_{i=1} \tau_i^2 = \xi^2$$
$$= (2\pi)^{-\frac{1}{2}c}\sigma^{-c-2}\xi^{\frac{1}{2}b}x^{1-\frac{1}{2}b}\exp\{-(r^2+\xi^2)/2\sigma^2\}I_{\frac{1}{2}b-1}(x\xi/\sigma^2). \quad (8)$$

Since the least index of x in $I_{\frac{1}{2}b-1}(x\xi/\sigma^2)$ is $\frac{1}{2}b-1$, the least index of x in (8) is zero, and so this integral is a monotonically increasing function of x. Consider now the integral of (8) over the critical region of the test. As proved above, $\mathfrak{D}$ encloses a proportion α of the surface area of every hypersphere (7), and the integral of (8) will therefore be maximized by choosing the part of the area where the values of x^2 are as large as possible. Hence x^2/r^2 is constant over the boundary of the critical region, and this quantity, or equivalently

$$x^2/(r^2-x^2) = \sum_{i=1}^{b} v_i^2 \bigg/ \sum_{j=1}^{c} w_j^2$$

must be chosen as large as possible to provide the critical region which maximizes the power of the test. This leads to the variance-ratio criterion, and so completes the proof.

Further optimum properties are proved by Lehmann (1950), who shows, for example, that the variance-ratio test is most stringent, and that it minimizes the maximum expected loss with respect to any invariant risk function. However, the general theory which he describes takes no account of the fact that slight reductions in power or increases in expected loss may be offset by considerable gains in time resulting from the calculation of simplified test criteria, and we therefore turn to discuss this aspect of the problem of testing hypotheses.

4.5. Alternative tests

Suppose that each observation has mean θ and variance σ^2. We wish to test the hypothesis that θ has a specified value μ. The corresponding variance-ratio is

$$F(1, n-1) = (y.-\mu)^2 n(n-1)\bigg/ \sum_{i=1}^{n}(y_i-y.)^2, \quad (1)$$

where $y.$ is the mean of $y_1, y_2, ..., y_n$. However, the first test criterion proposed for this problem ('Student', 1908) is

$$t = (y.-\mu)\bigg/\sqrt{\bigg\{n(n-1)\bigg/ \sum_{i=1}^{n}(y_i-y.)^2\bigg\}}, \quad (2)$$

and there is evidently greater scope in choosing a critical region for t than for t^2. Define

$$t_\alpha(c) = \sqrt{F_\alpha(1, c)}, \tag{3}$$

and suppress the argument c when its value is understood. If the alternatives to $\theta = \mu$ comprise only positive values of $\theta - \mu$, then a critical region of the form

$$t \geqslant t_{2\alpha}(n-1) \tag{4}$$

gives a uniformly most powerful test at significance level α (Neyman and Pearson, 1933), while a similar *one-sided* test is optimum for the class of alternatives $\theta - \mu < 0$. When the alternatives to $\theta = \mu$ comprise either positive or negative values of $\theta - \mu$, a *two-sided* test is obtained by using the critical region

$$|t| \geqslant t_\alpha(n-1), \tag{5}$$

and this leads to the most powerful unbiased test (Sato, 1937), where an *unbiased* test is one whose power never falls below the significance level. The probability statement

$$\Pr\{-t_\alpha < (y. - \theta)\sqrt{\{n(n-1)\big/ \sum (y_i - y.)^2\}} < t_\alpha\} = 1 - \alpha \tag{6}$$

is equivalent to

$$\Pr[y. - t_\alpha\sqrt{\{\sum (y_i - y.)^2/n(n-1)\}}$$
$$< \theta < y. + t_\alpha\sqrt{\{\sum (y_i - y.)^2/n(n-1)\}}] = 1 - \alpha,$$

and we describe

$$[y. - t_\alpha\sqrt{\{\sum (y_i - y.)^2/n(n-1)\}}, \quad y. + t_\alpha\sqrt{\{\sum (y_i - y.)^2/n(n-1)\}}]$$

as a *confidence interval*, which covers the value of θ with probability $1 - \alpha$, the *confidence coefficient*.

In the same situation, another possible test criterion (Daly, 1946; Lord, 1947) is

$$u = (y. - \mu)\sqrt{n}/w, \tag{7}$$

where w is the sample range. (Lord's u incorporates a factor d_n, such that w/d_n is an unbiased estimate of σ.) An obvious advantage of u is that it can be computed more easily than t. Analytical forms for its percentage points exist when $n = 2$ and 3 but when $n \geqslant 4$ the distribution must be handled numerically. Lord has calculated tables of percentage points for u and for a more general criterion based on the mean range of several samples. In a further paper (1950) he has also studied the power of his criteria and finds that the loss in power of the u-test as compared with the t-test is barely appreciable for many practical purposes.

These calculations are all based on the fact that $y_.$ and w are distributed independently, which can be proved as follows. Let $H(y_1, y_2, ..., y_n)$ be any function such that

$$H(y_1+k, y_2+k, ..., y_n+k) = H(y_1, y_2, ..., y_n), \qquad (8)$$

whatever is the value of k. Then w is a special case of H. Make an orthogonal transformation $z = My$, where each element in the first row of M is $1/\sqrt{n}$. The sum of every row of M, other than the first, is consequently zero. If $H(y_1, y_2, ..., y_n)$ transforms into $J(z_1, z_2, ..., z_n)$, then

$$J(z_1+k\sqrt{n}, z_2, ..., z_n) = J(z_1, z_2, ..., z_n)$$

for all k, which implies that J is a function of $z_2, z_3, ..., z_n$ only. The variables $z_1, z_2, ..., z_n$ are statistically independent and therefore z_1 is independent of J. Equivalently, $y_.$ is independent of H, and therefore of w.

The idea of using the sample range to estimate σ can be extended to other experimental designs. For example, suppose that the observations can be displayed in a rectangular array of β rows and τ columns such that the one in row i and column j, say y_{ij}, has expectation $\mu+\rho_i+\kappa_j$. This is the situation of Example 3 in Section 3 with one observation in each cell, and we take $\sum \rho_i = \sum \kappa_j = 0$. Our object is to test the hypothesis that

$$\kappa_1 = \kappa_2 = ... = \kappa_\tau.$$

Write $y_{.j}$ for the mean of the observations in the jth column, i.e. the estimate of $\mu+\tau_j$. Let w_0 be the range of the $\{y_{.j}\}$, and w_i the range of the residuals $y_{ij}-y_{.j}$ for i fixed. The test criterion proposed by Hartley (1950) is proportional to the ratio $w_0/w_.$, where $w_.$ is the mean of $w_1, w_2, ..., w_\beta$. The exact distribution of this criterion is untabulated but an approximate distribution theory follows from the device due to Patnaik (1950) of replacing the distribution of range by a χ-distribution with the same mean and variance. The agreement between exact and approximate values is good in the case of Lord's criterion u, and is inferred to be sufficiently close in other situations.

4.6. Multiple decisions

Few experiments are so simple that only one hypothesis is tested and it is usual to examine a system of linear hypotheses. If repeated use is made of statistical tests at significance level α when every hypothesis in the system is true, then the probability, say V, of at least one incorrect decision may greatly exceed α, and we therefore require procedures where $V \leqslant \alpha$. Many procedures with this property exist (Hartley, 1955) and the following examples show how they operate.

Suppose that we have available the vector estimate θ^*, normally distributed with $\mathscr{E}\theta^* = \theta$ and $\mathscr{D}\theta^* = \sigma^2 I/n$, together with an independent estimate s^2 of σ^2, such that cs^2/σ^2 is distributed as χ^2 with c degrees of freedom. We want a test of the $\frac{1}{2}p(p-1)$ hypotheses $\theta_j - \theta_k = 0$ $(j = k+1,...,p; k = 1, 2,...,p-1)$ which satisfies $V \leqslant \alpha$. Define the *studentized range* $w(k, c)$ as the ratio of (i) the range in a sample of size k from a normal distribution with variance σ^2, to (ii) an independent quantity distributed as s. Let $w_\alpha(k, c)$ be such that

$$\Pr\{w(k, c) \geqslant w_\alpha(k, c)\} = \alpha. \tag{1}$$

This criterion was first used in the present context by Newman (1939), and his technique refined by Keuls (1952). We arrange the elements of θ^* in ascending order:

$$\theta_1^* < \theta_2^* < ... < \theta_p^*$$

and record the difference $\theta_i - \theta_{i'}$, where $i > i'$, as non-zero if

$$(\theta_j^* - \theta_k^*) \geqslant w_\alpha(j-k+1, c)s/\sqrt{n} \tag{2}$$

for $j = i, i+1,...,p$ and $k = 1, 2,...,i'$. With this procedure, $V \leqslant \alpha$ provided that p' $(\geqslant 2)$ of $\theta_1, \theta_2,..., \theta_p$ have the same value μ, while the remainder are different from each other and from μ. In fact, suppose that θ_i^* is any element of θ^* with $\mathscr{E}\theta_i^* = \mu$, and let e be the number of elements θ_j^* satisfying

$$\min(\theta_i^*) \leqslant \theta_j^* \leqslant \max(\theta_i^*).$$

Then
$$V \leqslant \Pr\{\text{range of } p' \text{ elements } \theta_i^* \geqslant w_\alpha(e, c)s/\sqrt{n}\}$$

$$\leqslant \Pr\{\text{range of } p' \text{ elements } \theta_i^* \geqslant w_\alpha(p', c)s/\sqrt{n}\}$$

since $e \geqslant p'$. Thus $V \leqslant \alpha$ as stated.

Every procedure of this kind can alternatively be formulated as a set of confidence intervals, and we now explain how the variance-ratio test of a single linear hypothesis $\mathfrak{h}$ can also be used to provide an infinite system of intervals. Suppose that $\mathfrak{h}$ specifies the value of $Q\theta$. We have seen that

$$c(\theta^* - \theta)'Q'(QC^{-1}Q')^{-1}Q(\theta^* - \theta)/bR$$

is distributed as $F(b, c)$, so that $\mathfrak{h}$ can be tested by inserting the specified value of $Q\theta$ in the numerator and referring to a table of

$F_\alpha(b, c)$. Equivalently, the fact that

$$\Pr\{(\theta^* - \theta)'Q'(QC^{-1}Q')^{-1}Q(\theta^* - \theta) \leqslant bRF_\alpha(b, c)/c\} = 1 - \alpha \qquad (3)$$

leads to a closed confidence region for the elements of $Q\theta$. We proceed to find a confidence interval for any linear combination of the elements of θ having the form $m'Q\theta$. Consider what are the limits of variation of $m'Q(\theta^* - \theta)$ subject to

$$(\theta^* - \theta)'Q'(QC^{-1}Q')^{-1}Q(\theta^* - \theta) = bRF_\alpha(b, c)/c.$$

Put $Q(\theta^* - \theta) = g$, $QC^{-1}Q' = L$, and $bRF_\alpha(b, c)/c = d$. Differentiate

$$m'g - \tfrac{1}{2}\lambda g' L^{-1} g$$

with respect to the elements of g and obtain

$$m' = \lambda g' L^{-1}.$$

Hence $$\lambda = m'g/d,$$

and $$g = Lm/\lambda,$$

so that $$\lambda^2 = m'Lm/d.$$

The limits of $m'g$ are therefore $\pm\sqrt{\{d \cdot m'Lm\}}$, i.e. $\pm\sqrt{\{d \cdot \mathscr{V}(m'g/\sigma)\}}$. Thus, from (3), the probability is at least $1 - \alpha$ that the system of inequalities

$$m'Q\theta^* - \sqrt{\{bRF_\alpha(b, c)\mathscr{V}(m'Q\theta^*/\sigma)/c\}}$$
$$\leqslant m'Q\theta \leqslant m'Q\theta^* + \sqrt{\{bRF_\alpha(b, c)\mathscr{V}(m'Q\theta^*/\sigma)/c\}} \qquad (4)$$

is true simultaneously for any set of vectors m. Scheffé (1953) has made a careful study of this technique when $\mathfrak{h}$ is the hypothesis

$$\theta_1 = \theta_2 = \ldots = \theta_p.$$

4.7. Exercises

1. Verify that

$$\begin{bmatrix} C & Q' \\ \hline Q & 0 \end{bmatrix}^{-1} = \begin{bmatrix} C^{-1} - C^{-1}Q'(QC^{-1}Q')^{-1}QC^{-1} & C^{-1}Q'(QC^{-1}Q')^{-1} \\ \hline (QC^{-1}Q')^{-1}QC^{-1} & -(QC^{-1}Q')^{-1} \end{bmatrix}.$$

Hence, or otherwise, prove that the relative minimum of W, subject to the restriction $Q\theta = 0$, is

$$\begin{vmatrix} y'y & y'A & 0 \\ \hline A'y & C & Q' \\ \hline 0 & Q & 0 \end{vmatrix} \Bigg/ \begin{vmatrix} C & Q' \\ \hline Q & 0 \end{vmatrix}.$$

2. Let θ be partitioned in the form $\begin{bmatrix} \theta_1 \\ \hline \theta_2 \end{bmatrix}$ and partition

$$C^{-1} = \begin{bmatrix} C^{11} & C^{12} \\ \hline C^{21} & C^{22} \end{bmatrix}$$

correspondingly. After θ^*, C^{-1}, and R have been computed, a decision is taken that $\theta_2 = 0$. Show that the revised estimate of θ_1 is

$$\theta_1^+ = \theta_1^* - C^{12}(C^{22})^{-1}\theta_2^*.$$

Prove also that $\qquad \mathscr{D}\theta_1^+ = \sigma^2\{C^{11} - C^{12}(C^{22})^{-1}C^{21}\}$

and that the modified sum of squared residuals is

$$R + (\theta_2^*)'(C^{22})^{-1}\theta_2^*. \qquad\qquad \text{(Cochran, 1938.)}$$

3. Several observations are available for each of the expected values below:

$$\mu + \rho_1 + \kappa_1, \quad \mu + \rho_2 + \kappa_2, \quad \mu + \rho_2 + \kappa_3.$$

The sum of squares for the hypothesis that $\rho_1 = \rho_2$ is S_ρ. Show that S_ρ is identically zero.

4. For n pairs (x_{ij}, y_{ij}) $(j = 1, 2, ..., n_i; i = 1, 2, ..., k)$ define the following quantities:

$$x_{i0} = \sum_{j=1}^{n_i} x_{ij}; \qquad x_{i.} = x_{i0}/n_i; \qquad x_{00} = \sum_{i=1}^{k} x_{i0}; \qquad x_{..} = x_{00}/n;$$

$$y_{i0} = \sum_{j=1}^{n_i} y_{ij}; \qquad y_{i.} = y_{i0}/n_i; \qquad y_{00} = \sum_{i=1}^{k} y_{i0}; \qquad y_{..} = y_{00}/n;$$

$$X_i = \sum_{j=1}^{n_i} x_{ij}^2 - x_{i0}^2/n_i; \qquad Y_i = \sum_{j=1}^{n_i} y_{ij}^2 - y_{i0}^2/n_i; \qquad Z_i = \sum_{j=1}^{n_i} x_{ij}y_{ij} - x_{i0}y_{i0}/n_i;$$

$$X = \sum_{i=1}^{k} X_i; \qquad Y = \sum_{i=1}^{k} Y_i; \qquad Z = \sum_{i=1}^{k} Z_i;$$

$$X_m = \sum_{i=1}^{k} x_{i0}^2/n_i - x_{00}^2/n; \qquad Y_m = \sum_{i=1}^{k} y_{i0}^2/n_i - y_{00}^2/n;$$

$$Z_m = \sum_{i=1}^{k} x_{i0}y_{i0}/n_i - x_{00}y_{00}/n;$$

$$X_0 = X_m + X; \qquad Y_0 = Y_m + Y; \qquad Z_0 = Z_m + Z.$$

Suppose that $\mathscr{E}y_{ij} = \theta_i + \beta_i(x_{ij} - x_{i.})$ where the $\{\theta_i\}$ and $\{\beta_i\}$ are unknown. Derive the following sums of squares.

u	Hypothesis $\mathfrak{h}_u$	Sums of squares S_u	Degrees of freedom
1	$\beta_1 = \beta_2 = ... = \beta_k \ (= \beta, \text{ unspecified})$	$\sum_{i=1}^{k} Z_i^2/X_i - Z^2/X$	$k-1$
2	$\mathfrak{h}_1$ and $\theta_i = \theta + \beta_m(x_{i.} - x_{..})$	$Y_m - Z_m^2/X_m$	$k-2$
3	$\mathfrak{h}_1, \mathfrak{h}_2,$ and $\beta_m = \beta$	$Z^2/X + Z_m^2/X_m - Z_0^2/X_0$	1

(Kendall, § 24.30.)

5. (i) Under the conditions of Exercise 3.7.3, show that the sum of squares for testing that $Q\theta = 0$ is less than the corresponding sum of squares using $y - B\phi^0$ for the vector of observations and A for the design matrix.

(ii) Under the conditions of Exercise 3.7.4, show that the sum of squares for testing that $Q\theta = 0$ is less than the corresponding sum of squares using $\begin{bmatrix} y_1 \\ y_2 \end{bmatrix}$ for the vector of observations and A for the design matrix.

6. A sample of size n is taken from a normal distribution with mean μ and variance σ^2. The sample mean and variance are respectively

$$y. = \sum_{i=1}^{n} y_i/n \quad \text{and} \quad s^2 = \sum_{i=1}^{n} (y_i - y.)^2/(n-1).$$

For any fixed L, put $\delta = (L-\mu)\sqrt{n}/\sigma$.

Prove that the density function of $x = (L-y.)\sqrt{n}/s$ is

$$\frac{1}{2^{\frac{1}{2}(n-3)}\Gamma\{\frac{1}{2}(n-1)\}\sqrt{(2\pi)}}\left(\frac{n-1}{n-1+x^2}\right)^{\frac{1}{2}n} \exp\left\{-\frac{\frac{1}{2}(n-1)\delta^2}{(n-1+x^2)}\right\} \times$$

$$\times \int_0^\infty v^{n-1} \exp\left\{-\frac{1}{2}\left[v - \frac{x\delta}{(n-1+x^2)^{\frac{1}{2}}}\right]^2\right\} dv.$$

(Johnson and Welch, 1940.)

7. Let u be defined by (5.7) and u_α by

$$\Pr(|u| \geqslant u_\alpha) = \alpha.$$

Show that, when $n = 2$, $\quad u_\alpha = 2^{-\frac{1}{2}}\cot(\frac{1}{2}\pi\alpha)$;

and when $n = 3$, $\quad u_\alpha = \tau 2^{\frac{1}{2}}/(1-3\tau^2)^{\frac{1}{2}}$,

where $\quad \tau = \tan\{\pi(1-\alpha)/6\}.$ (Lord, 1947.)

8. In the Newman-Keuls procedure, let $\theta_i \neq \theta_{i'}$ and suppose that $\theta_i^* \geqslant \theta_{i'}^*$. Define α' by

$$t_\alpha(c)\sqrt{2} = w_\alpha(p, c).$$

Write P for the probability of deciding that $\theta_i \neq \theta_{i'}$, and $P_\alpha(\delta, c)$ for

$$\Pr\{\theta_i^* - \theta_{i'}^* \geqslant t_\alpha(c)s\sqrt{(2/n)}\},$$

where $\quad \delta = (\theta_i - \theta_{i'})/\sigma\sqrt{(2/n)}.$

Prove that $\quad P_{\alpha'}(\delta, c) \leqslant P \leqslant P_\alpha(\delta, c).$ (Hartley, 1955.)

9. The variables $x_1, x_2, ..., x_p$ are normally distributed about zero means with $\mathcal{D}x = \sigma^2\{(1-\rho)I + \rho 11'\}$, where $\rho > -1/(p-1)$. Show that their range w has the same distribution as when $\mathcal{D}x = \sigma^2(1-\rho)I$, and that w is distributed independently of $x.$.

The estimates $\theta_1^*, ..., \theta_p^*$ are normally distributed with $\mathcal{E}\theta^* = \theta$ and $\mathcal{D}\theta^* = \sigma^2\{(1-\rho)I + \rho 11'\}/n$. Prove that the probability is $1-\alpha$ that simultaneously

$$\theta_i^* - \theta_j^* - sw_\alpha(p, c)\sqrt{\{(1-\rho)/n\}} \leqslant \theta_i - \theta_j \leqslant \theta_i^* - \theta_j^* + sw_\alpha(p, c)\sqrt{\{(1-\rho)/n\}}.$$

(Hartley, 1950; Tukey, 1952.)

10. For $i = 1, 2, ..., p$, a sample of size n is taken from a normal distribution with mean μ_i and variance σ^2. $\mu_i = \mu$ for $i = 1, 2, ..., p-k$ and $\mu_i = \mu + \lambda\sigma$ for $i = p-k+1, ..., p$. Denote by $\phi(x)$ the standard normal density function, and by $\Phi(x)$ the corresponding distribution function. Show that the probability is

$$k \int_{-\infty}^{\infty} \{\Phi(x+\lambda\sqrt{n})\}^{p-k}\{1-\Phi(x)\}^{k-1}\phi(x)\,dx$$

that the k largest sample means come from the distributions with $\mu_i = \mu + \lambda\sigma$. (Bechhofer, 1954.)

4.8. References

BECHHOFER, R. E. (1954). A single-sample multiple decision procedure for ranking means of normal populations with known variances. *Ann. Math. Statist.* **25**, 16–39.

COCHRAN, W. G. (1938). The omission or addition of an independent variate in multiple linear regression. *Suppl. J. R. Statist. Soc.* **5**, 171–6.

CRAMÉR, H. (1946). *Mathematical Methods of Statistics.* Princeton University Press.

DALY, J. F. (1946). On the use of the sample range in an analogue of Student's *t*-test. *Ann. Math. Statist.* **17**, 71–74.

FISHER, R. A. (1922). The goodness of fit of regression formulae, and the distribution of regression coefficients. *J. R. Statist. Soc.* **85**, 597–612.

FLETCHER, A., MILLER, J. C. P., and ROSENHEAD, L. (1946). *Index of Mathematical Tables.* London: Scientific Computing Service.

HARTLEY, H. O. (1950). The use of range in analysis of variance. *Biometrika,* **37**, 271–80.

—— (1955). Some recent developments in analysis of variance. *Commun. Pure Appl. Math.* **8**, 47–72.

HSU, P. L. (1938). Contribution to the theory of 'Student's' *t*-test as applied to the problem of two samples. *Statist. Res. Mem.* **2**, 1–24.

—— (1941 a). Canonical reduction of the general regression problem. *Ann. Eugen. Lond.* **11**, 42–46.

—— (1941 b). Analysis of variance from the power function standpoint. *Biometrika,* **32**, 62–69.

JOHNSON, N. L., and WELCH, B. L. (1940). Applications of the non-central *t*-distribution. *Biometrika,* **31**, 362–89.

KENDALL, M. G. (1946). *The Advanced Theory of Statistics,* Vol. **2**. London: Griffin.

KEULS, M. (1952). The use of the 'studentized range' in connection with an analysis of variance. *Euphytica,* **1**, 112–22.

KOLODZIEJCZYK, S. (1935). On an important class of statistical hypotheses. *Biometrika,* **27**, 161–90.

LEHMANN, E. L. (1950). Some principles of the theory of testing hypotheses. *Ann. Math. Statist.* **21**, 1–26.

—— and SCHEFFÉ, H. (1950). Completeness, similar regions and unbiased estimation—part I. *Sankhyā,* **10**, 305–40.

LORD, E. (1947). The use of range in place of standard deviation in the *t*-test. *Biometrika,* **34**, 41–67.

—— (1950). Power of the modified *t*-test (*u*-test) based on range. *Biometrika,* **37**, 64–77.

NEWMAN, D. (1939). The distribution of range in samples from a normal population, expressed in terms of an independent estimate of standard deviation. *Biometrika,* **31**, 20–30.

NEYMAN, J., and PEARSON, E. S. (1933). On the problem of the most efficient tests of statistical hypotheses. *Phil. Trans.* A, **231**, 289–337.

PATNAIK, P. B. (1950). The use of mean range as an estimator of variance in statistical tests. *Biometrika,* **37**, 78–87.

Roy, S. N., and Bose, R. C. (1953). Simultaneous confidence interval estimation. *Ann. Math. Statist.* **24**, 513–36.

Sato, R. (1937). Unpublished. Quoted by Hsu (1938).

Scheffé, H. (1953). A method for judging all contrasts in the analysis of variance. *Biometrika*, **40**, 87–104.

'Student' (1908). The probable error of a mean. *Biometrika*, **6**, 1–25.

Tang, P. C. (1938). The power function of the analysis of variance tests with tables and illustrations of their use. *Statist. Res. Mem.* **2**, 126–57.

Tukey, J. W. (1952). Unpublished. Quoted by Roy and Bose (1953).

Wald, A. (1942). On the power function of the analysis of variance tests. *Ann. Math. Statist.* **13**, 434–9.

Wolfowitz, J. (1949). The power of the classical tests associated with the normal distribution. *Ann. Math. Statist.* **20**, 540–51.

DEPARTURES FROM STANDARD TEST CONDITIONS

5.1. Introduction

A LINEAR hypothesis $\mathfrak{h}$ is usually tested on the assumption that the observations $y_1, y_2, ..., y_n$ satisfy the following conditions:

    (i) $\mathscr{E}y = A\theta$, where A is fixed and θ unknown;

    (ii) $\mathscr{D}y = \sigma^2 I$, where σ^2 is unknown;

    (iii) $y_1, y_2, ..., y_n$ are normally distributed.

When these conditions are not all realized, we do not know what is the probability of rejecting $\mathfrak{h}$ when it is true, and thus lose control of the proportion of results wrongly classed as significant. A desirable characteristic of a test is that this probability should be insensitive to departures from the standard conditions listed above, and in what follows, we examine the magnitude of the effect on t- and F-tests when

    (a) the observations, while remaining independent with $\mathscr{E}y = A\theta$, have the same non-normal distribution;

    (b) the observations are normally distributed with $\mathscr{E}y = A\theta$, but $\mathscr{D}y$ is a diagonal matrix different from $\sigma^2 I$;

    (c) the observations are normally distributed with $\mathscr{D}y$ fixed, but the matrix A is varied.

The situation (b) can lead to serious discrepancies from the nominal significance level, and some remedial measures are presented.

5.2. t-test for one sample

A sample of n observations $y_1, y_2, ..., y_n$ is taken from a normal population with mean θ and variance σ^2, both unknown. The sample mean is $y_.$. When θ is zero, the random variable

$$t = y_. \sqrt{\left\{ n(n-1) \Big/ \sum_{j=1}^{n} (y_j - y_.)^2 \right\}} \tag{1}$$

has the density function

$$c_{n-1}(t) = 1/\mathrm{B}\{\tfrac{1}{2}, \tfrac{1}{2}(n-1)\}(n-1)^{\frac{1}{2}}\{1 + t^2/(n-1)\}^{\frac{1}{2}n}, \tag{2}$$

first given by 'Student' (1908). The use of t in testing linear hypotheses has already been described in Section 4.5. We now consider the distribution of t in samples from non-normal populations.

The method of experimental sampling has been widely used here, notably by Pearson and Adyanthaya (1929). This technique will by-pass great mathematical difficulties, and the experimenter can take his samples from a model of any population likely to be met in practice. A large number of samples is required to determine the tails of a distribution with reasonable accuracy, but although this repetitive task was once a disadvantage, it is now ideally suited to an electronic computor. The work done in the 1929 study indicated that the predictions of normal theory are approximately fulfilled for symmetrical populations, as 'Student' himself anticipated; but that the effect of skewness is more serious, positive skewness in the parent leading to negative skewness in the distribution of t, although the distribution of $|t|$ is not so greatly affected.

Confirmation of these results has been provided by mathematical analysis, and the distribution of t theoretically determined in samples from the Edgeworth series. Here the parameters can be chosen so that a variety of different populations is represented, but their values must be confined within certain limits (Barton and Dennis, 1952) if the series is to represent a non-negative density function. Of prime importance in this field is the work of Bartlett (1935) and we shall illustrate his method by finding the distribution of t in samples of size n from the population with density function

$$f(x) = (1 - \lambda_3 D^3/6)\phi(x). \tag{3}$$

Here D denotes $\partial/\partial x$, and

$$\phi(x) = (2\pi)^{-\frac{1}{2}}e^{-\frac{1}{2}x^2}. \tag{4}$$

The probability distribution defined by $f(x)$ has zero mean and unit variance; and its skewness is measured by the standardized third cumulant

$$\lambda_3 = \kappa_3/\kappa_2^{\frac{3}{2}}, \tag{5}$$

in which κ_j is the jth population cumulant. The distribution of t for this population was also derived by Geary (1936), but his approach is not so readily generalized.

A part of the argument depends on the following lemma. The Chebyshev–Hermite polynomial

$$H_v(x) = x^v - \frac{v(v-1)}{2}x^{v-2} + \frac{v(v-1)(v-2)(v-3)}{2 \cdot 4}x^{v-4} - \dots \tag{6}$$

satisfies the equation

$$D^v e^{-\frac{1}{2}x^2} = (-1)^v H_v(x)e^{-\frac{1}{2}x^2} \quad (v = 1, 2, \dots). \tag{7}$$

Consequently $\qquad D^v e^{-\frac{1}{2}ax^2} = (-1)^r H'_v(x) e^{-\frac{1}{2}ax^2},$

where $\qquad\qquad H'_v(x) = a^{\frac{1}{2}v} H_v(x\sqrt{a}),$

and we can express $H_v(x)$ in terms of $\{H'_v(x)\}$ by

$$H_v = \frac{1}{a^v} H'_v + \frac{v(v-1)}{2}\left(\frac{1-a}{a}\right)\frac{1}{a^{v-2}} H'_{v-2} +$$

$$+ \frac{v(v-1)(v-2)(v-3)}{2.4}\left(\frac{1-a}{a}\right)^2 \frac{1}{a^{v-4}} H'_{v-4} + \dots .$$

This result is used in the form

$$e^{-\frac{1}{2}x^2(a-1)} D^v e^{-\frac{1}{2}x^2} = \left\{\left(\frac{D}{a}\right)^v + \frac{v(v-1)}{2}\left(\frac{1-a}{a}\right)\left(\frac{D}{a}\right)^{v-2} +\right.$$

$$\left. + \frac{v(v-1)(v-2)(v-3)}{2.4}\left(\frac{1-a}{a}\right)^2\left(\frac{D}{a}\right)^{v-4} + \dots\right\} e^{-\frac{1}{2}ax^2}. \quad (8)$$

Turning now to the main issue, the joint characteristic function of x and x^2 is

$$\psi(r_1, r_2) = \int_{-\infty}^{\infty} e^{ir_1x + ir_2x^2}(1 - \lambda_3 D^3/6)\phi(x)\, dx.$$

Taking $a = 1 - 2ir_2$,

$$\psi(r_1, r_2) = \int_{-\infty}^{\infty} e^{ir_1x}\left[1 - \frac{\lambda_3}{6}\left\{\frac{D^3}{(1-2ir_2)^3} + \frac{6ir_2 D}{(1-2ir_2)^2}\right\}\right] e^{ir_2x^2}\phi(x)\, dx$$

$$= \int_{-\infty}^{\infty}\left[1 - \frac{\lambda_3}{6}\left\{\frac{(D-ir_1)^3}{(1-2ir_2)^3} + \frac{6ir_2(D-ir_1)}{(1-2ir_2)^2}\right\}\right] e^{ir_1x + ir_2x^2}\phi(x)\, dx.$$

When the operator is expanded, all the powers of D lead to expressions of the form $H_v(x)\phi(x)$ and therefore give zero on integration. Hence

$$\psi(r_1, r_2) = \left[1 + \frac{\lambda_3}{6}\left\{\frac{(ir_1)^3}{(1-2ir_2)^3} + \frac{6(ir_1)(ir_2)}{(1-2ir_2)^2}\right\}\right]\zeta(r_1, r_2),$$

where $\qquad \zeta(r_1, r_2) = (1-2ir_2)^{-\frac{1}{2}}\exp\{-r_1^2/2(1-2ir_2)\},$

which is the joint characteristic function of x and x^2 under normality. For a sample of n random variables $x_1, x_2, \dots, x_n$ independently distributed with the density function $f(x)$, the joint characteristic function of $s_1 = \sum x$ and $s'_2 = \sum x^2$ is $\psi^n(r_1, r_2)$. If we neglect all powers of λ_3 above the first,

$$\psi^n(r_1, r_2) \simeq \exp\{-nr_1^2/2(1-2ir_2)\}[(1-2ir_2)^{-\frac{1}{2}n} +$$

$$+ n\lambda_3\{(ir_1)^3(1-2ir_2)^{-\frac{1}{2}(n+6)} + 6(ir_1)(ir_2)(1-2ir_2)^{-\frac{1}{2}(n+4)}\}/6].$$

Under these conditions, the joint density function of s_1 and s_2' is

$$j(s_1, s_2') = w(n) - n\lambda_3\{D_1^3 w(n+6) - 6D_1 D_2 w(n+4)\}/6,$$

where $D_1 = \partial/\partial s_1$, $D_2 = \partial/\partial s_2'$, and

$$w(m) = (2\pi)^{-2} \int\int e^{-ir_1 s_1 - ir_2 s_2'}(1 - 2ir_2)^{-\frac{1}{2}m}\exp\{-nr_1^2/2(1-2ir_2)\}dr_1\,dr_2.$$

Integrate first with respect to r_1, and obtain

$$(2\pi)^{-1}\int e^{-ir_1 s_1}\exp\{-nr_1^2/2(1-2ir_2)\}\,dr_1$$
$$= \{(1-2ir_2)/2\pi n\}^{\frac{1}{2}}\exp\{-s_1^2(1-2ir_2)/2n\}.$$

The double integral becomes

$$\frac{\exp(-s_1^2/2n)}{\sqrt{(2\pi n)}}\frac{1}{2\pi}\int(1-2ir_2)^{-\frac{1}{2}(m-1)}\exp\{-ir_2(s_2'-s_1^2/n)\}\,dr_2$$

and hence

$$w(m) = \frac{\exp(-s_1^2/2n)}{\sqrt{(2\pi n)}}\frac{(s_2'-s_1^2/n)^{\frac{1}{2}(m-3)}\exp\{-\frac{1}{2}(s_2'-s_1^2/n)\}}{2^{\frac{1}{2}(m-1)}\Gamma\{\frac{1}{2}(m-1)\}}.$$

Denote $s_2'-s_1^2/n$ by s_2. Since the Jacobian of the transformation from s_1 and s_2' to s_1 and s_2 is unity, the joint density function of s_1 and s_2, say $q(s_1, s_2)$, is the same as $j(s_1, s_2')$. Evaluating the derivatives of $w(n+6)$ and $w(n+4)$, we find

$$q(s_1, s_2) = \frac{\exp(-s_1^2/2n)}{\sqrt{(2\pi n)}}\frac{s_2^{\frac{1}{2}(n-3)}\exp(-\frac{1}{2}s_2)}{2^{\frac{1}{2}(n-1)}\Gamma\{\frac{1}{2}(n-1)\}}\times$$
$$\times\left[1+\frac{n\lambda_3}{6}\left\{\left(\frac{s_1}{n}\right)^3 - 3\left(\frac{s_1}{n}\right) + 3\left(\frac{s_1}{n}\right)\left(\frac{s_2}{n}\right)\right\}\right].$$

Put $s_1 = \{ns_2/(n-1)\}^{\frac{1}{2}}t$, multiply $q(s_1, s_2)$ by $\{ns_2/(n-1)\}^{\frac{1}{2}}$, and integrate s_2 from 0 to ∞. The density function of t is

$$c(t) = \frac{\Gamma(\frac{1}{2}n)}{\{(n-1)\pi\}^{\frac{1}{2}}\Gamma\{\frac{1}{2}(n-1)\}}\frac{1}{\{1+t^2/(n-1)\}^{\frac{1}{2}n}}+$$
$$+\lambda_3\frac{3(n-1)t-(2n-1)t^3}{6(n-1)(2n\pi)^{\frac{1}{2}}\{1+t^2/(n-1)\}^{\frac{1}{2}(n+3)}}.\quad(9)$$

Gayen (1949) has used this approach when the density function of the population is

$$f(x) = \{1-\lambda_3 D^3/6+\lambda_4 D^4/24+\lambda_3^2 D^6/72\}\phi(x),\quad(10)$$

where λ_3 has the same meaning as before, and λ_4 is the standardized fourth cumulant, a measure of flatness defined by

$$\lambda_4 = \kappa_4/\kappa_2^2.\quad(11)$$

His results are based on neglecting higher powers of λ_3 and λ_4 than are

TABLE 5. *Probability that |t| exceeds a value close to $t_{0.015}(5)$ for different non-normal populations with zero means*

	λ_3^2	
λ_4	0·0	0·5
−1·0	0·0343	0·0447
−0·5	0·0322	0·0426
0·0	**0·0301**	0·0405
0·5	0·0280	0·0384
1·0	0·0259	0·0363
1·5	0·0237	0·0341
2·0	0·0216	0·0320

This table is abridged from A. K. Gayen (1949), table 4, and is reproduced by kind permission of the author and Professor E. S. Pearson, editor of *Biometrika*.

TABLE 6. *Probability that t exceeds $t_{0.05}(9)$ for different non-normal populations with various means*

			λ_3	
λ_4	$\theta\sqrt{n}/\sigma$	−0·6	0·0	0·6
−1·0	0	0·072	0·051	0·036
	2	0·556	0·559	0·550
	4	0·969	0·988	..
0·0	0	0·071	**0·050**	0·035
	2	0·576	**0·580**	0·571
	4	0·960	**0·979**	..
1·0	0	0·070	0·049	0·034
	2	0·597	0·601	0·591
	4	0·951	0·970	0·992
2·0	0	0·069	0·048	0·033
	2	0·618	0·621	0·612
	4	0·943	0·961	0·983

This table is abridged from A. B. L. Srivastava (1958), table 2, and is reproduced by kind permission of the author and Professor E. S. Pearson, editor of *Biometrika*.

given in $f(x)$, but his predictions agree well with several experimental investigations, and this suggests that the theory may possess quite a wide range of applicability. He also gives reasons for supposing that the distribution of t obtained is valid for any parent population if the samples are so large that terms of order $n^{-\frac{3}{2}}$ can be neglected. As an example of his calculations, Table 5, which refers to samples of 6, gives the probability with which $|t|$ exceeds a value close to $t_{0.015}(5)$.

The effect of non-normality on the power-function of the t-test has been examined by Ghurye (1949) and Srivastava (1958) for the populations whose density functions are given by (3) and (10) respectively. Srivastava takes the joint distribution of mean and standard deviation given by Gayen (1949), and integrates it over the region of acceptance for a one-sided test. When $n = 10$ and $\alpha = 0.05$, Table 6 gives the power for various combinations of λ_3 and λ_4. Srivastava concludes that the effects of λ_3 and λ_4 are broadly of the same order, and that the power is not seriously invalidated even when the samples are from considerably non-normal populations.

5.3. F-test for a single classification

Samples are taken from p normal populations, whose means are $\theta_1, \theta_2, ..., \theta_p$ and whose variances are assumed to be equal. The n_k observations of the kth sample are denoted by

$$y_{k1}, y_{k2}, ..., y_{kn_k} \quad (k = 1, 2, ..., p).$$

Write $y_k.$ for the kth sample mean and $y..$ for the mean of all observations. Corresponding to the hypothesis

$$\mathfrak{h}: \theta_1 = \theta_2 = ... = \theta_p$$

is the variance-ratio

$$F = (n-p) \sum_{k=1}^{p} n_k(y_k. - y..)^2 \Big/ (p-1) \sum_{k=1}^{p} \sum_{j=1}^{n_k} (y_{kj} - y_k.)^2. \qquad (1)$$

The density function of F is

$$g(F; b, c) = b^{\frac{1}{2}b} c^{\frac{1}{2}b} F^{\frac{1}{2}b-1} / B(\tfrac{1}{2}b, \tfrac{1}{2}c)(c+bF)^{\frac{1}{2}(b+c)}, \qquad (4.3.6)$$

where $b = (p-1)$ and $c = (n-p)$; and the optimum test of $\mathfrak{h}$ at significance level α is obtained by using the critical region

$$F > F_\alpha(p-1, n-p).$$

When the observations are independently and identically distributed with a common density function which departs only moderately from normality, the actual distribution of F is adequately represented by the function $g(F; b, c)$ as far as the practical application of statistical methods is concerned. This result was first established by Pearson (1931), mainly for groups of equal size, by taking experimental samples from six populations. Mathematical confirmation was provided by Gayen (1950): using an extension of the technique already described in the case of the t-test, he found the distribution of F when the common density function of the observations is given by (2.10). As before, his derivation neglects powers of λ_3 and λ_4

higher than those present in $f(x)$, but his results are valid asymptotically for any population. For five samples of five observations each, Table 7 gives his estimate of the probability with which $F_{0.05}(4, 20)$ is exceeded, but the results may be unreliable when λ_3^2 and λ_4 are large.

TABLE 7. *Probability that the variance-ratio exceeds $F_{0.05}(4, 20)$ for different non-normal populations*

	λ_3^2		
λ_4	0·00	0·25	0·50
−1·0	0·0524	0·0526	0·0529
−0·5	0·0512	0·0514	0·0517
0·0	**0·0500**	0·0502	0·0505
0·5	0·0488	0·0490	0·0493
1·0	0·0476	0·0478	0·0481
1·5	0·0464	0·0466	0·0469
2·0	0·0452	0·0454	0·0457
2·5	0·0440	0·0442	0·0445

This table is abridged from A. K. Gayen (1950), table 1, and is reproduced by kind permission of the author and Professor E. S. Pearson, editor of *Biometrika*.

Suppose next that all the observations are distributed normally and independently with the same mean, but with variances which differ according to the population sampled, the variance of the kth population being σ_k^2. For each population, $y_k.$ and

$$\sum_{j=1}^{n_k} (y_{kj} - y_k.)^2$$

are independently distributed, and so

$$S = \sum_{k=1}^{p} n_k (y_k. - y..)^2$$

and

$$R = \sum_{k=1}^{p} \sum_{j=1}^{n_k} (y_{kj} - y_k.)^2$$

remain statistically independent. Let $\chi^2(\nu)$ denote a random variable distributed as χ^2 on ν degrees of freedom. The sum of squares S is a quadratic form in $y_1., y_2., ..., y_p.$, with matrix

$$B = \{n_k \delta_{kj} - n_k n_j/n\}.$$

Since the $\{y_k.\}$ are normally distributed with dispersion matrix

$$W = \{\sigma_k^2 \delta_{kj}/n_k\},$$

S is distributed like $$\sum_{v=1}^{h} \beta_v \chi_v^2(1),$$

where the individual terms are statistically independent, and $\beta_1, \beta_2, ..., \beta_h$ are the non-zero latent roots of

$$BW = \{\sigma_k^2 \delta_{kj} - \sigma_k^2 n_j / n\}.$$

All the non-zero roots are positive, because W is positive definite and B non-negative definite. Furthermore, since

$$\sum_{j=1}^{n_k} (y_{kj} - y_{k.})^2$$

is distributed as $\sigma_k^2 \chi^2(n_k - 1)$, the sum of squared residuals R is distributed as

$$\sum_{k=1}^{p} \sigma_k^2 \chi^2(n_k - 1),$$

where the individual terms are statistically independent.

TABLE 8. *Probability that the variance ratio exceeds $F_{0.05}$ for different combinations of group variances and group sizes*

Group variances					Group sizes						Probability that
σ_1^2	σ_2^2	σ_3^2	σ_4^2	σ_5^2	n_1	n_2	n_3	n_4	n_5	n	F exceeds $F_{0.05}$
1	2	3	..	..	5	5	5	..	..	15	0·0558
1	2	3	..	..	3	9	3	..	..	15	0·0555
1	2	3	..	..	7	5	3	..	..	15	0·0925
1	2	3	..	..	3	5	7	..	..	15	0·0403
1	1	3	..	..	5	5	5	..	..	15	0·0587
1	1	3	..	..	7	5	3	..	..	15	0·1070
1	1	3	..	..	9	5	1	..	..	15	0·1741
1	1	3	..	..	1	5	9	..	..	15	0·0131
1	1	1	1	3	5	5	5	5	5	25	0·0742
1	1	1	1	3	9	5	5	5	1	25	0·1464
1	1	1	1	3	1	5	5	5	9	25	0·0249

This table is abridged from G. E. P. Box (1954), table 4, and is reproduced by kind permission of the author and the editor of *The Annals of Mathematical Statistics*.

The exact distribution of F when the population variances differ can now be found using the theory given in Chapter 2. In this way, Box (1954) has obtained the numerical results in Table 8. When the samples are of equal size, moderate differences between variances have no serious effect on the test. With unequal sizes, much larger discrepancies appear; and Box shows, by approximating to the numerator and denominator of F with multiples of χ^2, that these discrepancies persist when the sample sizes are increased proportionately.

5.4. Modified test for a single classification

The foregoing results indicate that the use of the variance-ratio to compare the means of several groups of observations may lead to erroneous conclusions unless there is good reason to believe that the population variances for the different groups are all equal. When nothing is known about the ratios of the population variances, the problem of constructing a valid test to compare the means is one for which no exact solution is available, and, indeed, such a solution may not exist. However, several approximate solutions have been put forward, of which the most important are those derived by a fundamental technique due to Welch (1947), and applied to this problem by James (1951) and Welch (1951).

The following argument is given by James. Denote σ_k^2/n_k by α_k, $y_k.$ by x_k, and

$$\sum_{j=1}^{n_k} (y_{kj}-y_k.)^2/n_k(n_k-1)$$

by a_k. Thus $x_1, x_2,..., x_p$ are normally distributed with means $\theta_1, \theta_2,..., \theta_p$ and variances $\alpha_1, \alpha_2,..., \alpha_p$ respectively; $a_1, a_2,..., a_p$ are estimates of $\alpha_1, \alpha_2,..., \alpha_p$ respectively, the probability element for a_k being

$$\frac{1}{\Gamma(\tfrac{1}{2}\nu_k)}\left(\frac{\nu_k a_k}{2\alpha_k}\right)^{\tfrac{1}{2}\nu_k-1} \exp\left(-\frac{\nu_k a_k}{2\alpha_k}\right) d\left(\frac{\nu_k a_k}{2\alpha_k}\right), \tag{1}$$

where $\nu_k = n_k-1$; and the variables $x_1, x_2,..., x_p, a_1, a_2,..., a_p$ are mutually independent. Write ω_k for $1/\alpha_k$ and w_k for $1/a_k$. Put $\omega = \sum \omega_k$ and $w = \sum w_k$. If $\alpha_1, \alpha_2,..., \alpha_p$ were known, we could test the hypothesis

$$\mathfrak{h}: \theta_1 = \theta_2 = ... = \theta_p$$

by calculating $\sum \omega_k x_k^2 - (\sum \omega_k x_k)^2/\omega$, and using the fact that

$$\Pr\{\sum \omega_k x_k^2 - (\sum \omega_k x_k)^2/\omega \leqslant 2\xi\} = G_\rho(\xi), \tag{2}$$

where $\rho = \tfrac{1}{2}(p-1)$ and

$$G_\rho(\xi) = \{\Gamma(\rho)\}^{-1} \int_0^\xi t^{\rho-1} e^{-t}\, dt. \tag{3}$$

With large values of ν_k, we could replace ω_k by w_k and continue to use the test as an approximation, but this procedure would be unsatisfactory for small ν_k. In order to take the sampling variation of

$a_1, a_2, ..., a_p$ properly into account, we attempt to find a series development of a function $h(a_1, a_2, ..., a_p; \xi) \equiv h(a)$ such that, in place of (2),

$$\Pr\{\sum w_k x_k^2 - (\sum w_k x_k)^2/w \leqslant 2h(a)\} = G_\rho(\xi). \qquad (4)$$

This can be written in the form

$$\int \Pr\{\sum w_k x_k^2 - (\sum w_k x_k)^2/w \leqslant 2h(a)|a\}\Pr(da) = G_\rho(\xi), \qquad (5)$$

where the first expression is a conditional probability for $a_1, a_2, ..., a_p$ fixed, the second is the product of p terms like (1), and the whole is integrated over 0 to ∞ in each a_k. By Taylor's theorem, we have

$$\Pr\{\sum w_k^2 x_k - (\sum w_k x_k)^2/w \leqslant 2h(a)|a\}$$
$$= \exp\{\sum (a_k - \alpha_k)\partial_k\}\Pr\{\sum \omega_k x_k^2 - (\sum \omega_k x_k)^2/\omega \leqslant 2h(\alpha)\}, \qquad (6)$$

where, after expansion of the exponential, ∂_k denotes $\partial/\partial \alpha_k$. These operators act on the α_k and $\omega_k = 1/\alpha_k$ which appear explicitly in $\Pr\{\sum \omega_k x_k^2 - (\sum \omega_k x_k)^2/\omega \leqslant 2h(\alpha)\}$; but they do not act on the α_k appearing in the distribution of the x_k, from which $\Pr\{...\}$ is calculated. From (5) and (6),

$$G_\rho(\xi) = \left[\int \exp\{\sum (a_k - \alpha_k)\partial_k\}\Pr\{da\}\right] \times$$
$$\times \Pr\{\sum \omega_k x_k^2 - (\sum \omega_k x_k)^2/\omega \leqslant 2h(\alpha)\}. \qquad (7)$$

On substituting for $\Pr\{da\}$, the integral becomes

$$\Theta = \prod e^{-\alpha_k \partial_k}(1 - 2\alpha_k \partial_k/\nu_k)^{-\frac{1}{2}\nu_k}$$
$$= 1 + \sum \alpha_k^2 \partial_k^2/\nu_k + \{4 \sum \alpha_k^3 \partial_k^3/3\nu_k^2 + \tfrac{1}{2}(\sum \alpha_k^2 \partial_k^2/\nu_k)^2\} + O(\nu^{-3}). \qquad (8)$$

We thus obtain

$$G_\rho(\xi) = \Theta \Pr\{\sum \omega_k x_k^2 - (\sum \omega_k x_k)^2/\omega \leqslant 2h(\alpha)\}. \qquad (9)$$

Suppose now that

$$h(a) = h_0(a) + h_+(a) = h_0(a) + h_1(a) + h_2(a) + ..., \qquad (10)$$

where $h_s(a)$ is of order ν^{-s}. Using Taylor's theorem again,

$$G_\rho(\xi) = \Theta \exp\{h_+(\alpha)D\}\Pr\{\sum \omega_k x_k^2 - (\sum \omega_k x_k)^2/\omega \leqslant 2h_0(\alpha)\}, \qquad (11)$$

where, after expansion of the exponential, D denotes differentiation with respect to $h_0(\alpha)$. Writing out (11) as far as the term of order ν^{-2}, we find

$$G_\rho(\xi) = [1 + \sum \alpha_k^2 \partial_k^2/\nu_k + \{4 \sum \alpha_k^3 \partial_k^3/3\nu_k^2 + \tfrac{1}{2}(\sum \alpha_k^2 \partial_k^2/\nu_k)^2\}] \times$$
$$\times [1 + h_1(\alpha)D + \{h_2(\alpha)D + \tfrac{1}{2}h_1^2(\alpha)D^2\}]\Pr\{...\}. \qquad (12)$$

G

Equating the terms of order ν^0, ν^{-1}, ν^{-2} in succession,

$$h_0(\alpha) = \xi, \tag{13}$$

$$\{h_1(\alpha)D + \sum \alpha_k^2 \partial_k^2/\nu_k\}\Pr\{\sum \omega_k x_k^2 - (\sum \omega_k x_k)^2/\omega \leqslant 2\xi\} = 0, \tag{14}$$

and

$$[h_2(\alpha)D + \tfrac{1}{2}h_1^2(\alpha)D^2 + \sum \alpha_k^2\{h_1^{(kk)}(\alpha) + 2h_1^{(k)}(\alpha)\partial_k + h_1(\alpha)\partial_k^2\}D/\nu_k +$$
$$+ 4\sum \alpha_k^3 \partial_k^3/3\nu_k^2 + \tfrac{1}{2}(\sum \alpha_k^2 \partial_k^2/\nu_k)^2]\Pr\{...\} = 0, \tag{15}$$

where $h_1^{(kk)} = \partial_k^2 h_1(\alpha)$, etc. The functions $h_1(a)$ and $h_2(a)$ are now determined by performing the differentiations indicated.

This completes James's illustration of Welch's technique. He continues with a general method of evaluating the derivatives of all orders, which involves a further lengthy analysis and will not be reproduced here. The result is that

$$h_1(a) = \tfrac{1}{4}\{3\xi^2/\rho(\rho+1) + \xi/\rho\}\sum (1 - w_k/w)^2/\nu_k, \tag{16}$$

while the expression for $h_2(a)$ is very complicated and unlikely to be of much practical utility. Thus, ignoring terms of order ν_k^{-2},

$$2h(a) = z\left\{1 + \frac{3z + (p+1)}{2(p^2 - 1)}\sum \frac{1}{\nu_k}\left(1 - \frac{w_k}{w}\right)^2\right\}, \tag{17}$$

where z is the value of $\chi^2(p-1)$ corresponding to the significance level chosen. For example, consider the following data, given by Welch (1951).

k	n_k	x_k	a_k	w_k	w_k/w	$(1-w_k/w)^2$	$(1-w_k/w)^2/\nu_k$
1	20	27·8	3·00	0·333	0·130	0·757	0·0398
2	10	24·1	0·63	1·587	0·618	0·146	0·0162
3	10	22·2	1·54	0·649	0·253	0·558	0·0620
				2·569			0·1180

The observed value of $\sum w_k x_k^2 - (\sum w_k x_k)^2/w$ is 6·90, and the 0·05 point of its distribution is

$$2h(a) = 5\cdot991[1 + \tfrac{1}{16}\{3(5\cdot991) + 4\}(0\cdot118)] = 6\cdot96.$$

Using techniques which are the same in principle but more elaborate in detail, James (1954) has found a test for any linear hypothesis in canonical form when the observations may have different variances, of which estimates are available as above. He has subsequently (1956) applied his extended results to give a solution of the problem of determining confidence limits for the common value of $\theta_1, \theta_2, ..., \theta_p$. Denote the common mean by μ and its estimate $\sum w_k x_k/w$ by $\hat{\mu}$. Then a function u of the ratios $\{w_i/w\}$ is obtained such that

$$\Pr\{|w^{\frac{1}{2}}(\hat{\mu}-\mu)| < u\} = P, \tag{18}$$

where P is an assigned probability.

5.5. Comparison of two independent variances

The following problem is not one in which a linear hypothesis is tested, but it has been included as an important example of the use of the F-test. We are given two populations. A sample of size n_j is taken from the jth population, and yields a sample variance

$$s_j^2 = \sum_{k=1}^{n_j} (y_{jk}-y_{j.})^2/(n_j-1),$$

based on $\nu_j = n_j-1$ degrees of freedom ($j = 1, 2$). Let κ_{1j}, κ_{2j}, κ_{3j} and κ_{4j} be the first four cumulants of the jth population, and define

$$\lambda_{3j} = \kappa_{3j}/\kappa_{2j}^{\frac{3}{2}}, \qquad \lambda_{4j} = \kappa_{4j}/\kappa_{2j}^2.$$

Suppose initially that both populations are normal, in which case $\lambda_{3j} = \lambda_{4j} = 0$, and denote the ratio of their variances by $\zeta = \kappa_{21}/\kappa_{22}$. On the hypothesis that $\zeta = 1$, the density function of s_1^2/s_2^2 is $g(x; \nu_1, \nu_2)$. If the set of admissible alternatives to $\zeta = 1$ is restricted to $\zeta > 1$, then the test which rejects $\zeta = 1$ whenever $s_1^2/s_2^2 > F_\alpha(\nu_1, \nu_2)$ is the uniformly most powerful test at significance level α; and, for the set of alternatives $\zeta < 1$, $s_1^2/s_2^2 < F_{1-\alpha}(\nu_1, \nu_2)$ gives a uniformly most powerful test (Neyman and Pearson, 1933). When the alternatives are not restricted, criteria affecting the choice of a critical region are discussed by Scheffé (1942). The usual practice is to refer $m = \max(s_1^2/s_2^2, s_2^2/s_1^2)$ to a critical region defined by $m > F_\alpha(\nu_1, \nu_2)$ and the corresponding significance level is then 2α. Since the density function of $s_1^2/\zeta s_2^2$ is $g(x; \nu_1, \nu_2)$, the power of any of these tests can easily be computed for different values of ζ.

The effect of non-normality on this test was investigated by Pearson (1931), who took 500 pairs of samples of 5 and 20 from six experimental populations and calculated the values of $\nu_1 s_1^2/(\nu_1 s_1^2+\nu_2 s_2^2)$, a criterion equivalent to s_1^2/s_2^2. He showed that the test can be seriously misleading, particularly when the value of λ_4 differs from zero. These conclusions were confirmed by Gayen (1950), who supposed that the density function of each population had the form (2.10). After a mathematical study of the type which has already been described in connexion with this population, he computed the results illustrated in Table 9. Here $\nu_1 = 4$, $\nu_2 = 20$ and $\Pr\{s_1^2/s_2^2 > F_{0\cdot05}(4, 20)\}$ is recorded.

TABLE 9. *Probability that the ratio of two independent variances exceeds* $F_{0\cdot05}(4, 20)$ *for different non-normal populations*

λ_4	λ_3^2		
	0·00	0·25	0·50
−1·0	0·0241	0·0229	0·0216
−0·5	0·0371	0·0358	0·0345
0·0	0·0500	0·0487	0·0474
0·5	0·0629	0·0617	0·0604
1·0	0·0759	0·0746	0·0733
1·5	0·0888	0·0875	0·0862
2·0	0·1017	0·1004	0·0992
2·5	0·1147	0·1134	0·1121

This table is abridged from A. K. Gayen (1950), Table 3, and is reproduced by kind permission of the author and Professor E. S. Pearson, editor of *Biometrika*.

The way in which non-normality affects the test can, however, be seen without laborious algebra, as Box (1953) has pointed out. Suppose that $s^2(\lambda_4; \nu)$ is the variance of a sample of size $n = \nu+1$ taken from a population whose variance is κ_2 and standardized fourth cumulant λ_4. Then

$$\mathscr{E} s^2(\lambda_4; \nu) = \kappa_2$$

and

$$\mathscr{V} s^2(\lambda_4; \nu) = \frac{2\kappa_2^2}{\nu}\left(1 + \frac{\nu\lambda_4}{2(\nu+1)}\right).$$

Since $s^2(\lambda_4; \nu)$ is asymptotically normal, it has the same limit distribution as $s^2(0; \delta\nu)$, where

$$\delta = \{1 + \nu\lambda_4/2(\nu+1)\}^{-1}.$$

Carrying both argument and notation a stage further, $F(\lambda_{41}, \lambda_{42}; \nu_1, \nu_2)$ has the same limit distribution as $F(0, 0; \delta_1\nu_1, \delta_2\nu_2)$. For finite samples, we infer that $F(\lambda_{41}, \lambda_{42}; \nu_1, \nu_2)$ has approximately an F distribution with $\delta_1\nu_1$ and $\delta_2\nu_2$ degrees of freedom; and numerical results derived by this method agree well with those in the table above. By a similar analysis, Box has shown that the sensitivity to non-normality of Bartlett's (1937) criterion for comparing several variances can be of the same order of magnitude as the sensitivity of criteria specifically designed to test normality. The empirical studies of Box and Andersen (1955) suggest that the replacement of λ_{41} and λ_{42} by sample estimates leads to a criterion insensitive to non-normality.

5.6. Variations in the design matrix

On the assumption that the three conditions given in Section 1 are satisfied, the hypothesis that the $p \times 1$ vector θ is zero can be tested by referring the criterion

$$E = y'A(A'A)^{-1}A'y/y'y \qquad (1)$$

to a table of the incomplete B-function ratio

$$I_E\{\tfrac{1}{2}p, \tfrac{1}{2}(n-p)\} = \int_0^E x^{\frac{1}{2}p-1}(1-x)^{\frac{1}{2}(n-p)-1}\,dx/B\{\tfrac{1}{2}p, \tfrac{1}{2}(n-p)\}. \qquad (2)$$

If, however, condition (ii) is replaced by

$$\mathscr{D}y = \sigma^2 V, \qquad (3)$$

then $\Pr(E < \epsilon)$ will differ from the value α given by

$$\alpha = I_\epsilon\{\tfrac{1}{2}p, \tfrac{1}{2}(n-p)\}. \qquad (4)$$

For fixed values of α and V, define ϵ_0 by

$$\Pr(E < \epsilon_0) = \alpha. \qquad (5)$$

Here ϵ_0 is a function of A, and the problem arises of finding the range of values of ϵ_0 when A is varied. The treatment which follows is based on Watson (1955), and serves to indicate the scope of his results, in which the effect on a regression analysis of wrongly assuming that $\mathscr{D}y = \sigma^2 I$ is studied in detail. The earlier papers of Durbin and Watson (1950, 1951) also contain relevant material.

In the first place, we note that $A'A$, being positive definite, admits the representation $X'X$, where X is upper triangular. Writing K for AX^{-1}, we have

$$E = y'KK'y/y'y$$

where

$$K'K = I. \qquad (6)$$

We thus require the range of ϵ_0 when K is varied subject to (6).

Suppose that the latent roots of V are distinct; and denote them by $\tau_1, \tau_2, ..., \tau_n$, where

$$\tau_1 < \tau_2 < ... < \tau_n.$$

Let $q_1, q_2, ..., q_n$ be the corresponding latent vectors and put

$$Q = [q_1, q_2, ..., q_n].$$

Thus

$$Q'VQ = T, \qquad (7)$$

where

$$Q'Q = I,$$

and

$$T = \mathrm{diag}(\tau_1, \tau_2, ..., \tau_n).$$

Define

$$x = T^{-\frac{1}{2}}Q'y,$$

where

$$T^{-\frac{1}{2}} = \mathrm{diag}(\tau_1^{-\frac{1}{2}}, \tau_2^{-\frac{1}{2}}, ..., \tau_n^{-\frac{1}{2}}).$$

Then
$$\mathscr{E}xx' = \sigma^2 T^{-\frac{1}{2}}Q'VQT^{-\frac{1}{2}} = \sigma^2 I. \tag{8}$$

Hence, when $\theta = 0$, the elements of x are normally and independently distributed with zero means, and the same variance, σ^2.

We now transform to the new variables and obtain
$$y'KK'y = x'T^{\frac{1}{2}}Q'KK'QT^{\frac{1}{2}}x.$$

Let $\mu_1, \mu_2, ..., \mu_p$ be the non-zero latent roots of $T^{\frac{1}{2}}Q'KK'QT^{\frac{1}{2}}$, ordered so that
$$\mu_1 \leqslant \mu_2 \leqslant \cdots \leqslant \mu_p.$$

According to Section 2.3, $y'KK'y$ is distributed as $z'Mz$, where the elements of z are normally and independently distributed with zero means and variance σ^2, and
$$M = \mathrm{diag}(\mu_1, \mu_2, ..., \mu_p).$$

The latent roots of the product of two matrices are independent of the order of multiplication (Macduffee, 1933, Th. 16.2), and since
$$K'QT^{\frac{1}{2}}T^{\frac{1}{2}}Q'K = K'VK,$$

it follows that $\mu_1, \mu_2, ..., \mu_p$ are also the roots of
$$|K'VK - \mu I| = 0. \tag{9}$$

Write the left-hand side in the form
$$|K'QTQ'K - \mu I| = |\{(T - \mu I)^{\frac{1}{2}}Q'K\}'\{(T - \mu I)^{\frac{1}{2}}Q'K\}|.$$

By the theorem on the multiplication of determinantal arrays (Aitken, 1951, § 36),
$$|K'VK - \mu I| = \sum (\tau_1 - \mu)(\tau_2 - \mu)...(\tau_p - \mu)J_{12...p}^2, \tag{10}$$

where $J_{12...p}$ is the minor formed by rows $1, 2, ..., p$ of $Q'K$, and the summation is over the $\binom{n}{p}$ selections of p integers from $1, 2, ..., n$.

We note that
$$\sum J_{12...p}^2 = |K'QQ'K| = 1. \tag{11}$$

When $p = n-1$, (10) implies that
$$\mathrm{sgn}|K'VK - \tau_r I| = (-1)^{r-1} \quad (r = 1, 2, ..., n). \tag{12}$$

This means that the $(n-1)$ roots of (9) are separated by $\tau_1, \tau_2, ..., \tau_n$. We now proceed by induction to prove in general that
$$\tau_1 \leqslant \mu_1 \leqslant \tau_{n-p+1}$$
$$\tau_2 \leqslant \mu_2 \leqslant \tau_{n-p+2}$$
$$\cdot \quad \cdot \quad \cdot \quad \cdot \quad \cdot \quad \cdot$$
$$\tau_p \leqslant \mu_p \leqslant \tau_n. \tag{13}$$

Let K_j be an orthogonal matrix of order $(n-j+1)\times(n-j)$ and write

$$K_{(i)} = K_1 K_2 ... K_{n-i}.$$

Thus $K_{(i)}$ is an orthogonal matrix of order $n\times i$, and K is a particular value of $K_{(p)}$. By the result just derived, the $(i-1)$ latent roots of $K'_{(i-1)} V K_{(i-1)}$ are separated by the i latent roots of $K'_{(i)} V K_{(i)}$. Allowing i to take in succession the values $n, n-1,..., p$ we obtain the system of inequalities (13). The minimum values of $\mu_1, \mu_2,..., \mu_p$ are attained only if $J_{12...p} = 1$, which occurs when

$$K = [q_1, q_2,..., q_p].$$

Similarly, the maximum values are attained when

$$K = [q_{n-p+1}, q_{n-p+2},..., q_n].$$

We have thus shown that the minimum value of $y'KK'y$, when y is fixed and K varies subject to (6), is

$$x'T^{\frac{1}{2}}\begin{bmatrix} I \\ 0 \end{bmatrix}\begin{bmatrix} I \\ 0 \end{bmatrix}' T^{\frac{1}{2}}x = x'T^{\frac{1}{2}}\begin{bmatrix} I & 0 \\ 0 & 0 \end{bmatrix} T^{\frac{1}{2}}x = \sum_{r=1}^{p} \tau_r x_r^2. \tag{14}$$

Similarly, the maximum value is

$$\sum_{r=n-p+1}^{n} \tau_r x_r^2.$$

The limits of ϵ_0, namely ϵ_L and ϵ_U, are therefore obtained by solving the two equations

$$\Pr\left\{ \sum_{r=1}^{p} \tau_r x_r^2 \Big/ \sum_{r=1}^{n} \tau_r x_r^2 < \epsilon_L \right\} = \alpha \tag{15}$$

and

$$\Pr\left\{ \sum_{r=n-p+1}^{n} \tau_r x_r^2 \Big/ \sum_{r=1}^{n} \tau_r x_r^2 < \epsilon_U \right\} = \alpha. \tag{16}$$

The problem of determining the latent roots is taken up by Watson and Hannan (1956) in the situation which we consider in Chapter 7, and their results indicate that the bounds on ϵ_0, though wide, are attainable in practice.

5.7. Exercises

1. A sample of size two is taken from the population with density function $f(x)$.

   (i) $f(x) = 1$ $(-\frac{1}{2} \leqslant x \leqslant \frac{1}{2})$.

Show that the density function of t is

$$c(t) = 1/2(1+|t|)^2.$$

   (ii) $f(x) = \frac{1}{2}e^{-|x|}$ $(-\infty < x < \infty)$.

Show that the density function of t is

$$c(t) = \begin{cases} 1/4 & (t \leqslant 1) \\ 1/4t^2 & (t \geqslant 1). \end{cases}$$

(iii) $f(x) = 1/\pi(1+x^2)$ $(-\infty < x < \infty)$.

Show that the density function of $u = (t+1)/(t-1)$ is

$$g(u) = 2\log|u|/\pi^2(u^2-1). \qquad \text{(Rider, 1929; Geary, 1936.)}$$

2. A sample of size three is taken from the population with density function

$$f(x) = 1 \quad (-\tfrac{1}{2} \leqslant x \leqslant \tfrac{1}{2}).$$

Show that the density function of t is

$$\frac{\sqrt{3}}{2(4-t^2)\sqrt{(1-t^2)}}\left(1-\frac{9t^2}{4-t^2}\right)+\frac{3^{\frac{3}{2}}(2+t^2)}{(4-t^2)^{\frac{3}{2}}}\tanh^{-1}\sqrt{\left(\frac{1-t^2}{4-t^2}\right)} \quad (0 \leqslant t \leqslant \tfrac{1}{2}),$$

$$\frac{-9}{4(t+1)(t^2-4)}\left(\frac{1}{t+1}+\frac{3t}{t^2-4}\right)+\frac{3^{\frac{3}{2}}(2+t^2)}{(4-t^2)^{\frac{3}{2}}}\tanh^{-1}\left\{\frac{\sqrt{(4-t^2)}}{(t+2)\sqrt{3}}\right\} \quad (\tfrac{1}{2} \leqslant t \leqslant 2),$$

$$\frac{-9}{4(t+1)(t^2-4)}\left(\frac{1}{t+1}+\frac{3t}{t^2-4}\right)+\frac{3^{\frac{3}{2}}(t^2+2)}{(t^2-4)^{\frac{3}{2}}}\tan^{-1}\left\{\frac{\sqrt{(t^2-4)}}{(t+2)\sqrt{3}}\right\} \quad (t \geqslant 2).$$

$$\text{(Perlo, 1933.)}$$

3. A sample of size n is taken from the population with density function

$$f(x) = (1-\lambda_3 D^3/6)\phi(x).$$

If λ_3^2 is negligible, show that the multiple of λ_3 to be added to the distribution function of t can be written either as

(i) $\quad \dfrac{1}{6\sqrt{(2n\pi)}}\dfrac{1+(2n-1)t^2/(n-1)}{\{1+t^2/(n-1)\}^{\frac{1}{2}(n+1)}}$

or (ii) $\left\{\dfrac{2n-1}{6\sqrt{(2n\pi)}}\right\}I_u\{\tfrac{1}{2}(n-1), 1\}-\left\{\dfrac{n-1}{3\sqrt{(2n\pi)}}\right\}I_u\{\tfrac{1}{2}(n+1), 1\},$

where $\qquad\qquad\qquad u = 1/\{1+t^2/(n-1)\}$

and $\qquad\qquad I_u(a,b) = \int_0^u x^{a-1}(1-x)^{b-1}\,dx/\mathrm{B}(a,b).$ $\qquad$ (Geary, 1936.)

4. The variables $y_1, y_2, ..., y_n$ are normally and independently distributed with the same variance σ^2 and means $\eta_1, \eta_2, ..., \eta_n$ respectively. Suppose that $\sum \eta_k = 0$ and denote $\sum \eta_k^2/2\sigma^2$ by λ. Show that

(i) $y_.$ and $\sum(y_k-y_.)^2$ are statistically independent;

(ii) the density function of t is

$c_{n-1}(t)\exp\{-\lambda t^2/(n-1+t^2)\}M[-\tfrac{1}{2}; \tfrac{1}{2}(n-1); -\lambda/\{1+t^2/(n-1)\}],$

where M is Kummer's confluent hypergeometric series. (Robbins 1948; Weibull, 1950.)

5. With the assumptions and notation of Section 5.4, show that

(i) $\mathscr{V}\hat{\mu} = \{1+2\sum \rho_k(1-\rho_k)/\nu_k+O(\sum \nu_k^{-2})\}/\omega,$

where ρ_k denotes ω_k/ω;

(ii) an approximately unbiased estimate of $\mathscr{V}\hat{\mu}$ is

$$\mathscr{V}^{*}\hat{\mu} = \{1+4\sum r_k(1-r_k)/\nu_k\}/w,$$

where r_k denotes w_k/w. (Meier, 1953.)

6. Suppose that $x = \begin{bmatrix} x_1 \\ x_2 \end{bmatrix}$ has a normal bivariate distribution with $\mathscr{E}x = \begin{bmatrix} \xi_1 \\ \xi_2 \end{bmatrix}$ and $\mathscr{D}x = \begin{bmatrix} \lambda_{11} & \lambda_{12} \\ \lambda_{12} & \lambda_{22} \end{bmatrix}\sigma^2$. An independent variable s^2 is such that cs^2/σ^2 is distributed as χ^2 on c degrees of freedom. Show that a confidence interval for $\zeta = \xi_1/\xi_2$ with confidence coefficient $1-\alpha$ consists of all the values of ζ which satisfy $(x_1-\zeta x_2)^2 \leqslant t_\alpha^2(c)s^2(\lambda_{11}-2\zeta\lambda_{12}+\zeta^2\lambda_{22})$,

and that this interval is closed if and only if the hypothesis $\xi_2 = 0$ is rejected at significance level α. (Fieller, 1954.)

7. Suppose that y has a Poisson distribution with mean m. Expand $\sqrt{\{(y+c)/(m+c)\}}$ as a Taylor series about 1 in powers of $(y-m)/(m+c)$ and hence show that, as $m \to \infty$, the variance of $\sqrt{(y+\frac{3}{8})}$ differs from the constant $\frac{1}{4}$ by terms which are $O(m^{-2})$. (Anscombe, 1948.)

8. The observations $\{y_{ij}\}$ are normally and independently distributed with expectations

$$\eta_{ij} = \mu+\rho_i+\kappa_j \quad (i = 1, 2,...,\beta;\ j = 1, 2,....,\tau)$$

and the same variance σ^2. Put

$$N = \{\sum\sum y_{ij}(y_{i.}-y_{..})(y_{.j}-y_{..})\}^2/\{\sum(y_{i.}-y_{..})^2\sum(y_{.j}-y_{..})^2\}$$

and

$$P = (\beta\tau-\beta-\tau)N/(R-N),$$

where R is the sum of squared residuals. Use the fact that $y_{1.},...,y_{\beta.}$ and $y_{.1},...,y_{.\tau}$ are distributed independently of R to show that P has an $F(b,c)$ distribution with $b = 1$ and $c = \beta\tau-\beta-\tau$. Prove also that P is sensitive to departures from linearity which take the form

$$\eta_{ij} = \mu+\rho_i+\kappa_j+\lambda(\rho_i+\kappa_j)^2,$$

where λ is small. (Tukey, 1949.)

9. A population has the density function

$$(\delta/2\sigma^2)^{\frac{1}{2}\delta}|y-\eta|^{\delta-1}\exp\{-\delta(y-\eta)^2/2\sigma^2\}/\Gamma(\tfrac{1}{2}\delta) \quad (-\infty < y < \infty;\ 0 < \delta < \infty).$$

Show that $\mathscr{E}y = \eta$, $\mathscr{V}y = \sigma^2$, $\lambda_3 = 0$, and $\lambda_4 = 2(1-\delta)/\delta$.

For a sample of size n from this population, define

$$s^2(\lambda_4;n) = \sum(y_k-\eta)^2/n.$$

Show that $s^2(\lambda_4;n)$ is distributed exactly like $s^2(0;\delta n)$. (Box, 1953.)

10. $\mathscr{E}y = A\theta$ and $\mathscr{D}y = \sigma^2 V$, but it is erroneously assumed that $\mathscr{D}y = \sigma^2 I$. Prove that the bias in the estimate of $\mathscr{D}\theta^*$ is

$$\sigma^2(A'A)^{-1}[\{\operatorname{tr}V-\operatorname{tr}A'VA(A'A)^{-1}\}I/(n-p)-A'VA(A'A)^{-1}].$$

If always $A'A = I$, show further that the bias when estimating the variance of an element of θ^* has the maximum value

$$\sigma^2\{(\text{mean of } n-p \text{ greatest roots of } V)-\text{least root of } V\},$$

and the minimum value

$$\sigma^2\{(\text{mean of } n-p \text{ least roots of } V)-\text{greatest root of } V\}. \quad (\text{Watson, 1955.})$$

5.8. References

AITKEN, A. C. (1951). *Determinants and Matrices*, seventh edition. Edinburgh: Oliver and Boyd.

ANSCOMBE, F. J. (1948). The transformation of Poisson, binomial and negative binomial data. *Biometrika*, **35**, 246–54.

BARTLETT, M. S. (1935). The effect of non-normality on the *t*-distribution. *Proc. Camb. Phil. Soc.* **31**, 223–31.

—— (1937). Properties of sufficiency and statistical tests. *Proc. Roy. Soc.* A, **160**, 268–82.

BARTON, D. E., and DENNIS, K. E. (1952). The conditions under which Gram-Charlier and Edgeworth curves are positive definite and unimodal. *Biometrika*, **39**, 425–7.

BOX, G. E. P. (1953). Non-normality and tests on variances. *Biometrika*, **40**, 318–35.

—— (1954). Some theorems on quadratic forms applied in the study of analysis of variance problems, I. Effect of inequality of variance in the one-way classification. *Ann. Math. Statist.* **25**, 290–302.

—— and ANDERSEN, S. L. (1955). Permutation theory in the derivation of robust criteria and the study of departures from assumption. *J. R. Statist. Soc.* B, **17**, 1–26.

DURBIN, J., and WATSON, G. S. (1950). Testing for serial correlation in least squares regression. I. *Biometrika*, **37**, 409–28.

—— —— (1951). Testing for serial correlation in least squares regression. II. *Biometrika*, **38**, 159–78.

FIELLER, E. C. (1954). Some problems in interval estimation. *J. R. Statist. Soc.* B, **16**, 175–85.

GAYEN, A. K. (1949). The distribution of 'Student's' *t* in random samples of any size drawn from non-normal universes. *Biometrika*, **36**, 353–69.

—— (1950). The distribution of the variance ratio in random samples of any size drawn from non-normal universes. *Biometrika*, **37**, 236–55.

GEARY, R. C. (1936). The distribution of 'Student's' ratio for non-normal samples. *Suppl. J. R. Statist. Soc.* **3**, 178–84.

GHURYE, S. G. (1949). On the use of Student's *t*-test in an asymmetrical population. *Biometrika*, **36**, 426–30.

JAMES, G. S. (1951). The comparison of several groups of observations when the ratios of the population variances are unknown. *Biometrika*, **38**, 324–9.

—— (1954). Tests of linear hypotheses in univariate and multivariate analysis when the ratios of the population variances are unknown. *Biometrika*, **41**, 19–43.

—— (1956). On the accuracy of weighted means and ratios. *Biometrika*, **43**, 304–21.

MACDUFFEE, C. C. (1933). *The Theory of Matrices*. Berlin: Springer.

MEIER, P. (1953). Variance of a weighted mean. *Biometrics*, **9**, 59–73.

NEYMAN, J., and PEARSON, E. S. (1933). On the problem of the most efficient tests of statistical hypotheses. *Phil. Trans.* A, **231**, 289–337.

PEARSON, E. S., assisted by ADYANTHAYA, N. K., *et al.* (1929). The distribution of frequency constants in small samples from non-normal symmetrical and skew populations. *Biometrika*, **21**, 259–86.

PEARSON, E. S. (1931). The analysis of variance in cases of non-normal variation. *Biometrika*, **23**, 114–33.

PERLO, V. (1933). On the distribution of Student's ratio for samples of three drawn from a rectangular distribution. *Biometrika*, **25**, 203–4.

RIDER, P. R. (1929). On the distribution of the ratio of mean to standard deviation in small samples from non-normal universes. *Biometrika*, **21**, 124–43.

ROBBINS, H. (1948). The distribution of Student's *t* when the population means are unequal. *Ann. Math. Statist.* **19**, 406–10.

SCHEFFÉ, H. (1942). On the ratio of the variances of two normal populations. *Ann. Math. Statist.* **13**, 371–88.

SRIVASTAVA, A. B. L. (1958). Effect of non-normality on the power function of *t*-test. *Biometrika*, **45**, 421–9.

'STUDENT' (1908). The probable error of a mean. *Biometrika*, **6**, 1–25.

TUKEY, J. W. (1949). One degree of freedom for non-additivity. *Biometrics*, **5**, 232–42.

WATSON, G. S. (1955). Serial correlation in regression analysis. I. *Biometrika*, **42**, 327–41.

—— and HANNAN, E. J. (1956). Serial correlation in regression analysis. II. *Biometrika*, **43**, 436–48.

WEIBULL, M. (1950). The distribution of the *t* and *z* variables in the case of stratified sample with individuals taken from normal parent populations with varying means. *Skand. Akt.* **33**, 137–67.

WELCH, B. L. (1947). The generalization of 'Student's' problem when several different population variances are involved. *Biometrika*, **34**, 28–35.

—— (1951). On the comparison of several mean values: an alternative approach. *Biometrika*, **38**, 330–6.

POLYNOMIAL REGRESSION

6.1. Introduction

SUPPOSE that an experiment is performed by fixing the value of a quantitative variable x, such as time or temperature, and observing the value taken by a random variable y, such as the corresponding yield of a chemical product. We say that x is a *factor* and y the observed *response*, while the different values assigned to x are the *levels* of that factor. Denoting them by $x_1, x_2, ..., x_n$, we assume that the expected response corresponding to the rth level of x is

$$\eta(x_r) \equiv \mathcal{E}y_r = \beta_0 + \beta_1 x_r + \beta_2 x_r^2 + ... + \beta_\nu x_r^\nu, \tag{1}$$

where ν is an unknown integer, zero or positive, and $\beta_0, \beta_1, ..., \beta_\nu$ are unknown parameters, whose values are unrestricted. Assuming further that the dispersion matrix of the observations is $\sigma^2 I$, we discuss here techniques for the estimation of ν, $\eta(x)$, and the variance of the estimate of $\eta(x)$. Some attention is given to experiments which involve several factors like x, and in which the expected response is a polynomial function of the corresponding variables.

6.2. Direct method of analysis

The estimation of ν is the first problem to be tackled. By inspection of the data, we decide what is the highest value of u necessary for a polynomial approximation of the form

$$\eta(x_r) = \beta_0 + \beta_1 x_r + \beta_2 x_r^2 + ... + \beta_u x_r^u \tag{1}$$

to represent an adequate fit to the observations $\{y_r\}$. If w is the maximum value of u anticipated, we now calculate the sum of squared residuals for each value of $u = 0, 1, 2, ..., w$. Denote by R_u the sum of squared residuals which corresponds to equation (1), and by S_u the sum of squares for testing the hypothesis $\beta_u = 0$ when (1) holds. Thus

$$S_u = R_{u-1} - R_u \quad (u \geqslant 1). \tag{2}$$

The values of $S_0 = (\sum y_r)^2/n$, $S_1, S_2, ..., S_w$ are generally large at first and then rapidly decrease. By referring the variance-ratio

$$(n - w - 1) S_w / R_w$$

to the F-distribution with 1 and $(n-w-1)$ degrees of freedom, we can determine whether or not $\beta_w x_r^w$ need be included in the expression for $\eta(x_r)$. (This involves the additional assumption that $y_1, y_2,..., y_n$ are normally distributed.) Should it be excluded, we test

$$(n-w)S_{w-1}/R_{w-1}$$

and continue the process until reaching the first variance-ratio which is clearly significant. The value of u corresponding to this ratio is v, the estimate of v. Its distribution evidently depends on the values of the unknowns, and the significance levels of the various tests, but we shall not go into details, which are likely to be somewhat involved and not very illuminating. Similar procedures are discussed by Bancroft (1944).

A convenient scheme of computing S_u and R_u has been given by Hayes and Vickers (1951). Let us adapt earlier notation and rewrite (1) as

$$\boldsymbol{\eta} = \mathbf{A}_u \boldsymbol{\beta}_u \qquad (1 \ bis)$$

where $\boldsymbol{\eta}$ is the column vector with elements $\eta(x_1)$, $\eta(x_2)$,..., $\eta(x_n)$; $\boldsymbol{\beta}_u$ is the column vector with elements $\beta_0, \beta_1,..., \beta_u$; and $\mathbf{A}_u$ is the matrix with elements x_r^j $(r = 1, 2,..., n; j = 0, 1,..., u)$. We assume that at least w of $x_1, x_2,..., x_n$ are distinct, in which case $\mathbf{A}_w$ has rank $(w+1)$, because the determinant formed by its first $(w+1)$ rows, for example, is

$$\prod_{p>q=1}^{w+1} (x_p - x_q).$$

Denote by $\mathbf{C}_u$ the matrix $\mathbf{A}_u' \mathbf{A}_u$ with elements

$$c_{jk} = \sum_{r=1}^{n} x_r^{j+k} \quad (j, k = 0, 1, 2,..., u);$$

by $\mathbf{b}_u$ the vector $\mathbf{A}_u' \mathbf{y}$ with elements

$$b_j = \sum_{r=1}^{n} x_r^j y_r \quad (j = 0, 1, 2,..., u);$$

by $\mathbf{T}_u$ the upper triangular matrix with positive diagonal elements such that $\mathbf{C}_u = \mathbf{T}_u' \mathbf{T}_u$; and by $\mathbf{h}_u$ the solution of the equations $\mathbf{T}_u' \mathbf{h}_u = \mathbf{b}_u$. Then

$$S_u = h_u^2 \qquad (3)$$

and

$$R_u = \mathbf{y}' \mathbf{y} - \mathbf{h}_u' \mathbf{h}_u. \qquad (4)$$

The great advantage of these formulae is that $\mathbf{T}_{u-1}$ is the first $(u-1)$ rows and columns of $\mathbf{T}_u$, and $\mathbf{h}_{u-1}$ is the first $(u-1)$ rows of $\mathbf{h}_u$. Consequently, when R_{u-1} and S_{u-1} have been computed, $t_{1u}, t_{2u},..., t_{uu}$ and h_u are the only additional quantities which are needed in order to determine S_u and R_u. No recalculation or modification of earlier work is necessary.

In practice the order of the computations differs slightly from what the last paragraph might suggest, and follows the routine described in Chapter 1. The first stage consists in choosing an origin and scale for x such that the transformed values corresponding to $x_1, x_2, ..., x_n$ are spread over the interval $(-1, 1)$ approximately. Unless $x_1, x_2, ..., x_n$ have a strong tendency to cluster, this means that sums of odd powers of the transformed values are small, and sums of even powers have the same order of magnitude for the low values of w which we envisage. In this connexion, a transformation to the interval $(0, 1)$ implies (Hilbert, 1894; Forsythe, 1957) that C_w is approximately a multiple of a principal minor of

$$H = \begin{bmatrix} 1 & \frac{1}{2} & \frac{1}{3} & \frac{1}{4} & \cdot & \cdot & \cdot & \cdot \\ \frac{1}{2} & \frac{1}{3} & \frac{1}{4} & \frac{1}{5} & \cdot & \cdot & \cdot & \cdot \\ \frac{1}{3} & \frac{1}{4} & \frac{1}{5} & \frac{1}{6} & \cdot & \cdot & \cdot & \cdot \\ \cdot & \cdot & \cdot & \cdot & \cdot & \cdot & \cdot & \cdot \end{bmatrix}.$$

These minors are known to become very ill-conditioned when $w \geqslant 6$ (Todd, 1954).

We now proceed to the computation of $[\mathbf{C}_w \vdots \mathbf{b}_w]$, which is greatly assisted by a table of powers; $[\mathbf{C}_w \vdots \mathbf{b}_w]$ is checked by forming the column $[\mathbf{A}_w \vdots \mathbf{y}]\mathbf{1}$, and evaluating both sides of

$$\mathbf{A}'_w([\mathbf{A}_w \vdots \mathbf{y}]\mathbf{1}) = [\mathbf{C}_w \vdots \mathbf{b}_w]\mathbf{1}.$$

Next $[\mathbf{T}_w \vdots \mathbf{h}_w]$ is calculated and checked row by row, using the identity $\mathbf{T}'_w \mathbf{a}_2 = \mathbf{a}_1$, where $\mathbf{a}_1 = [\mathbf{C}_w \vdots \mathbf{b}_w]\mathbf{1}$ and $\mathbf{a}_2 = [\mathbf{T}_w \vdots \mathbf{h}_w]\mathbf{1}$. The vector $\mathbf{h}_w$ then provides $\{S_u\}$ and $\{R_u\}$, from which v is obtained as already described. Finally, $\boldsymbol{\beta}^*_v$ is the solution of $\mathbf{T}_v \boldsymbol{\beta}^*_v = \mathbf{h}_v$—checked by $\mathbf{a}'_3 \boldsymbol{\beta}^*_v = a_4$, where $\mathbf{a}'_3 = \mathbf{1}'\mathbf{C}_v$ and $a_4 = \mathbf{1}'\mathbf{b}_v$; and $\mathbf{C}^{-1}_v$ is the solution of $\mathbf{T}_v \mathbf{C}^{-1}_v = (\mathbf{T}^{-1}_v)'$—checked by $\mathbf{a}'_3 \mathbf{C}^{-1}_v = \mathbf{1}'$. Since v is a random variable, we can no longer assert correctly that $\mathscr{E}\boldsymbol{\beta}^*_v = \boldsymbol{\beta}_v$ and $\mathscr{D}\boldsymbol{\beta}^*_v = \sigma^2 \mathbf{C}^{-1}_v$. However, these statements may be accepted as working approximations. To the same degree of approximation, $\eta(x)$ is predicted by

$$\eta^*(x) = \beta^*_0 + \beta^*_1 x + \beta^*_2 x^2 + ... + \beta^*_v x^v \tag{5}$$

and the variance of the predicted value is

$$\mathscr{V}\eta^*(x) = \sigma^2 \{c^{00} + (c^{01} + c^{10})x + (c^{02} + c^{11} + c^{20})x^2 + ... + c^{vv} x^{2v}\} \tag{6}$$

in which the coefficients are elements of $\mathbf{C}^{-1}_v$.

In the example presented in Table 10, the values $\{x_r\}$ have already been transformed to accord with the principles stated above, while $\mathbf{C}_w$ and $\mathbf{b}_w$ may be supposed to have been checked. Here $w = 3$ and the analysis leads to $v = 2$, since S_3 is smaller than $R_3/10$. The low value of S_1 is due to the small slope of the line which best fits the data.

TABLE 10. *Direct fit of regression polynomial*

x	y	x	y
-0.92	0.716	0.10	2.270
-0.84	1.052	0.24	2.260
-0.66	1.521	0.38	2.078
-0.56	1.598	0.50	2.040
-0.50	1.767	0.62	1.829
-0.38	1.948	0.66	1.705
-0.26	2.157	0.92	1.134

	$\mathbf{C}_w$			$\mathbf{b}_w$	$\mathbf{a}_1$
14.00000	-0.70000	4.89160	-0.53274	24.07500	41.73386
-0.70000	4.89160	-0.53274	2.73095	0.25590	6.64571
4.89160	-0.53274	2.73095	-0.38205	6.74937	13.45713
-0.53274	2.73095	-0.38205	1.85473	-0.05301	3.61788
18.19160	3.65886	7.08981		31.08027	a_4

	$\mathbf{T}_w$			$\mathbf{h}_w$	$\mathbf{a}_2$
3.74166	-0.18708	1.30733	-0.14238	6.43431	11.15384
	2.20377	-0.13076	1.22713	0.66233	3.96247
		1.00237	-0.03537	-1.57206	-0.60506
			0.57215	-0.00919	0.56296

$(\boldsymbol{\beta}_v^*)'$	2.27799	0.20749	-1.56834
t^{jj}	0.26726	0.45377	0.99764

	$\mathbf{C}_v^{-1}$	
0.19139	-0.01016	-0.34480
-0.01016	0.20941	0.05905
-0.34480	0.05905	0.99528

$\eta^*(x) = 2.27799 + 0.20749x - 1.56834x^2$

$\mathscr{V}\eta^*(x) = \sigma^2(0.19139 - 0.02032x - 0.48019x^2 + 0.11810x^3 + 0.99528x^4)$

$$\sum y_r^2 = 44.3345$$

u	S_u	R_u
0	41.4003	2.9342
1	0.4387	2.4955
2	2.4714	0.0241
3	0.0001	0.0240

The estimate of σ^2 is $0.0241/11 = 0.00219$.

6.3. Orthogonal polynomials

The use of orthogonal functions in polynomial regression was studied independently by Rushton (1951) and Hayes and Vickers

(1951), while Wishart and Metakides (1953) offer a recommended computation scheme. In the following account we continue to use the notation of the previous Section.

Any assumption of the form

$$\boldsymbol{\eta} = \mathbf{A}_u \boldsymbol{\beta}_u \qquad (2.1 \text{ bis})$$

can be transformed into

$$\boldsymbol{\eta} = \mathbf{A}_u \mathbf{T}_u^{-1} \boldsymbol{\varphi}_u, \qquad (1)$$

where

$$\boldsymbol{\varphi}_u = \mathbf{T}_u \boldsymbol{\beta}_u. \qquad (2)$$

The rth row of $\mathbf{A}_u \mathbf{T}_u^{-1}$ is a vector of $(u+1)$ polynomials, the $(j+1)$th of these polynomials being

$$t_j(x_r) = t^{0j} + t^{1j}x_r + \ldots + t^{jj}x_r^j \qquad (3)$$

$$(j = 0, 1, 2, \ldots, u).$$

Hence $\qquad \eta(x_r) = \phi_0 t_0(x_r) + \phi_1 t_1(x_r) + \ldots + \phi_u t_u(x_r). \qquad (4)$

The polynomials $\{t_j(x)\}$ do not depend on u, for if the assumption (1) is replaced by

$$\boldsymbol{\eta} = \mathbf{A}_w \mathbf{T}_w^{-1} \boldsymbol{\varphi}_w, \qquad (5)$$

then $\mathbf{T}_u^{-1}$ is the first $(u+1)$ rows and columns of $\mathbf{T}_w^{-1}$, whatever $w > u$, and remainder of the first $(u+1)$ columns of $\mathbf{T}_w^{-1}$ consists entirely of zeros. Further,

$$(\mathbf{A}_w \mathbf{T}_w^{-1})'(\mathbf{A}_w \mathbf{T}_w^{-1}) = (\mathbf{T}_w^{-1})' \mathbf{C}_w \mathbf{T}_w^{-1} = \mathbf{I},$$

giving $\qquad \sum_{r=1}^{n} t_j(x_r)t_k(x_r) = \delta_{jk} \quad (j, k = 0, 1, 2, \ldots, w). \qquad (6)$

Thus the $\{t_j(x)\}$ form a set of polynomials which are orthogonal over the set $\{x_r\}$ of values of x, a result implicit in Hsu (1941). Since also

$$(\mathbf{A}_w \mathbf{T}_w^{-1})' \mathbf{A}_w = \mathbf{T}_w,$$

$$\sum_{r=1}^{n} x_r^k t_j(x_r) = t_{jk}$$

$$= 0 \quad (j > k).$$

Hence $\qquad \sum_{r=1}^{n} \pi_k(x_r)t_j(x_r) = 0 \qquad (7)$

for an arbitrary polynomial $\pi_k(x)$ of degree $k < j$. Any such polynomial can be written in the form

$$\pi_k(x_r) = c_0 t_0(x_r) + c_1 t_1(x_r) + \ldots + c_k t_k(x_r), \qquad (8)$$

where the coefficients are given by

$$c_j = \sum_{r=1}^{n} \pi_k(x_r)t_j(x_r) \qquad (j = 0, 1, 2, \ldots, k). \qquad (9)$$

If several sets of observed responses $\{y_r\}$ are likely to be associated with the same set of levels $\{x_r\}$, then much numerical work will be saved by computing a table of the values of $t_j(x_r)$ for $r = 1, 2, ..., n$ and $j = 0, 1, 2, ..., w$ where w is the highest degree anticipated among polynomial approximations to $\eta(x_r)$. As (6) shows, the matrix of the normal equations for $\phi_1^*, \phi_2^*, ..., \phi_w^*$ is $\mathbf{I}$ when $\mathscr{D}\mathbf{y} = \sigma^2\mathbf{I}$, so that

$$\mathscr{D}\boldsymbol{\varphi}_w^* = \sigma^2\mathbf{I}.$$

Under these conditions,

$$\phi_u^* = \sum_{r=1}^{n} t_u(x_r)y_r, \tag{10}$$

$$S_u = (\phi_u^*)^2, \tag{11}$$

and $$R_u = \mathbf{y}'\mathbf{y} - (\boldsymbol{\varphi}_u^*)'(\boldsymbol{\varphi}_u^*). \tag{12}$$

In the previous Section $\boldsymbol{\varphi}_u^*$ was denoted by $\mathbf{h}_u$, but the meaning of this quantity as an estimate of $\boldsymbol{\varphi}_u$ is more important here than its former use as an intermediate computing device. Another advantage of the representation (1) is that replacement of this assumption by (5) leaves the estimates of $\phi_0, \phi_1, \phi_2, ..., \phi_u$ and the corresponding $S_0, S_1, S_2, ..., S_u$ both unaltered; the effect of the additional terms on the graduated value y_r^* corresponding to y_r is simply to add

$$\phi_{u+1}^* t_{u+1}(x_r) + \phi_{u+2}^* t_{u+2}(x_r) + ... + \phi_w^* t_w(x_r),$$

so that the approximating polynomials can, if desired, be successively constructed and inspected.

On the other hand, calculating the coefficients of the orthogonal polynomials—which necessarily involves determining the inverse of $\mathbf{T}_w$—is not worth while for a single set of observed responses. Although the diagonal elements of $\mathbf{C}_v^{-1}$, namely the variances of $\beta_0^*, \beta_1^*, \beta_2^*, ..., \beta_v^*$, are more rapidly obtained through the resolution $\mathbf{C}_v^{-1} = \mathbf{T}_v^{-1}(\mathbf{T}_v^{-1})'$ than by solving $\mathbf{T}_v\mathbf{C}_v^{-1} = (\mathbf{T}_v^{-1})'$, the principal object of the analysis usually consists in the estimation of $\eta(x)$ and $\mathscr{V}\eta^*(x)$, in which case the whole of $\mathbf{C}_v^{-1}$ is required and the direct method described in the preceding Section is preferable.

We illustrate in Table 11 the computation of a table of $\{t_j(x_r)\}$, given the same set of values $\{x_r\}$ as used in the previous example. The numerical methods up to the evaluation of $\mathbf{T}_w$ have been described and illustrated. Here $\mathbf{T}_w'$ is written down in place of $\mathbf{T}_w$ to facilitate the calculation of $\mathbf{T}_w^{-1}$; using the identity, $\mathbf{T}_w^{-1}\mathbf{T}_w = \mathbf{I}_w$, $\mathbf{T}_w^{-1}$ is then computed by columns, beginning with the first. The notation is $\mathbf{a}_1' = \mathbf{1}'\mathbf{C}_w$; $\mathbf{a}_2' = \mathbf{1}'\mathbf{T}_w'$; and $\mathbf{a}_3' = \mathbf{1}'\mathbf{T}_w^{-1}$. When computing $\mathbf{T}_w'$,

H

check that $\mathbf{a}_2' \mathbf{T}_w = \mathbf{a}_1'$; and when computing $\mathbf{T}_w^{-1}$, check that $\mathbf{a}_3' \mathbf{T}_w = \mathbf{1}'$, After $\mathbf{T}_w^{-1}$ has been checked, the values $\{t_j(x_r)\}$ are calculated from (3).

TABLE 11. *Computation of orthogonal polynomials*

x	x^2	x^3	x	x^2	x^3
-0.92	0·8464	-0.778688	0·10	0·0100	0·001000
-0.84	0·7056	-0.592704	0·24	0·0576	0·013824
-0.66	0·4356	-0.287496	0·38	0·1444	0·054872
-0.56	0·3136	-0.175616	0·50	0·2500	0·125000
-0.50	0·2500	-0.125000	0·62	0·3844	0·238328
-0.38	0·1444	-0.054872	0·66	0·4356	0·287496
-0.26	0·0676	-0.017576	0·92	0·8464	0·778688

$$\mathbf{C}_w$$

14·00000	-0.70000	4·89160	-0.53274
-0.70000	4·89160	-0.53274	2·73095
4·89160	-0.53274	2·73095	-0.38205
-0.53274	2·73095	-0.38205	1·85473
$\mathbf{a}_1'$ 17·65886	6·38981	6·70776	3·67089

$$\mathbf{T}_w'$$

3·74166			
-0.18708	2·20377		
1·30733	-0.13076	1·00237	
-0.14238	1·22713	-0.03537	0·57215
$\mathbf{a}_2'$ 4·71953	3·30014	0·96700	0·57215

$$\mathbf{T}_w^{-1}$$

0·26726	0·02269	-0.34561	-0.00352
	0·45377	0·05919	-0.96957
		0·99764	0·06167
			1·74779
$\mathbf{a}_3'$ 0·26726	0·47646	0·71122	0·83637

x	$t_1(x)$	$t_2(x)$	$t_3(x)$	x	$t_1(x)$	$t_2(x)$	$t_3(x)$
-0.92	-0.39478	$+0.44434$	-0.42030	$+0.10$	$+0.06807$	-0.32971	-0.09811
-0.84	-0.35848	$+0.30861$	-0.18149	$+0.24$	$+0.13159$	-0.27394	-0.20850
-0.66	-0.27680	$+0.04990$	$+0.16078$	$+0.38$	$+0.19512$	-0.17906	-0.26715
-0.56	-0.23142	-0.06590	$+0.25184$	$+0.50$	$+0.24957$	-0.06661	-0.25441
-0.50	-0.20419	-0.12579	$+0.27821$	$+0.62$	$+0.30403$	$+0.07458$	-0.16440
-0.38	-0.14974	-0.22404	$+0.27792$	$+0.66$	$+0.32218$	$+0.12803$	-0.11409
-0.26	-0.09529	-0.29356	$+0.22202$	$+0.92$	$+0.44016$	$+0.55325$	$+0.51766$

$$t_0(x_r) = 0·26726 = 1/\sqrt{14}.$$

In applying a table of $\{t_j(x_r)\}$, equations (10), (11), and (12) give $\{\phi_u^*\}$, $\{S_u\}$, and $\{R_u\}$; the estimate v is then chosen as before. The coefficient of x^j in $\eta^*(x)$ is the $(j+1)$th element of $(\boldsymbol{\varphi}_v^*)'(\mathbf{T}_v^{-1})'$. $\mathscr{V}\eta^*(x)$ is then given by (2.6), in which the elements $\{c^{jk}\}$ are calculated from the representation $C_v^{-1} = T_v^{-1}(T_v^{-1})'$. To illustrate the analysis we take the values $\{y_r\}$ which were used in the example of the preceding Section.

$$\sum y_r^2 = 44 \cdot 3345$$

u	ϕ_u^*	S_u	R_u
0	6·43428	41·4000	2·9345
1	0·66238	0·4387	2·4958
2	−1·57195	2·4710	0·0248
3	−0·00923	0·0001	0·0247

Adopting the estimate $v = 2$, the estimate of $\sigma^2 = 0{\cdot}0248/11 = 0{\cdot}00225$.

$$\eta^*(x) = 2{\cdot}27794 + 0{\cdot}20752x - 1{\cdot}56824x^2,$$

and $\mathscr{V}\eta^*(x) = \sigma^2(0{\cdot}19139 - 0{\cdot}02032x - 0{\cdot}48018x^2 +$

$$+ 0{\cdot}11810x^3 + 0{\cdot}99529x^4).$$

A comparison with the results got by direct analysis reveals only small discrepancies in $\eta^*(x)$ and $\mathscr{V}\eta^*(x)$.

6.4. Finite difference operators

The notation in this Section and the next follows Bickley (1948). Consider the values taken by a function $f(x)$ at integral values of x. The forward shift operator E is defined by

$$Ef(x) = f(x+1). \tag{1}$$

Positive or negative powers of E satisfy

$$E^k f(x) = f(x+k). \tag{2}$$

The forward difference operator Δ is defined by

$$\Delta f(x) = f(x+1) - f(x);$$

and the backward difference operator ∇ by

$$\nabla f(x) = f(x) - f(x-1).$$

Thus $\qquad\qquad\qquad \Delta = E-1 = \nabla E \tag{3}$

and $\qquad\qquad\qquad \nabla = 1 - E^{-1} = \Delta E^{-1}. \tag{4}$

$\Delta^k f(x)$ can be expressed in terms of the values of $f(x)$ at integral x by expanding $(E-1)^k$ and operating on $f(x)$ in accordance with (2). Similarly, powers of E can be expressed as polynomials in Δ or ∇. The kth forward or backward differences of a polynomial of degree j are values of a polynomial of degree $j-k$; for $k > j$, such differences are zero.

The symbol $\binom{s}{j}$ is defined for $j \geqslant 0$, and stands for

$$s(s-1)(s-2)...(s-j+1)/j!.$$

When $s > j$, $\binom{s}{j} = s!/(s-j)!j!$; when $0 \leqslant s \leqslant (j-1)$, $\binom{s}{j} = 0$; and

when $s < 0$, $\binom{s}{j} = (-)^j\binom{j-s-1}{j}$. Suppose that we require to

expand $\binom{x-n}{j}$ in terms of its forward differences at $\binom{x-j}{j}$ where

$0 \leqslant x \leqslant (n-1)$ and $0 \leqslant j \leqslant (n-1)$. Then

$$\binom{x-n}{j} = E^{-(n-j)}\binom{x-j}{j}$$

$$= \binom{x-j}{j} - \binom{n-j}{1}\Delta\binom{x-j}{j} + \binom{n-j+1}{2}\Delta^2\binom{x-j}{j} - \dots.$$

By induction,

$$\Delta^k\binom{x-j}{j} = \binom{x-j}{j-k}$$

$$= 0 \quad (k > j).$$

Hence

$$\binom{x-n}{j} = \binom{x-j}{j} - \binom{n-j}{1}\binom{x-j}{j-1} +$$

$$+ \binom{n-j+1}{2}\binom{x-j}{j-2} - \dots (-1)^j\binom{n-1}{j}. \quad (5)$$

The forward summation operator Σ is defined by

$$\Sigma f(x) = \Sigma f(x-1) + f(x);$$

and the backward summation operator $\mathfrak{Z}$ by

$$\mathfrak{Z} f(x) = \mathfrak{Z} f(x-1) + f(x-1).$$

Thus $$\Sigma = (1 - E^{-1})^{-1} = \nabla^{-1}, \quad (6)$$

and $$\mathfrak{Z} = (E-1)^{-1} = \Delta^{-1}. \quad (7)$$

Unless a lower limit of summation is specified, $\Sigma^j f(x)$ and $\mathfrak{Z}^j f(x)$ will contain arbitrary constants analogous to the constant of integration which occurs with an indefinite integral. We take $x = 0$ as a lower limit and, after expanding $(1 - E^{-1})^{-j}$ or $(E-1)^{-j}$, replace $E^{-k}f(x)$ by 0 if $k > x \geqslant 0$. This does not mean that $f(x)$ is assumed to be zero for $x < 0$ but merely ensures that the quantities $f(-1), f(-2),...$ do not enter into repeated summations. For example,

$$\mathfrak{Z}^j = (E-1)^{-j} = E^{-j} + \binom{j}{j-1}E^{-(j+1)} + \binom{j+1}{j-1}E^{-(j+2)} + \dots$$

giving $$\mathbb{Z}^j f(x) = 0 \quad (0 \leqslant x < j) \tag{8}$$

and $$\mathbb{Z}^j f(n) = \sum_{x=0}^{n-j} \binom{n-1-x}{j-1} f(x). \tag{9}$$

The kth forward or backward summations of a polynomial of degree j are values of a polynomial of degree $j+k$.

6.5. Orthogonal polynomials when $\Delta x = 1$

In this Section $p_j(x)$ denotes a polynomial of degree j such that the set of polynomials $\{p_j(x)\}$ is orthogonal over the set of values $0, 1, 2,..., (n-1)$ of x. We shall determine an explicit expression for $p_j(x)$; obtain a recurrence relation from which the set $\{p_j(x)\}$ can be constructed; and illustrate its use in fitting a polynomial to observations $\{y_r\}$ when the corresponding values $\{x_r\}$ are equally spaced. These polynomials and many of their properties were discovered by Chebyshev (1875); and they were first applied to statistical problems by Fisher (1920). The proofs of their properties which are given below are due to Aitken (1933), Lidstone (1933), and Weinberg (1947).

Given an arbitrary polynomial $\pi_k(x)$, of degree $k < j$, (3.7) shows that

$$\sum_{x=0}^{n-1} \pi_k(x) p_j(x) = 0. \tag{1}$$

Take $$\pi_k(x) = \binom{n-1-x}{k}.$$

$\pi_k(x)$ is zero for $x = (n-1), (n-2),..., (n-k)$ and so

$$\sum_{x=0}^{n-1} \pi_k(x) p_j(x) = \sum_{x=0}^{n-k-1} \binom{n-1-x}{k} p_j(x) = \mathbb{Z}^{k+1} p_j(n).$$

Hence $$\mathbb{Z}^{k+1} p_j(n) = 0 \quad (k = 0, 1, 2,..., j-1). \tag{2}$$

Denote $\mathbb{Z}^j p_j(x)$ by $g(x)$. This is a polynomial of degree $2j$. Since $\mathbb{Z} = \Delta^{-1}$,

$$p_j(x) = \Delta^j g(x). \tag{3}$$

From (2), $g(x)$ and its first $(j-1)$ forward differences are zero at $x = n$; building up the polynomial from its differences, $g(x) = 0$ at $x = n$, $(n+1),..., (n+j-1)$. Since, by (4.8), $g(x) = 0$ at $x = 0, 1, 2,..., (j-1)$, we have a total of $2j$ linear factors for $g(x)$, and therefore

$$g(x) = L_j \binom{x}{j} \binom{x-n}{j}, \tag{4}$$

where L_j is a coefficient depending on j but not on x.

We interrupt the main argument at this point in order to prove that $p_j(x)$, considered as a function of $x-\frac{1}{2}(n-1)$, is an even function if j is even and odd if j is odd. The identity

$$\binom{x}{j}\binom{x-n}{j} = (-1)^j\binom{x}{j}\binom{n-x+j-1}{j} = \binom{j-1-x}{j}\binom{n-x+j-1}{j}$$

gives

$$g(x) = g(n-x+j-1).$$

Hence

$$\Delta^i g(x) = (-1)^i \nabla^i g(n-x+j-1) = (-1)^i \Delta^i g(n-x+j-1-i).$$

On taking $i = j$, and using (3),

$$p_j(x) = (-1)^j p_j(n-x-1). \tag{5}$$

This is the result stated. It can also be derived from the supposition that the coefficient of x^j in a polynomial of degree j fitted to an arbitrary set of observations $\{y_r\}$ must also be the coefficient of $(n-1-x)^j$ in a polynomial of degree j fitted to the same observations in reverse order.

Returning to (4), we insert the expansion (4.5) for $\binom{x-n}{j}$ and obtain

$$g(x) = L_j \sum_{i=0}^{j} \binom{x}{j}(-1)^i\binom{x-j}{j-i}\binom{n-j+i-1}{i}$$

$$= L_j \sum_{i=0}^{j} (-1)^i\binom{x}{2j-i}\binom{2j-i}{j}\binom{n-j+i-1}{i}.$$

Now perform Δ^j, which gives

$$p_j(x) = L_j \sum_{i=0}^{j} (-1)^i\binom{x}{j-i}\binom{2j-i}{j}\binom{n-j+i-1}{i}. \tag{6}$$

To find the coefficient L_j, consider

$$\mathcal{Z}^{j+1}p_j(n) = \sum_{x=0}^{n-j-1} \binom{n-1-x}{j}p_j(x).$$

Expand $\binom{n-1-x}{j}$ as a sum of $\{p_i(x)\}$ for $i = 0, 1, 2, ..., j$. The coefficient of x^j in $\binom{n-1-x}{j}$ is $(-1)^j/j!$ whereas, from (6), the coefficient of x^j in $p_j(x)$ is $L_j\binom{2j}{j}\Big/j!$. Therefore

$$\binom{n-1-x}{j} = (-1)^j p_j(x)\Big/L_j\binom{2j}{j} + \text{terms in } \{p_k(x)\} \text{ for } k < j.$$

Multiply both sides by $p_j(x)$ and sum over x:

$$z^{j+1}p_j(n) = (-1)^j \Big/ L_j\binom{2j}{j}.$$

The left side here is $zg(n)$, and so

$$L_j \sum_{x=0}^{n-1} \binom{x}{j}\binom{x-n}{j} = (-1)^j \Big/ L_j\binom{2j}{j},$$

or

$$1/L_j^2 = \binom{2j}{j}\sum_{x=0}^{n-1}\binom{x}{j}\binom{n-x+j-1}{j}.$$

$\binom{x}{j}$ is the coefficient of $(-t)^{x-j}$ in the expansion of $(1+t)^{-(j+1)}$, and

$\binom{n-x+j-1}{j}$ is the coefficient of $(-t)^{n-x-1}$ in the same expansion.

Consequently

$$\sum_{x=0}^{n-1}\binom{x}{j}\binom{n-x+j-1}{j}$$

is the coefficient of $(-t)^{n-j-1}$ in the expansion of $(1+t)^{-(2j+2)}$, namely $\binom{n+j}{2j+1}$. Finally, then,

$$1/L_j^2 = \binom{2j}{j}\binom{n+j}{2j+1} \tag{7}$$

and the orthogonal polynomials $\{p_j(x)\}$ are completely determined by equations (6) and (7).

From the viewpoint of analysing observational data, any set of polynomials of the form

$$q_j(x) = M_j p_j(x)$$

is as useful as the set $p_j(x)$, because the basic property

$$\sum_{x=0}^{n-1} q_j(x)q_k(x) = 0 \quad (j \neq k)$$

is retained. The coefficients M_j can be chosen according to several different conventions. For example, integral values of $q_j(x)$ are desirable when tabulating these polynomials. The recurrence relation mentioned above is, however, conveniently obtained in terms of polynomials $\{q_j(x)\}$ where M_j is chosen such that the coefficient of x^j in $q_j(x)$ is unity. Using (6), this implies that

$$M_j = j! \Big/ L_j\binom{2j}{j},$$

whence

$$\sum_{x=0}^{n-1} [q_j(x)]^2 = M_j^2 = (j!)^2\binom{n+j}{2j+1}\Big/\binom{2j}{j}, \tag{8}$$

on substituting for $1/L_j^2$ from (7). Now consider the expansion of $q_1(x)q_j(x)$, a polynomial of degree $(j+1)$, in a series of orthogonal polynomials $\{q_i(x)\}$. The coefficient of $q_{j+1}(x)$ is unity, while the coefficient of $q_j(x)$ is

$$\sum_{x=0}^{n-1} q_1(x)[p_j(x)]^2,$$

which is zero because (5) shows that

$$q_1(x) = -q_1(n-1-x).$$

Furthermore, the coefficient of $q_{j+1-i}(x)$ in the expansion of $q_1(x)q_j(x)$ is M_j^2/M_{j+1-i}^2 times the coefficient of $q_j(x)$ in the expansion of $q_1(x)q_{j+1-i}(x)$, and is therefore zero when the degree of $q_1(x)q_{j+1-i}(x)$ is less than j, namely for $i > 2$. Consequently,

$$q_1(x)q_j(x) = q_{j+1}(x)+N_j q_{j-1}(x). \qquad (9)$$

Multiply both sides by $q_{j-1}(x)$ and sum over x:

$$\sum_{x=0}^{n-1} q_1(x)q_j(x)q_{j-1}(x) = N_j M_{j-1}^2.$$

Replace (9) by the corresponding expression for $j-1$, multiply both sides by $q_j(x)$ and sum over x:

$$\sum_{x=0}^{n-1} q_1(x)q_{j-1}(x)q_j(x) = M_j^2.$$

The last two equations give

$$N_j = M_j^2/M_{j-1}^2,$$

and using (8), $\qquad N_j = j^2(n^2-j^2)/4(4j^2-1).$

Combining this result with (9) gives

$$q_{j+1}(x) = q_1(x)q_j(x)-j^2(n^2-j^2)q_{j-1}(x)/4(4j^2-1). \qquad (10)$$

By means of the recurrence relation (10), a table of orthogonal polynomials can be constructed, beginning with $q_0(x) = 1$ and $q_1(x) = x-\frac{1}{2}(n-1)$; or any existing table can be extended to include polynomials of higher degree.

Suppose now that we wish to represent an arbitrary polynomial $\eta(x)$ in the form

$$\eta(x) = \chi_0 H_0 q_0(x)+\chi_1 H_1 q_1(x)+...+\chi_\nu H_\nu q_\nu(x),$$

where H_j is the smallest number giving integral values to $H_j q_j(x)$ at $x = 0, 1, 2,..., (n-1)$. Values of $H_j q_j(x)$ are tabulated in Fisher and Yates (1948). When fitting such a polynomial to a set of observations

$\{y_r\}$, the least squares estimate of the coefficient χ_j is

$$\chi_j^* = K_j/H_j^2 M_j^2,$$

where
$$K_j = \sum_{x=0}^{n-1} H_j q_j(x) y_{x+1}.$$

Because of the property

$$q_j(x) = (-1)^j q_j(n-x-1),$$

K_j is computed in terms of the sums $\{y_{n-x}+y_{x+1}\}$ when j is even, and in terms of the differences $\{y_{n-x}-y_{x+1}\}$ when j is odd. With the usual assumption that $\mathscr{D}\mathbf{y} = \sigma^2 \mathbf{I}$,

$$\mathscr{V}\chi_j^* = \sigma^2/H_j^2 M_j^2,$$

and the sum of squares for testing $\chi_j = 0$ is

$$S_j = K_j^2/H_j^2 M_j^2.$$

The remainder of the analysis has the pattern previously described. A numerical illustration is given in Table 12.

TABLE 12. *Orthogonal polynomials in regression analysis*

x_r	-4	-3	-2	-1	0	1	2	3	4
y_r	11·28	15·12	19·00	21·65	23·54	22·43	20·84	18·14	14·62

x_r	Sum (with even j)	Difference (with odd j)
0	(23·54)	..
± 1	44·08	0·78
± 2	39·84	1·84
± 3	33·26	3·02
± 4	25·90	3·34
Total	166·62	

x	$H_1 q_1$	$H_2 q_2$	$H_3 q_3$
5	0	-20	0
6	1	-17	-9
7	2	-8	-13
8	3	$+7$	-7
9	4	$+28$	$+14$
$H_j^2 M_j^2$	60	2772	990
H_j	1	3	5/6

$\Sigma y_r^2 = 3219\cdot9214$

j	K_j	χ_j^*	S_j	R_j
0	166·62	18·51333	3084·6916	135·2298
1	26·88	0·44800	12·0422	123·1876
2	$-580\cdot86$	$-0\cdot20955$	121·7166	1·4710
3	$-5\cdot32$	$-0\cdot00537$	0·0286	1·4424

The R_j column suggests a quadratic approximation to $\eta(x)$, the estimate being

$$\eta^* = 18\cdot51333 + 0\cdot44800 q_1 - 0\cdot62865 q_2$$

or
$$\eta^*(q_1) = 22\cdot70433 + 0\cdot44800 q_1 - 0\cdot62865 q_1^2.$$

6.6. Step-function methods

When n factorizes, the time taken to calculate estimates of $\beta_0 \beta_1,..., \beta_\nu$ is appreciably reduced by collecting neighbouring values of x into groups of equal size and applying the principle of least squares to the pairs $(\sum x, \sum y)$, where $\sum x$ is the total of a group of values of x and $\sum y$ the total of the corresponding values of y. A study of the resulting bias and loss in efficiency has been made by Guest (1954, 1956), who also points out that a further reduction in time can be obtained by the use of step-functions, which lead to unbiased estimates of high efficiency and are defined as follows.

Suppose that the values of x are equally spaced, so that they can be linearly transformed into values of a variable ϵ, which ranges by unit steps from $-\frac{1}{2}(n-1)$ to $+\frac{1}{2}(n-1)$. The observations on y are now denoted by $y(\epsilon)$, and

$$\mathscr{E}y(\epsilon) = \mu_0 + \mu_1\epsilon + \mu_2\epsilon^2 + ... + \mu_\nu\epsilon^\nu. \tag{1}$$

For $j = 1, 2,...$ let $w_j(\epsilon)$ be any function which satisfies

$$\sum \epsilon^k w_j(\epsilon) = 0 \quad (0 \leqslant k < j) \tag{2}$$

and

$$\sum \epsilon^j w_j(\epsilon) \neq 0. \tag{3}$$

In addition, put $w_0(\epsilon) \equiv 1$. Then the system of equations

$$\sum y(\epsilon)w_0(\epsilon) = n\mu_0^+ + \mu_1^+ \sum \epsilon \quad + \mu_2^+ \sum \epsilon^2 \quad + ... + \mu_\nu^+ \sum \epsilon^\nu$$

$$\sum y(\epsilon)w_1(\epsilon) = \quad \mu_1^+ \sum \epsilon w_1(\epsilon) + \mu_2^+ \sum \epsilon^2 w_1(\epsilon) + ... + \mu_\nu^+ \sum \epsilon^\nu w_1(\epsilon)$$

$$\cdot \quad \cdot \quad \cdot \quad \cdot \quad \cdot \quad \cdot \quad \cdot \quad \cdot \quad \cdot \quad \cdot \quad \cdot \quad \cdot$$

$$\sum y(\epsilon)w_\nu(\epsilon) = \qquad \qquad \mu_\nu^+ \sum \epsilon^\nu w_\nu(\epsilon) \tag{4}$$

can be solved for the estimates $\mu_\nu^+, \mu_{\nu-1}^+,..., \mu_0^+$ in turn. Taking the expectation of both sides, we see that these estimates are all unbiased.

A convenient set of functions $\{w_j(\epsilon)\}$ is provided by those which are constant in magnitude over different ranges of the variable ϵ. For example, let $w_1(\epsilon)$ be such that

$$\sum w_1(\epsilon)f(\epsilon) = \left\{ B_1\left(\sum_{0,\frac{1}{2}}^{\frac{1}{2}(n-1)} - \sum_{0,\frac{1}{2}}^{\frac{1}{2}(z_1-1)} \right) + B_2\left(\sum_{0,\frac{1}{2}}^{\frac{1}{2}(z_1-1)} - \sum_{0,\frac{1}{2}}^{\frac{1}{2}(z_2-1)} \right) + ... \right.$$

$$\left. ... + B_m\left(\sum_{0,\frac{1}{2}}^{\frac{1}{2}(z_{m-1}-1)} - \sum_{0,\frac{1}{2}}^{\frac{1}{2}(z_m-1)} \right) \right\}\{f(\epsilon) - f(-\epsilon)\}, \tag{5}$$

in which $B_1, B_2,..., B_m$ are positive and $z_1, z_2,..., z_m$ integers such that

$$n > z_1 > z_2 > ... > z_m.$$

The minimum value of z_m is 0 or 1 according as n is odd or even respectively; and the lower limit in the summations is 0 or $\frac{1}{2}$ correspondingly. Since $w_1(\epsilon)$ is an odd function, it satisfies (2). For a given value of m, we choose B_i and z_i so as to maximize the efficiency of

$$\mu_1^+ = \sum y(\epsilon)w_1(\epsilon)\Big/\sum \epsilon w_1(\epsilon), \qquad (6)$$

considered as an estimate of μ_1 in the polynomial $\mu_0+\mu_1 \epsilon$. Write ζ_i for z_i/n. Then

$$\mathscr{V}\mu_1^+ = \sigma^2 \sum w_1^2(\epsilon)\Big/\{\sum \epsilon w_1(\epsilon)\}^2, \qquad (7)$$

where

$$\sum \epsilon w_1(\epsilon) = \tfrac{1}{4}n^2\{B_1(1-\zeta_1^2)+B_2(\zeta_1^2-\zeta_2^2)+...+B_m(\zeta_{m-1}^2-\zeta_m^2)\}, \quad (8)$$

and

$$\sum w_1^2(\epsilon) = n\{B_1^2(1-\zeta_1)+B_2^2(\zeta_1-\zeta_2)+...+B_m^2(\zeta_{m-1}-\zeta_m)\}. \quad (9)$$

The variance of the least-squares estimate of μ_1 is

$$\mathscr{V}\mu_1^* = n(n^2-1)/12 \simeq n^3/12. \qquad (10)$$

Hence, to this degree of approximation, the efficiency of μ_1^+ relative to μ_1^* is

$$\frac{3\{B_1(1-\zeta_1^2)+B_2(\zeta_1^2-\zeta_2^2)+...+B_m(\zeta_{m-1}^2-\zeta_m^2)\}^2}{4\{B_1^2(1-\zeta_1)+B_2^2(\zeta_1-\zeta_2)+...+B_m^2(\zeta_{m-1}-\zeta_m)\}}. \qquad (11)$$

It attains its maximum value of $1-1/(2m+1)^2$ when

$$\zeta_i = \{2(m-i)+1\}/(2m+1), \qquad (12)$$

and B_i is proportional to $(m-i+1)$, the constant of proportionality being conveniently chosen as unity.

Similar step-functions can be constructed for higher values of j, and tables of them have been published by Guest (1951). The main disadvantage of this class of techniques is that the time gained from computing μ^+ rather than μ^* is lost when computing the sum of squared residuals. However, approximate methods can be used to estimate σ^2, as Gibson and Jowett (1957) show.

6.7. Experimental design for several factors

We now generalize the basis of previous Sections by supposing that the observed response, hitherto dependent on a single factor x, depends instead on k factors $x_1, x_2,..., x_k$. The rth level of $(x_1, x_2,..., x_k)$ is $(x_{1r}, x_{2r},..., x_{kr})$, where r ranges from 1 to n, and the origin and scale are chosen so that

$$\sum_{r=1}^{n} x_{jr} = 0 \quad (j = 1, 2,..., k) \qquad (1)$$

and

$$\sum_{r=1}^{n} x_{jr}^2 = 1 \quad (j = 1, 2,..., k). \qquad (2)$$

We shall assume that the expected response corresponding to the

rth level of $(x_1, x_2, ..., x_k)$ is

$$\eta_r \equiv \mathscr{E}y_r = \beta_0 x_{0r} + \beta_1 x_{1r} + ... + \beta_k x_{kr} + \beta_{11} x_{1r}^2 + ... + \beta_{kk} x_{kr}^2 +$$

$$+ \beta_{12} x_{1r} x_{2r} + ... + \beta_{k-1,k} x_{k-1,r} x_{kr} + \beta_{111} x_{1r}^3 + ... \quad (3)$$

where $x_{0r} \equiv 1$, and the right-hand side is a polynomial of degree d in $x_{1r}, x_{2r}, ..., x_{kr}$. As before, $\mathscr{D}y$ is taken to be $\sigma^2 I$.

The experimental design is determined by the $k \times n$ matrix D whose rth column is $(x_{1r}, x_{2r}, ..., x_{kr})'$. Corresponding to any D, let $\eta^*(x)$ be the value predicted for

$$\eta(x) = \beta_0 + \beta_1 x_1 + ... + \beta_k x_k + \beta_{11} x_1^2 + ... + \beta_{kk} x_k^2 +$$

$$+ \beta_{12} x_1 x_2 + ... + \beta_{k-1,k} x_{k-1} x_k + \beta_{111} x_1^3 + ... \quad (4)$$

from all the observations by the principle of least squares. The *variance function* of the design is

$$V(x_1, x_2, ..., x_k) = n\mathscr{V}\eta^*(x)/\sigma^2, \quad (5)$$

and it measures the precision with which the response at any point in the space of $x_1, x_2, ..., x_k$ can be estimated. If, as is usually the case, nothing is known in advance of how the expected response is related to $x_1, x_2, ..., x_k$, then it is a reasonable requirement on D to suppose that V is a function only of

$$\rho^2 = \sum_{j=1}^{k} x_j^2. \quad (6)$$

When this condition is satisfied, the design is said to be *rotatable*, and to have a *spherical* variance function. We proceed to derive a condition for rotatability, following the arguments of Box and Hunter (1957), to whom this concept is due.

Put $x' = (x_1, x_2, ..., x_k)$ and let $x'^{[d]}$ be the derived power and product vector of degree d (Aitken, 1951, 137–8). This contains all the powers and products of degree d obtainable from the elements of x, scalar multipliers being attached to them so that $x'^{[d]}x^{[d]} = (x'x)^d$. Thus, when $k = 2$,

$$x'^{[2]} = (x_1^2, x_2^2, 2^{\frac{1}{2}}x_1 x_2). \quad (7)$$

If $z = Hx$, then $H^{[d]}$ is defined by $z^{[d]} = H^{[d]}x^{[d]}$. Take $z = KHx$. Since $z^{[d]}$ can be expressed either as $(KH)^{[d]}x^{[d]}$ or as

$$K^{[d]}(Hx)^{[d]} = K^{[d]}H^{[d]}x^{[d]},$$

we obtain $$(KH)^{[d]} = K^{[d]}H^{[d]}. \quad (8)$$

On taking $K = H'$, it follows that if H is orthogonal, then so is $H^{[d]}$.

Put $x'_r = (1, x_{1r}, x_{2r},..., x_{kr})$. Then (3) can be written in the form

$$\eta_r = x_r'^{[d]}\beta, \tag{9}$$

where β is a column vector of the unknown parameters with suitable multipliers attached. Let X be the matrix whose rth row is $x_r'^{[d]}$, so that

$$\mathscr{D}\beta^* = \sigma^2(X'X)^{-1}. \tag{10}$$

Put $x'_0 = (1, x_1, x_2,..., x_k)$, whence

$$\eta(x) = x_0'^{[d]}\beta, \tag{11}$$

and

$$\mathscr{V}\eta^*(x) = \sigma^2 x_0'^{[d]}(X'X)^{-1}x_0^{[d]}. \tag{12}$$

Consider the effect on the variance function of replacing x by Hx, where H is a $k \times k$ orthogonal matrix. Let

$$P = \begin{bmatrix} 1 & 0 \\ \hline 0 & H \end{bmatrix}. \tag{13}$$

Since x_0 is replaced by $z_0 = Px_0$, the variance of the estimated response becomes

$$\mathscr{V}\eta^*(z) = \sigma^2 x_0'^{[d]}P'^{[d]}(X'X)^{-1}P^{[d]}x_0^{[d]}. \tag{14}$$

If (12) and (14) are identical for every x_0 and P, then

$$X'X = P'^{[d]}(X'X)P^{[d]} \tag{15}$$

for every orthogonal matrix H. The right-hand side here is the value taken by $X'X$ when D is replaced by HD. Hence the variance function is spherical if and only if the elements of $X'X$ are invariant under orthogonal transformations of D.

A second criterion for rotatability is derived as follows. The quantity

$$n^{-1} \sum_{r=1}^{n} x_{1r}^{\alpha_1} x_{2r}^{\alpha_2} ... x_{kr}^{\alpha_k}$$

is a *moment* of the experimental design, with order $\alpha = \alpha_1 + \alpha_2 + ... + \alpha_k$. We denote it by $[1^{\alpha_1}, 2^{\alpha_2},..., k^{\alpha_k}]$ and proceed to construct a generating function for all moments of order $2d$ or less. In fact, put

$$u' = (1, u_1, u_2,..., u_k)$$

and write

$$Q = n^{-1}u'^{[d]}X'Xu^{[d]}. \tag{16}$$

Since

$$X' = [x_1^{[d]}, x_2^{[d]},..., x_k^{[d]}], \tag{17}$$

we obtain

$$Q = n^{-1}u'^{[d]}\left(\sum_{r=1}^{n} x_r^{[d]}x_r'^{[d]}\right)u^{[d]}$$

$$= n^{-1}\sum_{r=1}^{n}(u'x_r x_r' u)^d.$$

Thus $\qquad Q = n^{-1} \sum_{r=1}^{n} (1+u_1 x_{1r}+u_2 x_{2r}+...+u_k x_{kr})^{2d},$ (18)

and the coefficient of $u_1^{\alpha_1} u_2^{\alpha_2} ... u_k^{\alpha_k}$ in Q is

$$[1^{\alpha_1}, 2^{\alpha_2},..., k^{\alpha_k}](2d)!/(2d-\alpha)! \prod_{j=1}^{k} \alpha_j!.$$ (19)

Returning to (15), we see that

$$u'^{[d]} X' X u^{[d]} = u'^{[d]} P'^{[d]} X' X P^{[d]} u^{[d]} = (Pu)'^{[d]} X' X (Pu)^{[d]},$$ (20)

for every orthogonal matrix H. Hence Q, considered as a function of u, must be a function of $u'u$ only, and so

$$Q = \sum_{s=0}^{d} \theta_{2s} \left(\sum_{j=1}^{k} u_j^2 \right)^s.$$ (21)

The coefficient of $u_1^{\alpha_1} u_2^{\alpha_2} ... u_k^{\alpha_k}$ in Q is therefore

$$\theta_\alpha (\tfrac{1}{2}\alpha)! \Big/ \prod_{j=1}^{k} (\tfrac{1}{2}\alpha_j)!$$ (22)

if all the α_j are even, but is otherwise zero. Comparing this result with (19), and denoting $\theta_\alpha 2^{\frac{1}{2}\alpha}(\tfrac{1}{2}\alpha)!(2d-\alpha)!/(2d)!$ by λ_α, we conclude that

$$[1^{\alpha_1}, 2^{\alpha_2},..., k^{\alpha_k}] = \begin{cases} \lambda_\alpha \prod_{j=1}^{k} \alpha_j! \Big/ 2^{\frac{1}{2}\alpha} \prod_{j=1}^{k} (\tfrac{1}{2}\alpha_j)! & \text{if all } \alpha_j \text{ are even;} \\ 0, & \text{otherwise.} \end{cases}$$ (23)

Hence the variance function is spherical if and only if the moments of the design are given by (23).

Example. Take $k = 2$ and $d = 2$. A rotatable design with $n = 6$ was given by Box and Wilson (1951). The points in two-dimensional space which correspond to the columns of D form the vertices of a regular pentagon, whose centre is the origin, together with the origin itself. We show that the variance function is spherical by proving that all moments up to order 4 are invariant under rotations of the pentagon about its centre.

Let the coordinates of the vth vertex be $\xi \cos(\psi+2\pi v/5)$ and $\xi \sin(\psi+2\pi v/5)$. Put $\omega = e^{2\pi i/5}$ and $\tau = e^{i\psi}$. Then

$$\sum_{r=1}^{6} x_{1r}^{\alpha} x_{2r}^{\beta}$$

$$= (\tfrac{1}{2}\xi)^{\alpha+\beta} i^{-\beta} \sum_{v=0}^{4} (\tau\omega^v+\tau^{-1}\omega^{-v})^{\alpha}(\tau\omega^v-\tau^{-1}\omega^{-v})^{\beta}$$

$$= (\tfrac{1}{2}\xi)^{\alpha+\beta} i^{-\beta} \sum_{a=0}^{\alpha} \sum_{b=0}^{\beta} (-1)^b \binom{\alpha}{a}\binom{\beta}{b} \tau^{\alpha+\beta-2a-2b} \sum_{v=0}^{4} \omega^{v(\alpha+\beta-2a-2b)}.$$

(24)

The value of
$$\sum_{v=0}^{4} \omega^{v(\alpha+\beta-2a-2b)}$$

is 5 if $\alpha+\beta-2a-2b$ is an integral multiple of 5, but otherwise it is zero. Since, however, $-(\alpha+\beta) \leqslant \alpha+\beta-2a-2b \leqslant (\alpha+\beta)$, and we are only concerned with $\alpha+\beta \leqslant 4$, $\sum \omega^{v(\alpha+\beta-2a-2b)}$ is zero unless $\alpha+\beta-2a-2b = 0$. In this case, $\tau^{\alpha+\beta-2a-2b} = 1$, and therefore

$$\sum_{r=1}^{6} x_{1r}^{\alpha} x_{2r}^{\beta} = 5(\tfrac{1}{2}\xi)^{\alpha+\beta} i^{-\beta} \sum_{a+b=\frac{1}{2}(\alpha+\beta)} \sum (-1)^b \binom{\alpha}{a}\binom{\beta}{b}. \qquad (25)$$

Thus $[1^{\alpha}, 2^{\beta}]$ is independent of ψ as required by rotatability.

The conditions on $\{x_{jr}\}$ given at the beginning of this Section imply that $[0] = [1^2] = [2^2] = 1$, whence, using (25),

$$\xi^2 = 12/5.$$

From (23), $\lambda_0 = \lambda_2 = 1$ and all the remaining moments $[1^{\alpha}, 2^{\beta}]$ are zero except $[1^2, 2^2] = \lambda_4$ and $[1^4] = [2^4] = 3\lambda_4$. Using (25) again,

$$\lambda_4 = 5\xi^4/48 = 3/5.$$

6.8. Exercises

1. Assuming only that the orthogonal polynomials $\{t_j(x)\}$ satisfy

$$\sum_{r=1}^{n} x_r^k t_j(x_r) = 0$$

for all $k < j$, prove that

$$t_j(x) = P_j \begin{vmatrix} m_0 & m_1 & m_2 & . & . & . & m_j \\ m_1 & m_2 & m_3 & . & . & . & m_{j+1} \\ . & . & . & . & . & . & . \\ m_{j-1} & m_j & m_{j+1} & . & . & . & m_{2j-1} \\ 1 & x & x^2 & . & . & . & x^j \end{vmatrix},$$

where $m_i = \sum_{r=1}^{n} x_r^i$ and P_j is independent of x. By considering $\sum_{r=1}^{n} x_r^j t_j(x_r)$, show that

$$P_j = (Z_j Z_{j-1})^{-\frac{1}{2}},$$

where

$$Z_j = \begin{vmatrix} m_0 & m_1 & m_2 & . & . & . & m_j \\ m_1 & m_2 & m_3 & . & . & . & m_{j+1} \\ . & . & . & . & . & . & . \\ m_j & m_{j+1} & m_{j+2} & . & . & . & m_{2j} \end{vmatrix}.$$

(Szegö, 1939, § 2.1.)

2. With the notation $x^{(a)} = x(x-1)(x-2)...(x-a+1)$ for factorial powers, prove that

$$\sum_{x=0}^{n-1} (x+k-1)^{(k+i-1)} = (n+k-1)^{(k+i)}/(k+i).$$

Assuming only that the orthogonal polynomials $\{p_j(x)\}$ satisfy

$$\sum_{x=0}^{n-1} (x+k-1)^{(k-1)} p_j(x) = 0$$

for all $k \leqslant j$, deduce that

$$\sum_{i=0}^{j} \binom{n-1}{i} \Delta^i p_j(0)/(k+i) = 0 \quad (k \leqslant j). \qquad \text{(Allan, 1930.)}$$

3. Show that the least squares estimate of ϕ_j is

$$\phi_j^* = \sum_{i=0}^{j} \Delta^i p_j(0) \sum_{x=i}^{n-1} y_{x+1} \binom{x}{i}.$$

4. Prove that

$$\sum_{x=0}^{n-1} y_{x+1} \Delta^i g(x) = (-1)^i \sum_{x=0}^{n-i-1} g(x+i) \Delta^i y_{x+1} \quad (i \leqslant j).$$

Hence show that

$$\phi_j^* = L_j \sum_{x=0}^{n-j-1} \binom{x+j}{j} \binom{n-x-1}{j} \Delta^j y_{x+1}.$$

5. Derive the following formulae:

$q_2 = q_1^2 - (n^2 - 1)/12;$

$q_3 = q_1^3 - (3n^2 - 7)q_1/20;$

$q_4 = q_1^4 - (3n^2 - 13)q_1^2/14 + 3(n^2 - 1)(n^2 - 9)/560;$

$q_5 = q_1^5 - 5(n^2 - 7)q_1^3/18 + (15n^4 - 230n^2 + 407)q_1/1008.$

6. There are n equally spaced values of x, and the expected response at x_r is the sum of (i) a polynomial in x_r of degree ν and (ii) one of t treatment effects. We require to assign treatments to the values of x such that the estimated differences between treatment effects are uncorrelated with the estimated polynomial coefficients. Thus, when $t = 2$, $\nu = 3$, and $n = 8$, a possible design is

-7	-5	-3	-1	1	3	5	7
T_2	T_2	T_1	T_1	T_1	T_1	T_2	T_2

where the upper row contains values of x and the lower row treatments.

Construct similiar designs for $t = 2$, $\nu = 3$, and $n = 24$. (Cox, 1951.)

7. The values $\{x_r\}$ are equally spaced and the observations $\{y_r\}$ are such that $\mathcal{E} y_r = \alpha + \beta x_r$. Denote by X_1 the sum of the smallest m values of x, and by X_2 the sum of the largest m values; similarly define Y_1 and Y_2. Prove that

$$\beta^+ = (Y_2 - Y_1)/(X_2 - X_1)$$

is an unbiased estimate of β; and that its efficiency, as compared with the least squares estimate of β, is

$$6(m/n)(1 - m/n)^2/(1 - 1/n^2).$$

Hence show that the best method of grouping is obtained when $m = n/3$ approximately. (Jeffreys, 1948, § 4.43.)

8. Let $w_2(\epsilon)$ be such that

$$\sum w_2(\epsilon) f(\epsilon) = \left\{ B_1 \left(\sum_{-\frac{1}{2}(n-1)}^{\frac{1}{2}(n-1)} - \sum_{-\frac{1}{2}(z_1-1)}^{\frac{1}{2}(z_1-1)} \right) - B_2 \sum_{-\frac{1}{2}(z_2-1)}^{\frac{1}{2}(z_2-1)} \right\} f(\epsilon),$$

where B_1 and B_2 are positive, and $n > z_1 > z_2$. Show that the efficiency of

$\sum y(\epsilon)w_2(\epsilon)/\sum \epsilon^2 w_2(\epsilon)$, considered as an estimate of μ_2 in the polynomial

$$\mu_0 + \mu_1\epsilon + \mu_2\epsilon^2,$$

is approximately
$$\frac{5\{B_1(1-\zeta_1^3) - B_2\,\zeta_2^3\}}{B_1^2(1-\zeta_1) + B_2^2\,\zeta_2}.$$

Verify that this has a maximum of $0{\cdot}8958$ when $B_1 = 1{\cdot}3042$, $B_2 = 0{\cdot}7793$, $\zeta_1 = 0{\cdot}7363$, and $\zeta_2 = 0{\cdot}4414$. (Guest, 1954.)

9. Prove that the variance function of a general rotatable design for $d = 2$ is

$$G[2(k+2)\lambda_4^2 + 2\lambda_4(\lambda_4-1)(k+2)\rho^2 + \{(k+1)\lambda_4 - (k-1)\}\rho^4],$$

where
$$1/G = 2\lambda_4\{(k+2)\lambda_4 - k\}.$$

10. An experimental design for $k = 2$ and $d = 2$ is constructed as follows. The columns of D correspond to s concentric rings of points, centred at the origin; the wth ring has radius ξ_w and contains n_w equally spaced points, where $n_w \geqslant 5$ if $\xi_w \neq 0$. Show that the design is rotatable and prove that

$$\lambda_4 = n \sum_{w=1}^{s} n_w \xi_w^4 \Big/ 2\Big(\sum_{w=1}^{s} n_w \xi_w^2 \Big)^2. \qquad \text{(Box \& Hunter, 1957.)}$$

6.9. References

AITKEN, A. C. (1933). On the graduation of data by the orthogonal polynomials of least squares. *Proc. Roy. Soc. Edin.* **53**, 54–78.

—— (1951). *Determinants and Matrices*, seventh edition. Edinburgh: Oliver and Boyd.

ALLAN, F. E. (1930). The general form of the orthogonal polynomials for simple series, with proofs of their simple properties. *Proc. Roy. Soc. Edin.* **50**, 310–20.

BANCROFT, T. A. (1944). On biases in estimation due to the use of preliminary tests of significance. *Ann. Math. Statist.* **15**, 190–204.

BICKLEY, W. G. (1948). Difference and associated operators, with some applications. *J. Math. Phys.* **27**, 183–92.

BIRGE, R. T. (1947). Least-squares fitting of data by means of polynomials. *Rev. Mod. Phys.* **19**, 298–347. Mathematical appendix by J. W. Weinberg, ibid. 348–60.

BOX, G. E. P., and WILSON, K. B. (1951). On the experimental attainment of optimum conditions. *J. R. Statist. Soc.* B, **13**, 1–38.

—— and HUNTER, J. S. (1957). Multi-factor experimental designs for exploring response surfaces. *Ann. Math. Statist.* **28**, 195–241.

CHEBYSHEV, P. L. (1875). Ob interpolirovanii velichin ravnootstoiashchikh, Republished (1948) in *Polnoe sobranie sochinenii*, **3**, 66–87. Izdatel'stvo Akademii Nauk SSSR Moskva-Leningrad.

COX, D. R. (1951). Some systematic experimental designs. *Biometrika*, **38**, 312–23.

FISHER, R. A. (1920). Studies in crop variation. I. An examination of the yield of dressed grain from Broadbalk. *J. Agric. Sci.* **11**, 107–35.

—— and YATES, F. (1948). *Statistical Tables for Biological, Agricultural and Medical Research*, third edition. Edinburgh: Oliver and Boyd.

FORSYTHE, G. E. (1957). Generation and use of orthogonal polynomials for data fitting with a digital computer. *J. Soc. Indust. Appl. Math.* **5**, 74–88.

GIBSON, W. M., and JOWETT, G. H. (1957). 'Three-group' regression analysis. Part I. Simple regression analysis. *Appl. Statist.* **7**, 114–22.

GUEST, P. G. (1951). The fitting of polynomials by the method of weighted grouping. *Ann. Math. Statist.* **22**, 537–48.

—— (1954). Grouping methods in the fitting of polynomials to equally spaced observations. *Biometrika*, **41**, 62–76.

—— (1956). Grouping methods in the fitting of polynomials to unequally spaced observations. *Biometrika*, **43**, 149–60.

HAYES, J. G., and VICKERS, T. (1951). The fitting of polynomials to unequally-spaced data. *Phil. Mag.* [7], **42**, 1387–1400.

HILBERT, D. (1894). Ein Beitrag zur Theorie des Legendre'schen Polynoms. *Acta Math.* **18**, 155–9.

HSU, P. L. (1941). Canonical reduction of the general regression problem. *Ann. Eugen. Lond.* **11**, 42–46.

JEFFREYS, H. (1948). *Theory of Probability*, second edition. Oxford: Clarendon Press.

LIDSTONE, G. J. (1933). Notes on orthogonal polynomials and their application to least-square methods of (1) fitting polynomial curves to data, (2) graduation by weighted means. *J. Inst. Actuar.* **64**, 128–59.

RUSHTON, S. (1951). On least squares fitting by orthonormal polynomials using the Choleski method. *J. R. Statist. Soc.* B, **13**, 92–99.

SZEGÖ, G. (1939). *Orthogonal Polynomials.* New York: American Mathematical Society.

TODD, J. (1954). The condition of the finite segments of the Hilbert matrix. Pp. 109–16 of O. Taussky (editor), *Contributions to the Solution of Systems of Linear Equations and the Determination of Eigenvalues.* Nat. Bureau Standards, Appl. Math. Ser. 39: U.S. Govt. Printing Office.

WEINBERG, J. W. (1947). *See* Birge (1947).

WISHART, J., and METAKIDES, T. (1953). Orthogonal polynomial fitting. *Biometrika*, **40**, 361–9.

STATIONARY ERROR PROCESSES

7.1. Introduction

W E suppose now that the observations $y_1, y_2,..., y_n$ have the structure

$$y_t = \sum_{j=1}^{p} a_{tj}\theta_j + u_t,$$ (1)

where the matrix $\{a_{tj}\}$ is known and $u_1, u_2,..., u_n$ form a stationary sequence of random variables, i.e. they have zero expectations and a dispersion matrix

$$\mathscr{D}u = \begin{bmatrix} \lambda_0 & \lambda_1 & \lambda_2 & . & . & . & \lambda_{n-1} \\ & \lambda_0 & \lambda_1 & . & . & . & \lambda_{n-2} \\ & & . & . & . & . & . \\ & & & & & \lambda_0 & \lambda_1 \\ & & & & & & \lambda_0 \end{bmatrix},$$ (2)

where $\lambda_0, \lambda_1,..., \lambda_{n-1}$ are unknown.

We have discussed how to estimate the $\{\theta_j\}$ from correlated data and test hypotheses concerning them when $\mathscr{D}u$ is known, apart from a scalar factor. The corresponding problems when $\mathscr{D}u$ has the form (2) are much more difficult, and this Chapter is intended as an introduction to them.

7.2. Stationary processes

A sequence of random variables

$$..., u_{-2}, u_{-1}, u_0, u_1, u_2,...$$

is *stationary to the second order* if both $\mathscr{E}u_t$ and $\mathscr{C}(u_t, u_{t+s})$ are independent of t. We take $\mathscr{E}u_t = 0$ and write

$$\lambda_s = \mathscr{C}(u_t, u_{t+s}) = \mathscr{E}u_t u_{t+s}.$$ (1)

This is the *autocovariance* of *lag s*. In what follows, *stationary to the second order* is abbreviated to *stationary*.

The autocovariance-generating function of a stationary process is defined by

$$L(z) = \sum_{-\infty}^{\infty} \lambda_s z^s$$ (2)

provided that there exist values of z for which the sum converges. Let $\{u_t\}$ be a stationary process whose autocovariance-generating function is $L_u(z)$. Introducing constants $\{d_j\}$, define

$$g_t = \sum_{j=-q}^{r} d_j u_{t-j}.$$
(3)

Then $\{g_t\}$ is also a stationary process and its autocovariance-generating function, $L_g(z)$, is given by

$$\sum_{s=-\infty}^{\infty} z^s \mathscr{E} g_t g_{t+s} = \sum_{s=-\infty}^{\infty} z^s \sum_{j=-q}^{r} \sum_{k=-q}^{r} d_j d_k \mathscr{E} u_{t-j} u_{t+s-k}$$

$$= \sum_{s=-\infty}^{\infty} z^{s+j-k} \mathscr{E} u_{t-j} u_{t+s-k} \sum_{j=-q}^{r} d_j z^{-j} \sum_{k=-q}^{r} d_k z^k.$$

Hence $\qquad L_g(z) = \left(\sum_{j=-q}^{r} d_j z^{-j} \right)\left(\sum_{k=-q}^{r} d_k z^k \right) L_u(z).$
(4)

This useful result is given by Moran (1949).

The autocovariances of a stationary process can be represented in the form

$$\lambda_s = \int_{-\pi}^{\pi} e^{is\omega}\, dF(\omega),$$
(5)

where $F(\omega)$ is a non-decreasing function such that

$$F(\pi) - F(-\pi) = \lambda_0$$
(6)

and $\qquad F(\omega_2) - F(\omega_1) = F(-\omega_1) - F(-\omega_2)$
(7)

at points ω_1, ω_2 where $F(\omega)$ is continuous. If $\sum_{0}^{\infty} |\lambda_s|$ converges, then $F(\omega)$ has a derivative given by

$$f(\omega) = \frac{1}{2\pi} \sum_{-\infty}^{\infty} \lambda_s e^{-is\omega} \quad (-\pi \leqslant \omega \leqslant \pi).$$
(8)

We begin the proof by noting that

$$\frac{1}{N} \sum_{s=0}^{N} |u_s e^{-is\omega}|^2 \geqslant 0,$$
(9)

where ω is real. On taking the expectation,

$$\frac{1}{N} \sum_{s=0}^{N} \sum_{t=0}^{N} \lambda_{s-t} e^{-i(s-t)\omega} = \sum_{s=-N}^{N} \left(1 - \frac{|s|}{N} \right) \lambda_s e^{-is\omega} \geqslant 0.$$
(10)

Write $\qquad f_N(\omega) = \frac{1}{2\pi} \sum_{-\infty}^{\infty} \lambda_N(s) e^{-is\omega},$
(11)

where $\qquad \lambda_N(s) = \begin{cases} \left(1 - \dfrac{|s|}{N} \right)\lambda_s & \text{for } s \leqslant N, \\ 0 & \text{for } s > N. \end{cases}$
(12)

On inverting the series for $f_N(\omega)$,

$$\lambda_N(s) = \int_{-\pi}^{\pi} e^{is\omega} f_N(\omega) \, d\omega. \qquad (13)$$

Now $\lambda_N(s)$ is the Fourier transform of the non-negative function $f_N(\omega)$. According to Cramér (1946, § 10.4) we can take the limit as $N \to \infty$ and obtain

$$\lambda_s = \int_{-\pi}^{\pi} e^{is\omega} \, dF(\omega),$$

where $F(\omega)$ is non-decreasing. This expression leads to (6) on putting $s = 0$, and (7) is a consequence of the relation $\lambda_s = \lambda_{-s}$. When $\sum_0^\infty |\lambda_s|$ converges, (11) gives

$$f(\omega) = \frac{1}{2\pi} \sum_{-\infty}^{\infty} \lambda_s e^{-is\omega} = \frac{1}{2\pi} \left\{ \lambda_0 + 2 \sum_1^\infty \lambda_s \cos(s\omega) \right\}. \qquad (14)$$

These theorems are due to Wold (1938, p. 66) and Doob (1953, p. 474). $F(\omega)$ is the *spectral function* of the stationary process and $f(\omega)$ is the *spectral density function*. By a proof similar to that preceding (4), the spectral density of the sequence

$$g_t = \sum_{-q}^{r} d_j u_{t-j}$$

is given in terms of the density for $\{u_t\}$ by

$$f_g(\omega) = \left| \sum_{-q}^{r} d_j e^{ij\omega} \right|^2 f_u(\omega). \qquad (15)$$

In the following examples, $\{\epsilon_t\}$ is a sequence of uncorrelated random variables with $\mathscr{E}\epsilon_t = 0$ and $\mathscr{V}\epsilon_t = \sigma^2$.

Example 1. $\qquad\qquad\qquad u_t = \epsilon_t.$

Here

$$\lambda_0 = \sigma^2 \quad \text{and} \quad \lambda_s = 0 \quad (s \neq 0).$$

$$L(z) = \sigma^2 \quad \text{and} \quad f(\omega) = \sigma^2/2\pi.$$

Example 2.

$$u_t = \epsilon_{t-1} + \epsilon_t + \epsilon_{t+1} \quad (t = \ldots, -2, -1, 0, 1, 2, \ldots).$$

Here

$$\lambda_0 = 3\sigma^2, \quad \lambda_1 = \lambda_{-1} = 2\sigma^2, \quad \lambda_2 = \lambda_{-2} = \sigma^2, \quad \lambda_s = 0 \quad (s \neq 0, \pm 1, \pm 2).$$

$$L(z) = 3\sigma^2 + 2\sigma^2(z + z^{-1}) + \sigma^2(z^2 + z^{-2})$$

and

$$f(\omega) = \sigma^2(3 + 4\cos\omega + 2\cos 2\omega)/2\pi.$$

Example 3. $\qquad u_t = \rho u_{t-1} + \epsilon_t \quad (t = 1, 2, ...),$

in which $|\rho| < 1; \sigma^2 = 1 - \rho^2$; and u_0 is a random variable uncorrelated with the sequence $\{\epsilon_t\}$, such that $\mathscr{E}u_0 = 0$ and $\mathscr{V}u_0 = 1$. Thus

$$u_1 = \rho u_0 + \epsilon_1,$$
$$u_2 = \rho^2 u_0 + \rho\epsilon_1 + \epsilon_2$$

and, in general,

$$u_t = \rho^t u_0 + \rho^{t-1}\epsilon_1 + \rho^{t-2}\epsilon_2 + ... + \epsilon_t.$$

Hence

$$\lambda_s = \rho^{|s|},$$
$$L(z) = (1 - \rho^2)(1 - \rho z)^{-1}(1 - \rho z^{-1})^{-1},$$

which converges provided that $|\rho| < |z| < 1/|\rho|$, and

$$f(\omega) = (1 - \rho^2)/2\pi(1 - 2\rho \cos \omega + \rho^2).$$

7.3. Autoregressive sequences

Suppose that we are given arbitrary real numbers $v_r, v_{r+1}, ..., v_{r+m-1}$ and a sequence of independent random variables $\epsilon_{r+m}, \epsilon_{r+m+1}, ...$ each with mean zero and variance σ^2. Define a sequence of random variables $\{v_t\}$ by

$$v_t + \alpha_1 v_{t-1} + \alpha_2 v_{t-2} + ... + \alpha_m v_{t-m} = \epsilon_t \quad (t = r+m, r+m+1, ...), \quad (1)$$

where $\alpha_1, \alpha_2, ..., \alpha_m$ are real constants. Let the characteristic equation (Milne-Thomson, 1933), namely

$$z^m + \alpha_1 z^{m-1} + \alpha_2 z^{m-2} + ... + \alpha_m = 0, \quad (2)$$

have m distinct roots $z_1, z_2, ..., z_m$ and denote by w the maximum value of $|z_j|$ for $j = 1, 2, ..., m$. The argument and conclusions given below remain essentially the same when roots are equal; only minor algebraic changes are involved. We shall prove that, when $w < 1$, the process $\{v_t\}$ tends, as $r \to -\infty$, to be independent of the initial values

$$v_r, v_{r+1}, ..., v_{r+m-1}$$

and becomes a stationary process $\{u_t\}$. From the manner of its definition, $\{u_t\}$ is called an *autoregressive* sequence of *order m*. The case $m = 1$ is usually described as a Markov process; and many properties for $m = 2$ were derived by Kendall (1944).

Consider first of all the system of equations

$$v_t + \alpha_1 v_{t-1} + \alpha_2 v_{t-2} + ... + \alpha_m v_{t-m} = 0 \quad (t = r+m, r+m+1, ...). \quad (3)$$

The solution of (3) is

$$v_t = b_1 z_1^{t-r} + b_2 z_2^{t-r} + ... + b_m z_m^{t-r}, \quad (4)$$

where $b_1, b_2, ..., b_m$ are determined from the values of $v_r, v_{r+1}, ..., v_{r+m-1}$.

The solution of (1) is thus

$$v_t = \sum_{j=1}^{m} b_j z_j^{t-r} + \sum_{j=0}^{t-r-m} h_j \epsilon_{t-j}. \tag{5}$$

In order to find $h_0, h_1, h_2, \ldots$ we substitute (5) in (1) and equate the coefficients of $\epsilon_t, \epsilon_{t-1}, \ldots, \epsilon_{r+m}$. The following equations result:

$$h_0 = 1, \quad h_1 + \alpha_1 h_0 = 0, \quad h_2 + \alpha_1 h_1 + \alpha_2 h_0 = 0, \quad \ldots$$

$$\ldots, \quad h_{t-r-m} + \alpha_1 h_{t-r-m-1} + \ldots + \alpha_m h_{t-r-2m} = 0. \tag{6}$$

They are summarized by the identity

$$(h_0 + h_1 z + h_2 z^2 + \ldots)(1 + \alpha_1 z + \alpha_2 z^2 + \ldots + \alpha_m z^m) \equiv 1.$$

Hence

$$\sum_{j=0}^{\infty} h_j z^j = (1 - z_1 z)^{-1}(1 - z_2 z)^{-1} \ldots (1 - z_m z)^{-1}, \tag{7}$$

which converges provided that $|z| < w^{-1}$. Using (7) on $|z| = 1$,

$$\sum_{j=0}^{\infty} h_j^2 \leqslant \left(\sum_{j=0}^{\infty} |h_j| \right)^2 \leqslant (1-w)^{-2m} < \infty.$$

According to the Riesz–Fischer theorem (Lévy, 1937, § 18; Titchmarsh, 1939, § 12.5) this proves the existence of a random variable u_t to which the sequence

$$\sum_{j=0}^{n} h_j \epsilon_{t-j}$$

converges in the mean, in the sense that

$$\lim_{n \to \infty} \mathscr{E} \left\{ u_t - \sum_{j=0}^{n} h_j \epsilon_{t-j} \right\}^2 = 0.$$

We write

$$u_t = \text{l.i.m.} \sum_{j=0}^{n} h_j \epsilon_{t-j}$$

or equivalently

$$u_t = \text{l.i.m.} \, v_t,$$

because the solution (4) disappears as $r \to -\infty$ when $w < 1$. Since

$$\mathscr{E} u_t = 0 \quad \text{and} \quad \mathscr{E} u_t u_{t+s} = \sigma^2 \sum_{j=0}^{\infty} h_j h_{j+s},$$

the process thus defined is stationary.

Having established that $\{u_t\}$ is a stationary process, we can find its autocovariance-generating function from the representation

$$u_t + \alpha_1 u_{t-1} + \alpha_2 u_{t-2} + \ldots + \alpha_m u_{t-m} = \epsilon_t, \tag{8}$$

which implies that

$$(1 + \alpha_1 z + \alpha_2 z^2 + \ldots + \alpha_m z^m) \times$$

$$\times (1 + \alpha_1 z^{-1} + \alpha_2 z^{-2} + \ldots + \alpha_m z^{-m}) L_u(z) = L_\epsilon(z).$$

$L_\epsilon(z) = \sigma^2$, and therefore

$$L_u(z) = \sigma^2/(1+\alpha_1 z+\alpha_2 z^2+...+\alpha_m z^m)(1+\alpha_1 z^{-1}+\alpha_2 z^{-2}+...+\alpha_m z^{-m}).$$
(9)

Similarly the spectral density of the autoregressive sequence is given by

$$f(\omega) = \sigma^2/(2\pi|1+\alpha_1 e^{i\omega}+\alpha_2 e^{2i\omega}+...+\alpha_m e^{mi\omega}|^2).$$

Writing the generating function in the form

$$L_u(z) = \sigma^2 \prod_{j=1}^{m} (1-z_j z)^{-1} \prod_{j=1}^{m} (1-z_j/z)^{-1},$$

the first product converges when $|z| < w^{-1}$, and the second when $|z| > w$. Thus $L_u(z)$ converges in the annulus

$$w < |z| < w^{-1}.$$

Equation (9) is an inconvenient expression from which to determine the autocovariances of an autoregressive sequence, and they are more easily obtained by a direct approach. On multiplying both sides of (8) by $u_t, u_{t-1},..., u_{t-s}$, and taking expectations, we get

$$\lambda_0+\alpha_1\lambda_1+...+\alpha_m\lambda_m = \sigma^2$$

and
$$\lambda_s+\alpha_1\lambda_{s-1}+...+\alpha_m\lambda_{s-m} = 0 \quad (s>0).$$
(10)

The general solution of (10) takes the form

$$\lambda_s = b_1 z_1^{|s|}+b_2 z_2^{|s|}+...+b_m z_m^{|s|}.$$
(11)

Alternatively, using the fact that $\lambda_s = \lambda_{-s}$, the first $m+1$ equations of (10) can be solved for $\lambda_0, \lambda_1,..., \lambda_m$—since we already know that a solution exists—and $\lambda_{m+1}, \lambda_{m+2},...$ can be derived from subsequent equations.

Suppose that we define a sequence $\{g_t\}$ by

$$g_t = \sum_{j=-k}^{k} d_j u_{t-j},$$
(12)

where
$$\sum_{j=-k}^{k} d_j = 1.$$
(13)

Then g_t is a *moving average* of the sequence $\{u_t\}$; and the corresponding *trend-reduced* sequence is

$$x_t = u_t-g_t,$$

which has the form of (12) with

$$\sum_{j=-k}^{k} d_j = 0.$$

For example, take

$$g_t = (u_{t-1}+u_t+u_{t+1})/3 = (E^{-1}+1+E)u_t/3,$$

where E is the forward shift operator. Then

$$x_t = (-E^{-1}+2-E)u_t/3,$$

and $\qquad \lambda_s(x) = (E^{-1}-2+E)^2\lambda_s(u)/9 \quad (s \geqslant 2).$

Thus the autocovariances for $\{x_t\}$ are the fourth differences of those for $\{u_t\}$. If $\lambda_s(u)$ tends steadily to zero without changing sign, then $\lambda_s(x)$ tends to zero with greater rapidity; whereas if $\lambda_s(u)$ oscillates, then $\lambda_s(x)$ oscillates more. On the other hand, an average extending over many terms of the series will always tend to produce oscillations, and tables comparing $\lambda_s(u)$ and $\lambda_s(x)$ under these conditions have been computed by Spencer-Smith (1947). The use of trend-reduction in regression analysis is fully discussed by Jowett (1955 a) and will be referred to in the next Section.

7.4. Regression analysis

Given n observations $y_1, y_2, ..., y_n$ we assume that

$$y_t = \sum_{j=1}^{p} a_{tj}\theta_j + u_t, \tag{1}$$

where $u_1, u_2, ..., u_n$ are n successive variables in a stationary process. The coefficients $\{a_{tj}\}$ are known and we want to solve the usual problems of statistical inference which arise in connexion with the parameters $\{\theta_j\}$.

Exact tests. We begin with an exact solution which is available whenever $u_1, u_2, ..., u_n$ form an autoregressive sequence of normal variables. Suppose, for example, that

$$u_t = \rho u_{t-1} + w_t \quad (t = ...-2, -1, 0, 1, 2, ...), \tag{2}$$

where $|\rho| < 1$ and the increments $\{w_t\}$ are normally and independently distributed with mean zero and variance σ^2. Then $u_1, u_2, ..., u_n$ have a joint normal distribution with $\mathscr{E}u_t = 0$ and $\mathscr{C}(u_t, u_{t+s}) = \sigma^2\rho^{|s|}$. Let $n = 2k+1$. We shall derive the joint distribution of $u_2, u_4, ..., u_{2k}$ conditional upon fixed values of $u_1, u_3, ..., u_{2k+1}$. The derivation rests on the following lemma: if u has a multivariate normal distribution with $\mathscr{E}u = 0$ and $\mathscr{D}u = R = C^{-1}$, then the conditional distribution of u_2 given u_1 is multivariate normal with

$$\mathscr{E}u_2 = R_{21}R_{11}^{-1}u_1 \quad \text{and} \quad \mathscr{D}u_2 = C_{22}^{-1},$$

where
$$u = \begin{bmatrix} u_1 \\ u_2 \end{bmatrix}, \quad R = \begin{bmatrix} R_{11} & R_{12} \\ R_{21} & R_{22} \end{bmatrix}, \quad C = \begin{bmatrix} C_{11} & C_{12} \\ C_{21} & C_{22} \end{bmatrix}$$

and the partitions are made so that R_{11} and C_{11} are square matrices with the same number of rows as u_1. Here

$$R_{11} = \begin{bmatrix} 1 & \rho^2 & \rho^4 & . & . & . & . & \rho^{2k} \\ & 1 & \rho^2 & . & . & . & . & \rho^{2k-2} \\ & & 1 & & & & & \rho^2 \\ & & & & & & & 1 \end{bmatrix},$$

$$R_{11}^{-1} = (1-\rho^4)^{-1} \begin{bmatrix} 1 & -\rho^2 & 0 & 0 & . & . & . & 0 \\ & 1+\rho^4 & -\rho^2 & 0 & . & . & . & 0 \\ & & & & . & . & . & . \\ & & & & & 1+\rho^4 & -\rho^2 \\ & & & & & & 1 \end{bmatrix}$$

and

$$R_{21} = \begin{bmatrix} \rho & \rho & \rho^3 & . & . & . & \rho^{2k-1} \\ \rho^3 & \rho & \rho & . & . & . & \rho^{2k-3} \\ . & . & . & . & . & . \\ \rho^{2k-1} & \rho^{2k-3} & \rho^{2k-5} & . & . & . & \rho \end{bmatrix}.$$

Substitution of these values in the formula for $\mathscr{E}u_2$ yields

$$\mathscr{E}u_{2i} = \rho(1+\rho^2)^{-1}(u_{2i-1}+u_{2i+1}) \quad (i = 1, 2,..., k). \tag{3}$$

Again, $C_{22} = \{\sigma^2(1-\rho^2)\}^{-1}(1+\rho^2)I$, whence we deduce that the $\{u_{2i}\}$ are normally and independently distributed with the same variance $\sigma^2(1-\rho^2)/(1+\rho^2)$. Replacing u by $y-A\theta$ throughout the foregoing analysis, we find that, if $y_1, y_3,..., y_{2k+1}$ are fixed, then the remaining observations $y_2, y_4,..., y_{2k}$ are normally and independently distributed with the same variance $\sigma^2(1-\rho^2)/(1+\rho^2)$ and mean values given by

$$\mathscr{E}y_{2i} = \sum_{j=1}^p a_{2i,j}\theta_j + \psi(y_{2i-1}+y_{2i+1}) + \sum_{j=1}^p \phi_j(a_{2i-1,j}+a_{2i+1,j}), \tag{4}$$

in which

$$\psi = \rho(1+\rho^2)^{-1} \tag{5}$$

and

$$\phi_j = -\psi\theta_j. \tag{6}$$

If we ignore the fact that $\phi_j = -\psi\theta_j$, the problem has now been reformulated in such a way that the principle of least squares and its associated techniques can at once be applied. Some information is lost by overlooking relations between the parameters, but this is offset by ease of calculation; if maximum likelihood is employed, the equations of estimation become much more difficult to solve. Similar results are available for the situation where $u_1, u_2,..., u_n$ form an autoregressive sequence of order $m > 1$, in which case we require $n = (m+1)k+m$ and consider the joint distribution of $y_{(m+1)i}$ $(i = 1, 2,..., k)$ conditional upon fixed values of $y_{(m+1)i-j}$ and $y_{(m+1)i+j}$

$(j = 1, 2, ..., m)$. However, the predominance of fixed observations as m increases suggests a steady decline in the efficiency with which $\theta_1, \theta_2, ..., \theta_p$ are estimated by this method. The device on which the method rests was first explored by Ogawara (1951). Its application to regression analysis was developed by Hannan (1955), who discusses, when $m = p = 1$, the asymptotic efficiency of the resulting estimates as compared with those obtained by applying least squares on the assumption that $\mathscr{D}u = \sigma^2 I$. The fact that the partial correlation coefficient between non-adjacent pairs of observations is zero is also exploited by Williams (1952) to construct experimental designs which are relatively simple to analyse.

Direct methods. When errors are autocorrelated, the straightforward extension of standard estimation procedures for linear regression has been studied by Wold (1950). The resulting methods are valid provided that the number of parameters to be estimated from the data is small compared with the number of observations. We illustrate this point by considering the simple model

$$y_t = \eta + u_t. \tag{7}$$

Suppose that $\eta^* = y.$ is the estimate of η given by the principle of least squares on the assumption that $u_1, u_2, ..., u_n$ are uncorrelated. Whatever the distribution of these variables, η^* is unbiased and therefore, if x_t denotes the tth residual, namely $y_t - y.$, we have $\mathscr{E}x_t = 0$. Moreover, we can often assume, with an error of $O(n^{-1})$, that the residuals form a stationary process having the same autocovariances as those of the process $\{u_t\}$. In fact,

$$\mathscr{E}\{(y_t - y.)(y_{t+s} - y.)\}$$
$$= \lambda_s - n^{-1} \sum_{1-t}^{n-t} \lambda_j - n^{-1} \sum_{1-t-s}^{n-t-s} \lambda_j + n^{-2} \sum_{1-n}^{n-1} (n - |j|)\lambda_j.$$

Hence $\qquad |\mathscr{E}\{(y_t - y.)(y_{t+s} - y.)\} - \lambda_s| < n^{-1}\Big(\lambda_0 + 2\sum_1^\infty \lambda_j\Big).$

The infinite series converges for an autoregressive scheme, when

$$\mathscr{E}\{(y_t - y.)(y_{t+s} - y.)\} = \lambda_s + O(n^{-1}). \tag{8}$$

This justifies the estimation of λ_s by

$$c_s = (n - s)^{-1} \sum_{t=1}^{n-s} (y_t - y.)(y_{t+s} - y.). \tag{9}$$

In what follows, we require an expression for $\mathscr{C}(c_s, c_t)$. Let $u_1, u_2, ..., u_n$ be a sample of n successive observations from a stationary process with autocovariances $\{\lambda_s\}$. Then an unbiased estimate of λ_s is

$$c_s = (n-s)^{-1} \sum_{j=1}^{n-s} u_j\, u_{j+s}. \tag{10}$$

The covariance of two such estimates is

$$\mathscr{C}(c_s, c_t) = (n-s)^{-1}(n-t)^{-1}\mathscr{E} \sum_{j=1}^{n-s} u_j\, u_{j+s} \sum_{k=1}^{n-t} u_k\, u_{k+t} - \lambda_s \lambda_t.$$

If u_1, u_2, u_3, u_4 have a joint normal distribution with zero means, unit variances, and correlation coefficients $\{\rho_{jk}\}$, their joint characteristic function is

$$\phi(t_1, t_2, t_3, t_4) = \exp\left\{-\tfrac{1}{2} \sum_{j,k=1}^{4} \rho_{jk}\, t_j\, t_k\right\}.$$

$\mathscr{E} u_1 u_2 u_3 u_4$ is the coefficient of $t_1 t_2 t_3 t_4$ in the expansion of ϕ, whence

$$\mathscr{E} u_1 u_2 u_3 u_4 = \rho_{12} \rho_{34} + \rho_{13} \rho_{24} + \rho_{14} \rho_{23}.$$

Hence, if we suppose that $u_1, u_2, \ldots, u_n$ have a joint normal distribution,

$$\mathscr{E} u_j u_{j+s} u_{j+v} u_{j+v+t} = \lambda_s \lambda_t + \lambda_v \lambda_{v+t-s} + \lambda_{v+t} \lambda_{v-s}$$

and consequently

$$\mathscr{C}(c_s, c_t) \sim n^{-1} \sum_{v=-\infty}^{\infty} (\lambda_v \lambda_{v+t-s} + \lambda_{v+t} \lambda_{v-s}). \tag{11}$$

This result remains true for any autoregressive sequence $\{u_t\}$ provided that the fourth cumulant of ϵ_t is finite (Bartlett, 1955, § 9.1).

Returning to the model $y_t = \eta + u_t$, we consider now the estimation of

$$\mathscr{V}\eta^* = \sum_{1-n}^{n-1} (1 - |s|/n)\lambda_s. \tag{12}$$

When the values of c_s tend to zero as s increases, we look for an integer s_0 which is small compared with n and such that λ_s can be taken as zero for $s \geqslant s_0$. If such an integer exists, we substitute the values of c_s for $s < s_0$ directly for the corresponding autocovariances in the formula for $\mathscr{V}\eta^*$. Thus an estimate of

$$\lambda = \sum_{1-n}^{n-1} (1 - |s|/n)\lambda_s \tag{13}$$

is

$$\lambda^* = \sum_{1-s_0}^{s_0-1} c_s. \tag{14}$$

Other estimates of λ are proposed by Hannan (1957). When the observations are normally distributed,

$$\mathscr{V}\lambda^* \sim n^{-1} \sum_{s=1-s_0}^{s_0-1} \sum_{t=1-s_0}^{s_0-1} \sum_{v=-\infty}^{\infty} (\lambda_v \lambda_{v+s-t} + \lambda_{v-s} \lambda_{v+t}). \tag{15}$$

Under the conditions stated, $\mathscr{V}(\lambda^*/n)$ is therefore $O(s_0^3/n^3)$. Consequently

$$\mathscr{V}\left\{\frac{y.-\eta}{(\lambda^*/n)}\right\} = \mathscr{V}\left\{\frac{y.-\eta}{(\lambda/n)+z/n^{\frac{3}{2}}}\right\} \sim \mathscr{V}\left\{\frac{y.-\eta}{(\lambda/n)}[1-z/\lambda n^{\frac{1}{2}}]\right\} = 1+O(n^{-\frac{1}{2}}),$$

(16)

where z is used to denote a variable with finite variance. This justifies the comparison of $y.-\eta$ with its standard error in large samples. The technique is evidently invalidated if s_0 is large compared with n. However, if the values of c_s tend steadily to zero without changing sign, a trend-reduction of the original observations will result in a sequence whose expected values remain linear in η and whose auto-covariances tend more rapidly to zero. Further details of this method of approach are given by Jowett (1955a, 1955b) who takes $\frac{1}{2}\mathscr{E}(u_t-u_{t+s})^2$ as the fundamental quantity instead of $\mathscr{E}u_t u_{t+s}$.

When the autocovariances oscillate, we can attempt to fit an auto-regressive scheme, although difficulties arise even in over-simplified situations. For example, suppose that the order of the scheme is known, and that $\{u_t\}$ is observed directly. Given a sample of $m+n$ successive observations $u_{1-m},...,u_n$ from the process in which

$$u_t+\alpha_1 u_{t-1}+...+\alpha_m u_{t-m} = \epsilon_t,$$

(17)

we can obtain estimates of $\alpha_1, \alpha_2,..., \alpha_m$ by minimizing

$$\sum_{t=1}^{n} \epsilon_t^2 = \sum_{t=1}^{n} (u_t+\alpha_1 u_{t-1}+...+\alpha_m u_{t-m})^2$$

with respect to these parameters. The resulting equations are

$$\sum_{t=1}^{n} u_t u_{t-j}+\alpha_1^* \sum_{t=1}^{n} u_{t-1} u_{t-j}+...+\alpha_m^* \sum_{t=1}^{n} u_{t-m} u_{t-j} = 0 \quad (j = 1,..., m).$$

(18)

Although these equations have the standard least-squares appearance, the standard results are inapplicable here because the coefficients of $\alpha_1^*,..., \alpha_m^*$ are constructed from the observations. In particular, the estimates can be seriously biased in small samples, and expressions for the bias when $m = 1$ are given by Marriott and Pope (1954) and Kendall (1954). However, if n is large, the bias disappears. For large samples, we can treat the residuals $\{y_t-y.\}$ as forming a stationary process with autocovariances $\{\lambda_s\}$, replace the preliminary estimates $\{c_s\}$ by smoothed values calculated from the autoregressive model, and compute the standard error of η^* by substituting the smoothed estimates for the corresponding autocovariances in formula (13).

Usually, of course, m is unknown, and the distribution theory which is relevant when estimating it from a finite sample of observations with the structure (1) is at present incompletely understood, although the problem of testing for independent $\{u_t\}$ against a Markov alternative has been put on a numerical basis by Durbin and Watson (1950, 1951).

Asymptotic theory. If the dispersion matrix of $u_1, u_2,..., u_n$ were known, we could compute the best linear unbiased (B.L.U.) estimates of $\theta_1, \theta_2,..., \theta_p$ and they would, in general, differ from the ordinary least-squares (L.S.) estimates obtained by supposing that $u_1, u_2,..., u_n$ are uncorrelated and have the same variance. Under certain conditions on the design matrix A, the asymptotic relative efficiency of the L.S. estimates compared with the B.L.U. estimates can be expressed in terms of the spectrum of $u_1, u_2,..., u_n,...$ and a similar function defined for the regression variables. The results, which are due to Grenander (1954) and Grenander and Rosenblatt (1957), show, for example, that the L.S. estimates are asymptotically efficient when $\sum a_{tj}\theta_j$ is a polynomial or trigonometric function. We shall indicate how this is proved in the relatively simple case when $p = 1$, omitting some points of detail which will be found in the first reference cited.

Let the observations have the structure

$$y_t = b_t\theta + u_t \quad (t \geqslant 0). \tag{19}$$

Here $\{u_t\}$ is an autoregressive sequence generated by

$$\alpha_0 u_t + \alpha_1 u_{t-1} + ... + \alpha_m u_{t-m} = \epsilon_t \tag{20}$$

where

$$\mathscr{E}\epsilon_t\epsilon_s = \delta_{ts}. \tag{21}$$

The corresponding spectral density function is

$$f(\omega) = 1 \Big/ \Big(2\pi\Big| \sum_{j=0}^{m} \alpha_j e^{ij\omega}\Big|^2\Big). \tag{22}$$

The sequence $\{b_t\}$ has the following properties. Put

$$B(N) = \sum_{t=0}^{N} b_t^2. \tag{23}$$

We suppose that

$$\lim_{N\to\infty} B(N) = \infty \tag{24}$$

and

$$\lim_{N\to\infty} \{B(N+h)/B(N)\} = 1 \tag{25}$$

for every integer h. If

$$R_s = \lim_{N\to\infty} \Big\{ \sum_{t=0}^{N} b_t b_{t+s}/B(N)\Big\} \tag{26}$$

exists, then the conditions on $B(N)$ are necessary and sufficient for the existence of a distribution function $\beta(\omega)$ such that

$$R_s = \int_{-\pi}^{\pi} e^{is\omega} \, d\beta(\omega). \tag{27}$$

We now evaluate the variance of θ^*, the B.L.U. estimate of θ. According to Section 3.6, there exists a linear transformation carrying $y_0, y_1, \ldots, y_{m-1}$ into $z_0, z_1, \ldots, z_{m-1}$ such that

$$z_t = c_t \theta + \epsilon_t \quad (0 \leqslant t \leqslant m-1)$$

where the $\{\epsilon_t\}$ satisfy (21). Define

$$z_t = \alpha_0 y_t + \alpha_1 y_{t-1} + \ldots + \alpha_m y_{t-m} \quad (t \geqslant m).$$

Thus

$$z_t = c_t \theta + \epsilon_t \quad (t \geqslant 0),$$

where

$$c_t = \sum_{j=0}^{m} \alpha_j b_{t-j} \quad (t \geqslant m)$$

and the $\{\epsilon_t\}$ satisfy (21).

Since $B(N)$ is unbounded,

$$\lim_{N \to \infty} \left\{ \sum_{t=0}^{N} c_t^2 / B(N) \right\} = \lim_{N \to \infty} \left\{ \sum_{t=m}^{N} c_t^2 / B(N) \right\}.$$

However, for $t \geqslant m$,

$$c_t^2 = \sum_{j=0}^{m} \sum_{k=0}^{m} \alpha_j \alpha_k b_{t-j} b_{t-k}$$

and therefore

$$\lim_{N \to \infty} \left\{ \sum_{t=0}^{N} c_t^2 / B(N) \right\} = \sum_{j=0}^{m} \sum_{k=0}^{m} \alpha_j \alpha_k R_{j-k}.$$

Substituting for R_{j-k} from (27),

$$\sum_{j=0}^{m} \sum_{k=0}^{m} \alpha_j \alpha_k R_{j-k} = \int_{-\pi}^{\pi} \left| \sum_{j=0}^{m} \alpha_j e^{ij\omega} \right|^2 d\beta(\omega) = \int_{-\pi}^{\pi} d\beta(\omega) / 2\pi f(\omega).$$

The variance of the B.L.U. estimate from N observations is

$$\mathscr{V} \theta^* = 1 \Big/ \sum_{t=0}^{N} c_t^2,$$

and hence

$$\mathscr{V} \theta^* \sim 2\pi \Big/ \left\{ B(N) \int_{-\pi}^{\pi} d\beta(\omega) / f(\omega) \right\}. \tag{28}$$

We next evaluate the variance of θ^+, the L.S. estimate of θ. Since

$$\theta^+ = \frac{1}{B(N)} \sum_{t=0}^{N} b_t y_t,$$

we obtain

$$\mathscr{V} \theta^+ = \frac{1}{B^2(N)} \sum_{p=0}^{N} \sum_{q=0}^{N} b_p b_q \lambda_{p-q},$$

whence

$$B(N)\mathscr{V}\theta^+ = 2\sum_{t=1}^{N}\frac{\lambda_t}{B(N)}\sum_{q=0}^{N-t}b_q b_{q+t} + \frac{\lambda_0}{B(N)}\sum_{q=0}^{N}b_q^2.$$

From (3.11), $\lambda_s \leqslant Kw^{|s|}$ where $0 < w < 1$, and by the Schwarz inequality

$$\sum_{q=0}^{N-t}b_q b_{q+t}/B(N) \leqslant 1.$$

We can therefore take the limit as $N \to \infty$, and get

$$\lim_{N\to\infty} B(N)\mathscr{V}\theta^+ = \lambda_0 R_0 + 2\sum_{t=1}^{\infty}\lambda_t R_t = \sum_{s=-\infty}^{\infty}\lambda_s \int_{-\pi}^{\pi} e^{-is\omega}\,d\beta(\omega)$$

$$= 2\pi \int_{-\pi}^{\pi} f(\omega)\,d\beta(\omega).$$

Hence

$$\mathscr{V}\theta^+ \sim \frac{2\pi}{B(N)}\int_{-\pi}^{\pi} f(\omega)\,d\beta(\omega). \tag{29}$$

These results hold, in fact, for every stationary process $\{u_t\}$ with a continuous spectrum since such a process can be represented by an autoregressive scheme to any required degree of approximation.

The efficiency of θ^+ relative to θ^* is

$$\mathscr{V}\theta^*/\mathscr{V}\theta^+ \sim 1\Big/\int_{-\pi}^{\pi} f(\omega)\,d\beta(\omega)\int_{-\pi}^{\pi} d\beta(\omega)/f(\omega). \tag{30}$$

We are considering real processes only so that both $f(\omega)$ and $d\beta(\omega)$ are even functions. Consequently

$$\int_{-\pi}^{\pi} f(\omega)\,d\beta(\omega)\int_{-\pi}^{\pi} d\beta(\omega)/f(\omega) = 4\int_{0}^{\pi} f(\omega)\,d\beta(\omega)\int_{0}^{\pi} d\beta(\omega)/f(\omega).$$

Now

$$\int_{0}^{\pi} f(\omega)\,d\beta(\omega)\int_{0}^{\pi} d\beta(\omega)/f(\omega) \geqslant \left\{\int_{0}^{\pi} d\beta(\omega)\right\}^2 = \tfrac{1}{4},$$

with equality for all functions $f(\omega)$ if and only if $\beta(\omega)$ has a single point of increase in the interval $(0, \pi)$.

Example. Take $b_t = \cos t\xi$ $(0 < \xi < \pi)$. Then

$$2b_t b_{t+s} = \cos s\xi + \cos(2t+s)\xi,$$

so that

$$R_n = \lim_{N\to\infty}\frac{\sum_{t=0}^{N}\{\cos s\xi + \cos(2t+s)\xi\}}{\sum_{t=0}^{N}(1+\cos 2t\xi)} = \cos s\xi.$$

The corresponding function $\beta(\omega)$ has increments of $\tfrac{1}{2}$ at $\omega = \pm\xi$ and thus the least-squares estimate of θ is asymptotically efficient for all stationary processes $\{u_t\}$ with a continuous spectrum.

7.5. Exercises

1. A circular stationary process of size N is a set of N random variables $u_1, u_2, ..., u_N$ such that $\mathcal{E}u_t = 0$, $\mathcal{V}u_t = \sigma^2$ and $\mathcal{E}u_t u_{t+s} = \sigma^2 \rho_s$ $(t = 1, 2, ..., N)$, where $\rho_{N+s} = \rho_{N-s} = \rho_s$. Thus the first row of $\mathcal{D}u$ is

$$\sigma^2(1, \rho_1, \rho_2, ..., \rho_2, \rho_1)$$

and other rows are obtained by cyclic permutations of it. Show that the latent roots of $\mathcal{D}u$ are the values of the spectral density function for $\omega = 2\pi r/N$ $(r = 1, 2, ..., N)$. (Wise, 1955.)

2. $$y_t = \sum_j \theta_j \cos(2\pi t j/N) + \sum_k \phi_k \sin(2\pi t k/N) + u_t \quad (t = 1, 2, ..., N),$$

where $\{u_t\}$ is the circular stationary process defined in the previous Exercise. Show that the columns of the design matrix are latent vectors of $\mathcal{D}u$ and deduce that the least-squares estimates of θ_j and ϕ_k are fully efficient.

3. $$y_t = \alpha + \beta x_t + u_t,$$

where α and β are constants, while $\{x_t\}$ and $\{u_t\}$ are independent stationary processes such that

$$\mathcal{E}x_t = \mu, \qquad \mathcal{V}x_t = \sigma_x^2, \qquad \mathcal{C}(x_t, x_{t+s}) = \sigma_x^2 \rho_{(x)s}$$

and
$$\mathcal{E}u_t = 0, \qquad \mathcal{V}u_t = \sigma_u^2, \qquad \mathcal{C}(u_t, u_{t+s}) = \sigma_u^2 \rho_{(u)s}.$$

Let $$\beta^* = \sum_{t=1}^n (x_t - x.)(y_t - y.) \Big/ \sum_{t=1}^n (x_t - x.)^2.$$

If $\sum_{s=1}^\infty |\rho_{(x)s}|$ and $\sum_{s=1}^\infty |\rho_{(u)s}|$ converge, show that

$$\mathcal{E}\beta^* \sim \beta$$

and
$$\mathcal{V}\beta^* \sim \left(1 + 2\sum_{s=1}^{n-1} \rho_{(x)s}\rho_{(u)s}\right)\sigma_u^2/n\sigma_x^2. \qquad \text{(Wold, 1950.)}$$

4. $$y_t = \alpha + \beta x_t + u_t,$$

where α and β are constants, while $\{x_t\}$ and $\{u_t\}$ are independent stationary processes such that

$$\mathcal{E}x_t = \mu, \qquad \mathcal{V}x_t = \sigma_x^2, \qquad \mathcal{C}(x_t, x_{t+s}) = \sigma_x^2 \rho_x^{|s|}$$

and
$$\mathcal{E}u_t = 0, \qquad \mathcal{V}u_t = \sigma_u^2, \qquad \mathcal{C}(u_t, u_{t+s}) = \sigma_u^2 \rho_u^{|s|}.$$

Let $$\beta^* = \sum_{t=1}^n (x_t - x.)(y_t - y.) \Big/ \sum_{t=1}^n (x_t - x.)^2.$$

Show that $$\mathcal{V}\beta^* \sim \sigma_u^2(1 + \rho_u \rho_x)/n\sigma_x^2(1 - \rho_u \rho_x). \qquad \text{(Bartlett, 1935.)}$$

5. Under the conditions of the previous Exercise, let β^+ be the least-squares estimate of β from the first differences of the $\{y_t\}$. Show that

$$\mathcal{V}\beta^+ \sim \sigma_u^2(1 - \rho_u)(3 - \rho_u\rho_x - \rho_u - \rho_x)/2n\sigma_x^2(1 - \rho_x)(1 - \rho_u\rho_x).$$

$$\text{(Hannan, 1955.)}$$

6. Under the conditions of the previous two Exercises, let $\hat{\beta}$ be the least-squares estimate of β from $y_2, y_4, ..., y_{2k}$ for given values of $y_1, y_3, ..., y_{2k+1}$. Show that

$$\mathscr{V}\hat{\beta} \sim \sigma_u^2 (1-\rho_u^2)(1+\rho_x^2)/n\sigma_x^2(1+\rho_u^2)(1-\rho_x^2). \quad \text{(Hannan, 1955.)}$$

7. Let $\{u_t\}$ be a stationary process generated by

$$u_t = \rho u_{t-1} + \epsilon_t$$

where $|\rho| < 1$ and ϵ_t is normally distributed with mean zero and variance σ^2 independently of $...\epsilon_{t-1}, \epsilon_{t+1}, ...$ and $u_{t-1}, u_{t-2}, ...$ Show that the joint density function of $u_1, u_2, ..., u_n$ is

$$\left(\frac{1}{2\pi\sigma^2}\right)^{\frac{1}{2}n}(1-\rho^2)^{\frac{1}{2}}\exp\left[-\frac{1}{2\sigma^2}\left\{u_1^2+u_n^2+(1+\rho^2)\sum_{t=2}^{n-1}u_t^2-2\rho\sum_{t=1}^{n-1}u_t u_{t+1}\right\}\right].$$

8. Each of p treatments $1, 2, ..., p$ is used m times in an experimental design, the order of application being

$$1, 2, ..., p, 1, 2, ..., p, ..., 1, 2, ..., p.$$

The effects of the treatments are $\theta_1, \theta_2, ..., \theta_p$ so that the tth observation is $\theta_{[t]}+u_t$, where $\theta_{[t]}$ is the effect of the corresponding treatment and $\{u_t\}$ is the stationary process of the previous Exercise. Let y_{jk} be the observation resulting from the jth application of the kth treatment. Show that the maximum likelihood estimate of θ_k is

$$\hat{\theta}_k = y_{.k} - c_1\hat{\rho}^k - c_2\hat{\rho}^{-k},$$

where

$$c_1 = \frac{1}{m}\left\{\frac{\hat{\rho}}{m}(y_{11}-y_{.1}) + \left(\hat{\rho}^p\frac{m-1}{m}-1\right)(y_{mp}-y_{.p})\right\}\left\{\left(\hat{\rho}^p\frac{m-1}{m}-1\right)^2-\left(\frac{\hat{\rho}}{m}\right)^2\right\}^{-1},$$

$$c_2 = \frac{1}{m}\left\{\left(\hat{\rho}^p\frac{m-1}{m}-1\right)(y_{11}-y_{.1}) + \frac{\hat{\rho}}{m}(y_{mp}-y_{.p})\right\}\left\{\left(\hat{\rho}^p\frac{m-1}{m}-1\right)^2-\left(\frac{\hat{\rho}}{m}\right)^2\right\}^{-1}$$

and $\hat{\rho}$ is the maximum likelihood estimate of ρ. (Williams, 1952.)

9. $$y_t = b_t\theta + u_t,$$

where $\{u_t\}$ is a stationary process with a continuous spectrum. Show that the least-squares estimate of θ is asymptotically efficient when (i) $b_t = \sin t\xi$, (ii) $b_t = t^k$, where $k > 0$.

7.6. References

BARTLETT, M. S. (1935). Some aspects of the time-correlation problem in regard to tests of significance. *J. R. Statist. Soc.* **98**, 536–43.

—— (1955). *An Introduction to Stochastic Processes with Special Reference to Methods and Applications.* Cambridge University Press.

CRAMÉR, H. (1946). *Mathematical Methods of Statistics.* Princeton University Press.

DOOB, J. L. (1953). *Stochastic Processes.* New York: Wiley.

DURBIN, J., and WATSON, G. S. (1950, 1951). Testing for serial correlation in least squares regression. *Biometrika,* **37**, 409–28; **38**, 159–78.

GRENANDER, U. (1954). On the estimation of regression coefficients in the case of an autocorrelated disturbance. *Ann. Math. Statist.* **25**, 252–72.

—— and ROSENBLATT, M. (1957). *Statistical Analysis of Stationary Time Series.* New York: Wiley.

HANNAN, E. J. (1955). Exact tests for serial correlation. *Biometrika*, **42**, 133–42.

—— (1957). The variance of the mean of a stationary process. *J. R. Statist. Soc.* B, **19**, 282–5.

JOWETT, G. H. (1955 a). Least squares regression analysis for trend-reduced time series. *J. R. Statist. Soc.* B, **17**, 91–104.

—— (1955 b). The comparison of means of sets of observations from sections of independent stochastic series. *J. R. Statist. Soc.* B, **17**, 208–27.

KENDALL, M. G. (1944). On autoregressive time series. *Biometrika*, **33**, 105–22.

—— (1954). Note on bias in the estimation of autocorrelation. *Biometrika*, **41**, 403–4.

LÉVY, P. (1937). *Théorie de l'addition des variables aléatoires.* Paris: Gauthier-Villars.

MARRIOTT, F. H. C., and POPE, J. A. (1954). Bias in the estimation of auto-correlations. *Biometrika*, **41**, 390–402.

MILNE-THOMSON, L. M. (1933). *The Calculus of Finite Differences.* London: Macmillan.

MORAN, P. A. P. (1949). The spectral theory of discrete stochastic processes. *Biometrika*, **36**, 63–70.

OGAWARA, M. (1951). A note on the test of serial correlation coefficients. *Ann. Math. Statist.* **22**, 115–18.

SPENCER-SMITH, J. L. (1947). The oscillatory properties of the moving average. *Suppl. J. R. Statist. Soc.* **9**, 104–13.

TITCHMARSH, E. C. (1952). *The Theory of Functions.* Oxford University Press.

WILLIAMS, R. M. (1952). Experimental designs for serially correlated observations. *Biometrika*, **39**, 151–67.

WISE, J. (1955). The autocorrelation function and the spectral density function. *Biometrika*, **42**, 151–9.

WOLD, H. (1938). *A Study in the Analysis of Stationary Time Series.* Uppsala: Almqvist and Wiksells.

—— (1950). On least square regression with autocorrelated variables and residuals. *Bull. Inst. Int. Statist.* **32**, 277–89.

SYMMETRICAL FACTORIAL EXPERIMENTS

8.1. Introduction

THE concept of an experiment with quantitative factors was introduced in Chapter 6 by a specific illustration, and we now give a parallel illustration to define qualitative factors—the kind with which the present Chapter is mainly concerned.

Consider an agricultural experiment where different varieties of a plant are grown on plots which are grouped by rows and columns. The yield from a particular plant depends on the corresponding variety, row, and column which are the *factors* of the experiment. Individual varieties are described as *levels* of the factor varieties, and similarly for rows and columns. Any experimental unit formed by associating a level from each of the factors is a *treatment combination*, and the set of treatment combinations which are used constitutes the experimental design.

We shall discuss the problem of how best to choose the design. It calls for a different approach from the one followed previously since we now take account of factors where differences between levels cannot be expressed in numerical terms. The results are applicable to experiments with quantitative factors, but may not then provide the best methods of design and analysis.

8.2. Basis of factorial design

Suppose that the experiment involves v factors $F_1, F_2, ..., F_v$ which can appear at $q_1, q_2, ..., q_v$ specified levels respectively. Let $\eta(x, y, ..., z)$ be the expected value of an observation resulting from the treatment combination formed by the xth level of F_1, the yth level of $F_2, ...,$ and the zth level of F_v. We shall assume, until Section 5 is reached, that

$$\eta(x, y, ..., z) = \rho_x + \kappa_y + ... + \lambda_z. \tag{1}$$

The corresponding design matrix, S, has $q_1 + q_2 + ... + q_v$ columns, but its rank is $(v-1)$ less, as the following argument shows. Let $(r_1, r_2, ..., r_v)$ be any row vector orthogonal to the v-rowed unit vector, and let r be the column vector in which the first q_1 elements are r_1, the next q_2

elements are $r_2,...,$ and the last q_v elements are r_v. Then

$$Sr = 0. \tag{2}$$

However, there exist $(v-1)$ linearly independent vectors like $(r_1, r_2,..., r_v)$ and the rank of S is therefore

$$g = q_1+q_2+...+q_v-(v-1). \tag{3}$$

Denote by ρ the column vector of $\rho_1, \rho_2,..., \rho_{q_1}$, and similarly define $\kappa,..., \lambda$. Put

$$\theta = L^{-1}\rho,$$
$$\phi = M^{-1}\kappa,$$

and

$$\psi = N^{-1}\lambda, \tag{4}$$

where $L, M,..., N$ are non-singular matrices, each with a first column of unit elements. Since $LL^{-1} = I$, the rows of L^{-1}, after the first, sum to zero. The corresponding parameters, $\theta_2, \theta_3,..., \theta_{q_1}$ are therefore said to be *contrasts* of $\rho_1, \rho_2,..., \rho_{q_1}$. Put

$$\mu = \theta_1+\phi_1+...+\psi_1. \tag{5}$$

Then

$$\eta(x, y,..., z) = \mu+ \sum_{i=2}^{q_1} a_{xi}\theta_i+ \sum_{j=2}^{q_2} b_{yj}\phi_j+...+ \sum_{k=2}^{q_v} c_{zk}\psi_k, \tag{6}$$

where $L = \{a_{xi}\}$, $M = \{b_{yj}\},...,$ and $N = \{c_{zk}\}$. If R is the design matrix corresponding to (6), then its rank is g, equal to the number of parameters in the new system.

We shall suppose that R satisfies

$$R'R = nI, \tag{7}$$

where n is the total number of treatment combinations in the experiment. This condition is introduced for two reasons:

(i) the equations of estimation are then soluble immediately;
(ii) the contrasts are each estimated with the minimum possible variance.

Property (ii) is proved as follows. The dispersion matrix of the estimated contrasts is proportional to D^{-1} where $D = R'R$. According to Aitken (1951, § 31)

$$|D| = d_{11}|D_{11}|- \sum_{j=2}^{g} \sum_{k=2}^{g} d_{1j} d_{1k}|D_{jk}^{11}|, \tag{8}$$

where $|D_{11}|$ is the cofactor of d_{11} in $|D|$, and $|D_{jk}^{11}|$ is the cofactor of d_{jk} in $|D_{11}|$. Since the matrix with elements $\{|D_{jk}^{11}|\}$ is the adjugate of the matrix formed from D by omitting the first row and column, and is therefore positive definite,

$$|D| \leqslant d_{11}|D_{11}|. \tag{9}$$

Equivalently, $\qquad d^{11} \geqslant 1/d_{11},$

with equality if and only if $d_{12},...,d_{1g}$ are all zero. Let us now fix the values of the diagonal elements of D. On applying the same argument to other diagonal elements of D^{-1}, we see that they are simultaneously minimized when D is diagonal. From (6), $d_{11} = n$, and the choice of $D = nI$ merely represents a convenient choice of scale in defining the parameters other than μ. This argument for choosing D was put forward by Hotelling (1944).

We now examine the implications of (7). Suppose that the xth level of F_1 and the yth of F_2 appear together in a design w_{xy} times. Then F_1 appears at level x with frequency w_{x0} where

$$w_{x0} = \sum_y w_{xy},$$

and similarly F_2 appears at level y with frequency w_{0y}. Within the columns corresponding to F_1 we have

$$\sum_x a_{xj} a_{xk} w_{x0} = n\delta_{jk}. \tag{10}$$

The product of a column of F_1 with one of F_2 is

$$\sum_{x,y} a_{xj} w_{xy} b_{yk} = n\delta_{1j}\delta_{1k}. \tag{11}$$

In (10) put $j = 1$ and obtain

$$\sum_x a_{xk} w_{x0} = n\delta_{1k},$$

whence $\qquad\qquad w_{x0} = na^{1x}. \tag{12}$

Similarly $\qquad\qquad w_{0y} = nb^{1y}.$

Since (10) gives $\qquad w_{xy} = na^{1x}b^{1y},$

we have finally $\qquad nw_{xy} = w_{x0} w_{0y}. \tag{13}$

This condition, which is due to Plackett and Burman (1946) and Plackett (1946), is required to hold for every pair of factors in the experiment.

If we denote the q_1 levels of F_1 by q_1 different symbols, and similarly allot symbols for the levels of $F_2, F_3,..., F_v$, then any experimental design can be represented by a *factorial array*, which is a rectangular array of symbols where the rows correspond to individual factors while the columns give the treatment combinations used. We give below an example with three factors, appearing at $2, 2$, and 4 levels respectively, in which (13) is satisfied for each pair.

Treatment combinations

	F_1	0	0	0	0	1	1	1	1
Factors	F_2	0	0	1	1	0	0	1	1
	F_3	0	1	σ	τ	σ	τ	0	1

Here the levels of F_1 and F_2 are denoted by 0, 1, and those of F_3 by 0, 1, σ, τ.

To obtain the design matrix from the factorial array, we transpose the array; replace the xth symbol in the column giving levels of F_1 by a row consisting of the coefficients $\{a_{xi}\}$ for $i = 2, 3, ..., q_1$; replace the symbols giving levels of $F_2, ..., F_v$ in the same way; and finally adjoin a column 1 for the parameter μ. Row F_1 in the factorial array thus represents $(q_1 - 1)$ columns in the design matrix, and the corresponding set of $(q_1 - 1)$ parameters is termed the *main effect* of F_1.

We now make two simplifications.

(a) Each factor appears at the same number of levels, say q. A design with this property is described as a *symmetrical* factorial experiment.

(b) The contrasts for each factor form an orthogonal set, so that

$$L'L = M'M = ... = N'N = qI. \qquad (14)$$

From (12), and the fact that $L^{-1} = qL'$, we find

$$w_{x0} = n/q.$$

Similarly
$$w_{0y} = n/q,$$

whence
$$w_{xy} = n/q^2. \qquad (15)$$

The same condition holds for each pair of factors.

A factorial array which satisfies (15) for every pair of factors is known as an *orthogonal array of strength two* (Rao, 1946, 1947). We proceed to give some results from the theory of finite groups which form a necessary preliminary to the construction and combinatorial properties of such arrays.

8.3. A class of Abelian groups

The following account of topics discussed in Chapters 9, 10, and 11 of Carmichael (1937) is expressed in a notation which is convenient for applications to the study of factorial experiments.

Let p be a prime number and m a positive integer. Denote p^m by q. Consider a collection of q^s elements, which are individually denoted by $E_1^{g_1} E_2^{g_2} \dots E_s^{g_s}$, where the indices $g_1, g_2, \dots, g_s$ range independently over the marks of the Galois field $GF(q)$. The law of combination for these elements is given by

$$(E_1^{g_1} E_2^{g_2} \dots E_s^{g_s})(E_1^{h_1} E_2^{h_2} \dots E_s^{h_s}) = E_1^{g_1+h_1} E_2^{g_2+h_2} \dots E_s^{g_s+h_s}$$

and they therefore form an Abelian group G, in which $E_1^0 E_2^0 \dots E_s^0$ is the identity, I. In writing down a particular element, we omit any letter with index zero, and omit unit indices: thus $E_1^0 E_2^1 E_3^{g_3} \dots E_s^{g_s}$ becomes $E_2 E_3^{g_3} \dots E_s^{g_s}$. Similarly, we denote by $\{e_1^{v_1} e_2^{v_2} \dots e_s^{v_s}\}$ the elements of an Abelian group H which is isomorphic with G, where $v_1, v_2, \dots, v_s$ are further quantities which range over $GF(q)$. The identity of this group is denoted by 1.

Now suppose that $E_1^{g_1} E_2^{g_2} \dots E_s^{g_s}$ is any fixed element of G, except I; and form a set of elements $\{E_1^{cg_1} E_2^{cg_2} \dots E_s^{cg_s}\}$ by allowing c to range over $GF(q)$. All these elements are different and the product of any two of them belongs to the set, so that they form a subgroup of order q. We shall describe subgroups of this kind as *cyclic*. A cyclic subgroup can be identified by any element it contains, except I, because $E_1^{g_1} E_2^{g_2} \dots E_s^{g_s}$ and $E_1^{kg_1} E_2^{kg_2} \dots E_s^{kg_s}$ generate the same subgroup. Denote by G_1 the subgroup generated by $E_1^{g_1} E_2^{g_2} \dots E_s^{g_s}$. If $E_1^{h_1} E_2^{h_2} \dots E_s^{h_s}$ is any element of G not contained in G_1, then the cyclic subgroup G_2 generated by $E_1^{h_1} E_2^{h_2} \dots E_s^{h_s}$ has no element in common with G_1, except I. This is because the equation

$$(E_1^{g_1} E_2^{g_2} \dots E_s^{g_s})^{j_1} = (E_1^{h_1} E_2^{h_2} \dots E_s^{h_s})^{j_2},$$

where $j_1, j_2 \neq 0$, implies

$$h_1 = cg_1, \quad h_2 = cg_2, \quad \dots, \quad h_s = cg_s,$$

where $c = j_1/j_2$. Proceeding in this way, the elements of G, excluding I, can be divided into $(q^s-1)/(q-1)$ sets of $(q-1)$ elements, each set forming, with I, a cyclic subgroup of order q. Each of the $(q^s-1)/(q-1)$ sets can be identified by a single element of G, and these $(q^s-1)/(q-1)$ elements are *pairwise independent*, in the sense that none is contained in the cyclic subgroup generated by any of the others.

For example, when $q = 3$ and $s = 2$, the elements

$$I, \; A, \; A^2, \; B, \; B^2, \; AB, \; A^2B^2, \; AB^2, \; A^2B$$

can be divided into $(3^2-1)/(3-1) = 4$ cyclic subgroups, as follows.

$$
\begin{array}{cccc}
I & I & I & I \\
A & B & AB & AB^2 \\
A^2 & B^2 & A^2B^2 & A^2B
\end{array}
$$

The four elements A, B, AB, AB^2 are pairwise independent.

Let
$$A_1 = E_1^{g_{11}} E_2^{g_{12}} \ldots E_s^{g_{1s}}$$
be any element of G, except I; and form the subgroup of elements
$$\{A_1^{c_1}\} = \{E_1^{c_1 g_{11}} E_2^{c_1 g_{12}} \ldots E_s^{c_1 g_{1s}}\},$$
where c_1 ranges over $GF(q)$. If
$$A_2 = E_1^{g_{21}} E_2^{g_{22}} \ldots E_s^{g_{2s}}$$
is any element of G not in this subgroup, then the elements
$$\{A_1^{c_1} A_2^{c_2}\} = \{E_1^{c_1 g_{11}+c_2 g_{21}} E_2^{c_1 g_{12}+c_2 g_{22}} \ldots E_s^{c_1 g_{1s}+c_2 g_{2s}}\},$$
where c_1, c_2 range over $GF(q)$, form a subgroup of order q^2, and
$$
\begin{bmatrix}
g_{11} & g_{12} & \cdot & \cdot & \cdot & g_{1s} \\
g_{21} & g_{22} & \cdot & \cdot & \cdot & g_{2s}
\end{bmatrix}
$$
has rank 2. Continuing in this way, we find that any element of G can be expressed in the form
$$A_1^{c_1} A_2^{c_2} \ldots A_s^{c_s},$$
where
$$A_s = E_1^{g_{s1}} E_2^{g_{s2}} \ldots E_s^{g_{ss}},$$
and the matrix
$$
\begin{bmatrix}
g_{11} & g_{12} & \cdot & \cdot & \cdot & g_{1s} \\
g_{21} & g_{22} & \cdot & \cdot & \cdot & g_{2s} \\
 & & \cdot & \cdot & \cdot & \\
g_{s1} & g_{s2} & \cdot & \cdot & \cdot & g_{ss}
\end{bmatrix}
$$
has rank s. The elements $A_1, A_2, \ldots, A_s$ are said to comprise a set of completely independent *generators* of G.

8.4. Orthogonal arrays of strength two

When each factor appears at q levels, an upper bound to the number of factors which can be accommodated in a design which uses n treatment combinations is $(n-1)/(q-1)$, because the numerator is the number of permissible columns in the design matrix, excluding the column for μ, while the denominator is the number required for each of the sets of orthogonal contrasts. In particular, when

$$n = q^s, \tag{1}$$

the number of factors cannot exceed

$$u = 1+q+q^2+...+q^{s-1}. \tag{2}$$

We proceed to show that when

$$q = p^m, \tag{3}$$

where p is prime, q^s treatment combinations suffice for an orthogonal array of strength two involving u factors $F_1, F_2,..., F_u$, each at q levels. The omission of rows from this array will not affect its orthogonality, and allows for the estimation of experimental error, because the number of parameters to be estimated is then less than n. If v factors are present, where

$$s < v \leqslant u,$$

the design requires only q^s treatment combinations out of a total of q^v different combinations, and is thus termed a $1/q^{v-s}$ *fractional replicate* of the *complete factorial* experiment formed by all possible treatment combinations.

We construct this array by the following method (Bose and Kishen, 1940) based on the groups G and H defined in the previous Section. The rows are labelled by any u elements $\{E_1^{q_1} E_2^{q_2} ... E_s^{q_s}\}$ which identify different cyclic subgroups of G; the columns are labelled by the q^s elements $\{e_1^{v_1} e_2^{v_2} ... e_s^{v_s}\}$ of H; and the symbol in row $E_1^{q_1} E_2^{q_2} ... E_s^{q_s}$ and column $e_1^{v_1} e_2^{v_2} ... e_s^{v_s}$ is

$$x = v_1 g_1 + v_2 g_2 + ... + v_s g_s, \tag{4}$$

where all the operations of addition and multiplication are conducted in the field $GF(p^m)$. For example, take $q = 4$ and $s = 2$. The marks of $GF(2^2)$ are denoted by $0, 1, \sigma, \tau$ and are combined according to Tables 13 and 14.

TABLE 13

Addition in $GF(2^2)$

	0	1	σ	τ
0	0	1	σ	τ
1	1	0	τ	σ
σ	σ	τ	0	1
τ	τ	σ	1	0

TABLE 14

Multiplication in $GF(2^2)$

	0	1	σ	τ
0	0	0	0	0
1	0	1	σ	τ
σ	0	σ	τ	1
τ	0	τ	1	σ

We write $E_1 = A$, $E_2 = B$, $e_1 = a$, $e_2 = b$, and label the rows A, B, AB, AB^σ, AB^τ. Thus the symbol in row AB^σ and column $a^\sigma b^\tau$ is

$$1.\sigma + \sigma.\tau = \sigma + 1 = \tau.$$

The complete array is shown in Table 15.

TABLE 15. *Orthogonal array for four factors each at two levels*

	1	b	b^σ	b^τ	a	ab	ab^σ	ab^τ	a^σ	$a^\sigma b$	$a^\sigma b^\sigma$	$a^\sigma b^\tau$	a^τ	$a^\tau b$	$a^\tau b^\sigma$	$a^\tau b^\tau$
A	0	0	0	0	1	1	1	1	σ	σ	σ	σ	τ	τ	τ	τ
B	0	1	σ	τ	0	1	σ	τ	0	1	σ	τ	0	1	σ	τ
AB	0	1	σ	τ	1	0	τ	σ	σ	τ	0	1	τ	σ	1	0
AB^σ	0	σ	τ	1	1	τ	σ	0	σ	0	1	τ	τ	1	0	σ
AB^τ	0	τ	1	σ	1	σ	0	τ	σ	1	τ	0	τ	0	σ	1

Next, we show that any array constructed on these lines is an orthogonal array of strength two. Consider the factors

$$F_1 = E_1^{q_1} E_2^{q_2} \ldots E_s^{q_s} \quad \text{and} \quad F_2 = E_1^{h_1} E_2^{h_2} \ldots E_s^{h_s};$$

and let $e_1^{v_1} e_2^{v_2} \ldots e_s^{v_s}$ label any treatment combination in which F_1 and F_2 appear at levels x_1 and x_2 respectively. Then

$$x_1 = v_1 g_1 + v_2 g_2 + \ldots + v_s g_s,$$

and

$$x_2 = v_1 h_1 + v_2 h_2 + \ldots + v_s h_s.$$

If these equations are regarded as a system of simultaneous linear equations in which $x_1, g_1, g_2, \ldots, g_s$ and $x_2, h_1, h_2, \ldots, h_s$ are known, whereas $v_1, v_2, \ldots, v_s$ are to be determined, then the matrix of the system has rank two because $E_1^{q_1} E_2^{q_2} \ldots E_s^{q_s}$ and $E_1^{h_1} E_2^{h_2} \ldots E_s^{h_s}$ belong to different cyclic subgroups, so that we cannot have

$$g_1 = kh_1, \quad g_2 = kh_2, \quad \ldots, \quad g_s = kh_s$$

in all pairs of indices. We can thus insert arbitrary values for $v_1, v_2, \ldots, v_{s-2}$ say, and solve for v_{s-1} and v_s. The arbitrary values can be chosen in q^{s-2} ways, which is therefore the number of treatment combinations having the factors F_1 and F_2 at levels x_1 and x_2 respectively. This is true for any pair of levels and any pair of factors, so that the array has the properties required. We shall denote by $O_2(q^s)$ any orthogonal array of strength two for $(q^s-1)/(q-1)$ factors, each at q levels, using q^s treatment combinations, and constructed by the method described.

When $s = 2$, the number of treatment combinations (q^2) is the number of different combinations (x, y) of the levels of F_1 and F_2, so that each such combination defines a unique level z of F_3, with which it occurs in the factorial array. The factorial array for F_1, F_2, and F_3 only is therefore equivalent to a square array containing the symbol z in row x and column y; since all pairs (x, z) and (y, z) occur once each, every symbol z appears once in every row and once in every column. A square array with these properties is termed a *Latin square*. An orthogonal array for $(q+1)$ factors, using q^2 treatment combinations, can therefore be presented as a set of $(q-1)$ Latin squares. In each square the rows refer to levels of F_1, and the columns to levels of F_2; the inserted symbols refer to levels of one of the remaining factors. Any two squares are described as orthogonal, because when they are superimposed, all the q^2 ordered combinations of pairs of elements from $GF(q)$ each appear once (Bose, 1938; Stevens, 1939). In the above example, we obtain three squares, in which the inserted symbols refer respectively to levels of F_3, F_4, and F_5. They are shown in Table 16.

TABLE 16. *Set of mutually orthogonal Latin squares of side four*

0	1	σ	τ
1	0	τ	σ
σ	τ	0	1
τ	σ	1	0

0	σ	τ	1
1	τ	σ	0
σ	0	1	τ
τ	1	0	σ

0	τ	1	σ
1	σ	0	τ
σ	1	τ	0
τ	0	σ	1

We note that the p^{mu} different treatment combinations of the factors $F_1, F_2, ..., F_u$ can be represented by the elements $\{f_1^{x_1} f_2^{x_2} ... f_u^{x_u}\}$ of an Abelian group J, of order p^{mu}. Here $x_1, x_2, ..., x_u$ range independently over the marks of $GF(p^m)$. The array $O_2(q^s)$ is defined by a set of p^{ms} elements of J, and we denote this set by U. It includes the identity of J, namely $f_1^0 f_2^0 ... f_u^0$, which is described as the *control*, and which appears in the column labelled by the identity of H, $e_1^0 e_2^0 ... e_s^0$. Moreover, U is a subgroup of J. To prove this, suppose that column $e_1^{v_1} e_2^{v_2} ... e_s^{v_s}$ of the array yields the treatment combination $f_1^{x_1} f_2^{x_2} ... f_u^{x_u}$, and that $e_1^{w_1} e_2^{w_2} ... e_s^{w_s}$ yields $f_1^{y_1} f_2^{y_2} ... f_u^{y_u}$. Then $e_1^{v_1+w_1} e_2^{v_2+w_2} ... e_s^{v_s+w_s}$ is certainly a column of the array, and it yields the treatment combination $f_1^{x_1+y_1} f_2^{x_2+y_2} ... f_u^{x_u+y_u}$. The elements of U are therefore closed with respect to multiplication and hence they form a subgroup.

Lastly, we comment on the numerical analysis to which the use of these designs leads. Any factor, say F_1, divides the observations on $O_2(q^s)$ into q sets of size q^{s-1}, all the observations in a particular set being on treatment combinations in which F_1 has the same level. If the totals of these sets are $T_1, T_2, ..., T_q$, then

$$n\mu^* = T_1 + T_2 + ... + T_q,$$

and, e.g.,

$$n\theta_i^* = \sum_{x=1}^{q} a_{xi} T_x.$$

The parameters $\{\theta_i\}$ are therefore estimated by orthogonal contrasts of $T_1, T_2, ..., T_q$; and any two such estimates are uncorrelated, whether they refer to the same factor, or to different factors. Since $E_1^{q_1} E_2^{q_2} ... E_s^{q_s}$ and $E_1^{kg_1} E_2^{kg_2} ... E_s^{kg_s}$ divide the observations into the same q sets of q^{s-1} observations each, we conclude that the set of $(q-1)$ parameters represented by any row of $O_2(q^s)$ is in correspondence, not merely with a single element of G, but with every member, excluding I, of the cyclic subgroup based on that element. Hence each element of G, except I, has its counterpart in one of the (q^s-1) orthogonal contrasts of the q^s observations. The identity is always at level zero throughout any set of treatment combinations, and therefore effects no subdivision of them: it corresponds to the column 1 in the design matrix.

8.5. Interactions

When $s = 2$ and q is a prime power, we obtain by the methods of the previous Section an orthogonal array for $(q+1)$ factors, each at q levels, using q^2 treatment combinations. In this array, $O_2(q^2)$, we label the factors A, B, and $\{AB^h\}$, where h ranges through the non-zero marks of $GF(q)$. The treatment combination denoted by $a^x b^y$ then has factor A at level x, factor B at level y, and factor AB^h at level $x+hy$.

Suppose that A and B are the only factors present, so that $a^x b^y$ simply signifies the combination of level x of A with level y of B, each possible combination appearing once. According to the assumptions of Section 2, the q^2 values $\eta(x,y)$ are expressed in terms of $(2q-1)$ parameters by the system of equations

$$\eta(x,y) = \mu + \sum_{i=2}^{q} a_{xi}\theta_i + \sum_{j=2}^{q} b_{yj}\phi_j, \tag{1}$$

where the $(q-1)$ parameters $\{\theta_i\}$ represent the main effect of A, the $(q-1)$ parameters $\{\phi_j\}$ represent the main effect of B, and x, y belong to $GF(q)$. This system imposes $(q-1)^2$ restrictions on the values of $\eta(x,y)$. We now withdraw these restrictions, in which case the specification of $\eta(x,y)$ calls for $(q-1)^2$ parameters in addition to μ, $\{\theta_i\}$ and $\{\phi_j\}$. The coefficients of the additional parameters are conveniently provided by treating the rows of $O_2(q^2)$ labelled $\{AB^h\}$ just as if they corresponded to the main effects of $(q-1)$ factors, other than A and B. The resulting extension of (1) takes the form

$$\eta(x,y) = \mu + \sum_{i=2}^{q} a_{xi}\theta_i + \sum_{j=2}^{q} b_{yj}\phi_j + ... + \sum_{k=2}^{q} c_{x+hy,k}\psi_k + ..., \tag{2}$$

where the $(q-1)$ parameters $\{\psi_k\}$ correspond to the row AB^h and

x, y, $x+hy$ belong to $GF(q)$. The set of $(q-1)^2$ parameters typified by $\{\psi_k\}$ is termed the $A \times B$ *interaction*, and is thus represented by the rows in $O_2(q^2)$ which are labelled $\{AB^h\}$.

Similar considerations apply to an orthogonal array for q^2+q+1 factors, each at q levels, using q^3 treatment combinations. We label the factors of $O_2(q^3)$ by combinations of the letters A, B, and C so that the treatment combination denoted by $a^x b^y c^z$ has factor A at level x, B at level y, and C at level z. Every possible combination of levels of A, B, and C occurs once, and we suppose again that these are the only factors present. Each requires one row of $O_2(q^3)$ to represent its main effect; each of the interactions $A \times B$, $B \times C$, and $C \times A$ requires $(q-1)$ rows; and there remain

$$(q^2+q+1)-3-3(q-1) = (q-1)^2$$

rows. If the parameters corresponding to main effects and two-factor interactions are insufficient for a linear representation of the expected values $\{\eta(x, y, z)\}$, these $(q-1)^2$ rows of $O_2(q^3)$ correspond to the $(q-1)^3$ parameters required for the $A \times B \times C$ interaction. The rows of an array $O_2(q^3)$ which correspond to a three-factor interaction may conveniently be labelled according to the following system.

$$ABC, \ ABC^2,..., \ ABC^h,...$$
$$AB^2C, \ AB^2C^2,..., \ AB^2C^h,...$$
$$\cdot \quad \cdot \quad \cdot \quad \cdot \quad \cdot \quad \cdot$$
$$AB^qC, \ AB^qC^2,..., \ AB^qC^h,...$$
$$\cdot \quad \cdot \quad \cdot \quad \cdot \quad \cdot \quad \cdot$$

For example, take $q = s = 3$. The marks of $GF(3)$ are denoted by 0, 1, 2 and Table 17 shows the resulting representation of the effects, separate or combined, of three factors at three levels each. Treatment combinations are given by the first three rows of the array.

In general, we can represent the main effects and interactions of s factors $E_1, E_2,..., E_s$ at q levels each by the $(q^s-1)/(q-1)$ rows of $O_2(q^s)$. One row is required for each of s main effects, $(q-1)$ rows for each of $\binom{s}{2}$ two-factor interactions, $(q-1)^2$ rows for each of $\binom{s}{3}$ three-factor interactions, and so on, the total being

$$s+\binom{s}{2}(q-1)+\binom{s}{3}(q-1)^2+...+(q-1)^{s-1} = (q^s-1)/(q-1).$$

The columns are labelled by the q^s treatment combinations of these factors, namely $\{e_1^{r_1} e_2^{r_2} \dots e_s^{r_s}\}$. Any effect $E_1^{q_1} E_2^{q_2} \dots E_s^{q_s}$ divides the treatment combinations into q sets according to the q different symbols in the corresponding row; and it is estimated by orthogonal contrasts of the totals of the observations from each set. From the viewpoint of estimation, interactions are on the same footing as main effects, and for convenience in terminology, we shall refer to the symbols in any row $E_1^{q_1} E_2^{q_2} \dots E_s^{q_s}$ as the levels of this effect.

TABLE 17. *Main effects and interactions of three factors at three levels each*

A	000	000	000	111	111	111	222	222	222
B	000	111	222	000	111	222	000	111	222
C	012	012	012	012	012	012	012	012	012
AB	000	111	222	111	222	000	222	000	111
AB^2	000	222	111	111	000	222	222	111	000
BC	012	120	201	012	120	201	012	120	201
BC^2	021	102	210	021	102	210	021	102	210
CA	012	012	012	120	120	120	201	201	201
CA^2	012	012	012	201	201	201	120	120	120
ABC	012	120	201	120	201	012	201	012	120
ABC^2	021	102	210	102	210	021	210	021	102
AB^2C	012	201	120	120	012	201	201	120	012
AB^2C^2	021	210	102	102	021	210	210	102	021

8.6. Confounding

We can estimate all the main effects and interactions of u factors at q levels each by testing once every possible treatment combination —this is termed a q^u factorial experiment. An estimate of the experimental error can be obtained either by replicating the design—so that each treatment combination appears d times ($d \geqslant 2$)—or by regarding interactions which involve many factors as negligible, in which case the relevant columns of an array $O_2(q^u)$ each provide $(q-1)$ degrees of freedom towards the sum of squared residuals. Practical limitations may compel the treatment combinations of a complete factorial experiment to be subdivided into q^{u-v} sets of q^v; each set forms a possible fractional replicate, the observations on which are made under uniform conditions. However, conditions may vary from one set to another, so that we can regard the treatment combinations of a set as being further combined with some particular level of an additional factor, which is termed blocks, and which appears at q^{u-v} levels. We assume that this extra factor does not interact with any of those already present. Table 18 shows an example with $q = u = 3$ and $v = 1$.

TABLE 18. *A 3^3 design subdivided into 3^2 blocks of 3*

	Block 1			Block 2			Block 3			Block 4			Block 5			Block 6			Block 7			Block 8			Block 9		
A	0	1	2	0	1	2	0	1	2	0	1	2	0	1	2	0	1	2	0	1	2	0	1	2	0	1	2
B	0	2	1	0	2	1	0	2	1	1	0	2	1	0	2	1	0	2	2	1	0	2	1	0	2	1	0
C	0	1	2	1	2	0	2	0	1	0	1	2	1	2	0	2	0	1	0	1	2	1	2	0	2	0	1

This represents the experimental design, the treatment combinations being given by the 27 columns. The levels of AB, AC^2, BC, and AB^2C in the 9 blocks are in Table 19.

TABLE 19. *Interaction levels for the design of Table 18*

	Block 1			Block 2			Block 3			Block 4			Block 5			Block 6			Block 7			Block 8			Block 9		
AB	0	0	0	0	0	0	0	0	0	1	1	1	1	1	1	1	1	1	2	2	2	2	2	2	2	2	2
AC^2	0	0	0	2	2	2	1	1	1	0	0	0	2	2	2	1	1	1	0	0	0	2	2	2	1	1	1
BC	0	0	0	1	1	1	2	2	2	1	1	1	2	2	2	0	0	0	2	2	2	0	0	0	1	1	1
AB^2C	0	0	0	1	1	1	2	2	2	2	2	2	0	0	0	1	1	1	1	1	1	2	2	2	0	0	0

These interactions are therefore estimated by contrasts between block totals and we say that they are *confounded* with blocks, since we are unable to distinguish between them and the main effect of the factor blocks.

We now examine the relation between the subdivision of treatment combinations used, and the structure of the effects confounded with blocks, in the particular case when each factor appears at $q = p^m$ levels, where p is prime (Bose and Kishen, 1940; Fisher, 1942, 1945, 1951). As noted in Section 4, the treatment combinations of u factors $F_1, F_2, ..., F_u$ at q levels each can be represented by the elements $\{f_1^{x_1} f_2^{x_2} ... f_u^{x_u}\}$ of an Abelian group J of order p^{mu}. Similarly, the effects of these factors, acting singly or in combination, correspond to the elements $\{F_1^{i_1} F_2^{i_2} ... F_u^{i_u}\}$ of a group K, which is isomorphic with J. All effects are at level zero in the control ($f_1^0 f_2^0 ... f_u^0$) and any confounded effect $F_1^{i_1} F_2^{i_2} ... F_u^{i_u}$ is therefore at level zero throughout the block containing the control. Hence, if $f_1^{x_1} f_2^{x_2} ... f_u^{x_u}$ and $f_1^{y_1} f_2^{y_2} ... f_u^{y_u}$ are any two treatment combinations in this block,

$$i_1 x_1 + i_2 x_2 + ... + i_u x_u = 0, \tag{1}$$

and

$$i_1 y_1 + i_2 y_2 + ... + i_u y_u = 0,$$

giving

$$i_1(x_1 + y_1) + i_2(x_2 + y_2) + ... + i_u(x_u + y_u) = 0.$$

This means that the set of treatment combinations, in which all confounded interactions are at level zero, is closed with respect to multiplication and consequently forms a subgroup of J, which we denote by Y. All the treatment combinations of Y occupy the same block and they form the *intrablock* subgroup. If $f_1^{c_1} f_2^{c_2} \dots f_u^{c_u}$ and $f_1^{d_1} f_2^{d_2} \dots f_u^{d_u}$ both occupy another block, throughout which $F_1^{i_1} F_2^{i_2} \dots F_u^{i_u}$ is at level w, then

$$c_1 i_1 + c_2 i_2 + \dots + c_u i_u = w,$$

and

$$d_1 i_1 + d_2 i_2 + \dots + d_u i_u = w,$$

giving

$$i_1(c_1 - d_1) + i_2(c_2 - d_2) + \dots + i_u(c_u - d_u) = 0.$$

Hence $f_1^{c_1-d_1} f_2^{c_2-d_2} \dots f_u^{c_u-d_u}$ is a member of the intrablock subgroup so that we obtain the set of treatment combinations in the same block as $f_1^{c_1} f_2^{c_2} \dots f_u^{c_u}$ on multiplying $f_1^{c_1} f_2^{c_2} \dots f_u^{c_u}$ by each element of Y. In the above example, block 1 contains the intrablock subgroup, consisting of *1*, ab^2c, and a^2bc^2. To construct the remaining blocks, we multiply successively by c, c^2, b, bc, bc^2, b^2, b^2c, and b^2c^2.

By identical reasoning, the set of effects, which are confounded with blocks, forms a subgroup of K, denoted by W. The order of W is found as follows. Since each block contains q^v treatment combinations, this is the order of Y, which can therefore be generated by v elements of J, none of which is contained in the subgroup generated by the remaining $(v-1)$. Hence we arrive at v linearly independent equations of the form (1), from which to determine $i_1, i_2, \dots, i_u$; on noting that $(u-v)$ of the unknowns can be given arbitrary values from $GF(q)$, we see that the number of solutions is q^{u-v}, which is the order of W. The elements of W, excluding I, are thus associated with the $q^{u-v}-1$ degrees of freedom available for contrasts between block totals. Since the design matrix is orthogonal, the remaining effects must be estimated from contrasts within blocks, and are unconfounded; every block supplies (q^v-1) contrasts and the number of parameters obtained in this way is

$$q^{u-v}(q^v - 1) = q^u - q^{u-v},$$

equal to the number of elements in $(K-W)$. In our example, each member $A^{i_1} B^{i_2} C^{i_3}$ of W is such that

$$i_1 + 2i_2 + i_3 = 0,$$

whence

$$W = (I, AB, A^2B^2, AC^2, A^2C, BC, B^2C^2, A^2BC^2, AB^2C).$$

The unconfounded effects are

$$A, A^2, B, B^2, C, C^2; \quad AB^2, A^2B, AC^2, A^2C, BC^2, B^2C;$$

and $\quad ABC, A^2B^2C^2, ABC^2, A^2B^2C, AB^2C^2, A^2BC.$

We summarize the significance of equation (1) by describing $f_1^{x_1} f_2^{x_2} \dots f_u^{x_u}$ and $F_1^{i_1} F_2^{i_2} \dots F_u^{i_u}$ as *orthogonal*; and the subgroups Y and W as *completely orthogonal*.

8.7. Orthogonal arrays in confounding

Suppose that we select from the group J of q^u treatment combinations the subgroup U of q^s treatment combinations formed by the columns of $O_2(q^s)$ and take U for the intrablock subgroup. The factors thus correspond to elements of G which identify different cyclic subgroups, say

$$F_1 = E_1^{g_1} E_2^{g_2} \dots E_s^{g_s},$$
$$F_2 = E_1^{h_1} E_2^{h_2} \dots E_s^{h_s},$$
$$\cdot \quad \cdot \quad \cdot \quad \cdot$$

and $\quad F_u = E_1^{i_1} E_2^{i_2} \dots E_s^{i_s}.$

Any confounded effect $F_1^{j_1} F_2^{j_2} \dots F_u^{j_u}$ now has the property that its representation in G reduces to the identity:

$$(E_1^{g_1} E_2^{g_2} \dots E_s^{g_s})^{j_1} (E_1^{h_1} E_2^{h_2} \dots E_s^{h_s})^{j_2} \dots (E_1^{i_1} E_2^{i_2} \dots E_s^{i_s})^{j_u} = I. \tag{1}$$

Equivalently,

$$\left. \begin{aligned} g_1 j_1 + h_1 j_2 + \dots + i_1 j_u &= 0 \\ g_2 j_1 + h_2 j_2 + \dots + i_2 j_u &= 0 \\ \cdot \quad \cdot \quad \cdot \quad \cdot \quad \cdot \quad \cdot \\ g_s j_1 + h_s j_2 + \dots + i_s j_u &= 0 \end{aligned} \right\}. \tag{2}$$

and

In fact, $F_1^{j_1} F_2^{j_2} \dots F_u^{j_u}$ is confounded if, for all $\{v_1, v_2, \dots, v_s\}$,

$$j_1(v_1 g_1 + v_2 g_2 + \dots + v_s g_s) + \dots + j_u(v_1 i_1 + v_2 i_2 + \dots + v_s i_s) = 0,$$

or $\quad v_1(g_1 j_1 + h_1 j_2 + \dots + i_1 j_u) + \dots + v_s(g_s j_1 + h_s j_2 + \dots + i_s j_u) = 0. \tag{3}$

There are q^s possible combinations $\{v_1, v_2, \dots, v_s\}$. The matrix, of which they form the rows, has rank s, so that (2) is the only solution of the system represented by (3). This proves the result stated.

Example. Let an array $O_2(3^2)$ constitute an intrablock subgroup for four factors A, B, C, and D at three levels each.

A		0	0	0	1	1	1	2	2	2
B		0	1	2	0	1	2	0	1	2
$C = AB$		0	1	2	1	2	0	2	0	1
$D = AB^2$		0	2	1	1	0	2	2	1	0

The interaction AB^2D^2 is confounded because

$$(A)(B)^2(AB^2)^2 = I;$$

whereas AC^2D^2 is unconfounded because

$$(A)(AB)^2(AB^2)^2 = A^2.$$

Another consequence of taking U for the intrablock subgroup is that no interaction involving less than three factors is confounded, since, for any pair of factors, all combinations of levels appear with equal frequency, so that main effects and two-factor interactions are estimated by contrasts within blocks.

When the row corresponding to the factor F_1 is omitted from an $O_2(q^s)$, the array is still an orthogonal array of strength two, and the treatment combinations it represents again form a subgroup of the group of all treatment combinations, which—since there remain $(u-1)$ factors—now has order q^{u-1}. The new array is therefore a permissible intrablock subgroup of order q^s. The subgroup of confounded interactions has order q^{u-1-s} and can be obtained by deleting from W all interactions involving $F_1^{i_1}$ ($i_1 \neq 0$). This is because the elements of W involving F_1^0 form the subgroup of effects $\{F_2^{i_2} \ldots F_u^{i_u}\}$ which are orthogonal to every $\{f_2^{x_2} \ldots f_u^{x_u}\}$ in the new intrablock subgroup. Similar adjustments are made when further factors $F_2, F_3, \ldots$ are omitted; and in all cases, confounded interactions reduce to the identity in G. In the preceding example the indices of confounded interactions form an array identical with the one given, so that

$$W = (I, BCD^2, B^2C^2D, ACD, ABC^2, AB^2D^2, A^2C^2D^2, A^2BD, A^2B^2C).$$

Hence, when only B, C, and D take part, the confounded interactions become I, BCD^2, and B^2C^2D.

We are now in a position to reconsider fractional replication (Finney, 1945; Kempthorne, 1947). Suppose that an intrablock subgroup is formed by retaining any v ($< u$) rows of $O_2(q^s)$ and that it constitutes the entirety of treatment combinations used in an experiment. All the q^{v-s} elements in the subgroup of confounded effects, X, are then indistinguishable from one another since there is now only one block, throughout which they all appear at level zero. Moreover, whenever an effect E is at level w, so is every member of EX, and we say that every effect has $q^{v-s}-1$ *aliases*. For example, take $q = 4$, $s = 2$, and $v = 3$. A possible fractional replicate is obtained by using rows A, B, and AB^σ of the array $O_2(4^2)$ constructed in Section 4. Denote AB^σ by C.

A	0	0	0	0	1	1	1	1	σ	σ	σ	σ	τ	τ	τ	τ
B	0	1	σ	τ	0	1	σ	τ	0	1	σ	τ	0	1	σ	τ
C	0	σ	τ	1	1	τ	σ	0	σ	0	1	τ	τ	1	0	σ

This subgroup of treatment combinations is generated by bc^σ and ac, so that any interaction $A^{i_1} B^{i_2} C^{i_3}$ in X must satisfy

$$i_2 + \sigma i_3 = 0$$

and

$$i_1 + i_3 = 0.$$

A solution is $AB^\sigma C$ and it generates

$$X = (I,\ AB^\sigma C,\ A^\sigma B^\tau C^\sigma,\ A^\tau BC^\tau).$$

These effects cannot be identified, and similarly

$$AC = B^\sigma = A^\tau B^\tau C^\tau = A^\sigma BC^\sigma,$$

on multiplying the elements of X by AC.

The disadvantage of using an $O_2(q^s)$ for the purposes of fractional replication is that main effects are confounded with two-factor interactions, which are likely to be of the same order of magnitude in many practical situations. Suppose that we can construct a factorial array for k factors, each at q levels, using q^s treatment combinations, with the property that each set of t rows contains all possible combinations of levels with the same frequency, q^{s-t}. The result is denoted by (q^s, k, q, t) and described as an orthogonal array of strength t, size q^s, with k constraints at q levels. This array can be used to provide a fractional replicate in which no main effect is confounded with an interaction involving less than t factors, no two-factor interaction with one involving less than $(t-1)$ factors,..., the general rule being that no two interactions are confounded if the total number of factors which they involve is less than $t+1$. If, in addition, the treatment combinations of the array form a subgroup, they can supply the generating block of a design, where the q^k possible combinations are divided into blocks of q^s, such that no interaction involving less than $t+1$ factors is confounded.

Further methods of constructing orthogonal arrays, and inequalities concerning the maximum number of factors which can be accommodated in them, are given by Bose (1947), Rao (1947), and Bose and Bush (1952). Tables published by the National Bureau of Standards

(1957) enumerate fractional replicates of 2^k factorial experiments in which all main effects and the maximum number of two-factor interactions are confounded with interactions of three or more factors.

8.8. Exercises

1. A factorial experiment involves three factors, F_1, F_2 and, F_3, at q_1, q_2, and q_3 levels respectively. Prove that the least number of treatment combinations for a factorial array which satisfies (2.13) is $q_1 q_2 q_3/h$, where h is the highest common factor of q_1, q_2, and q_3. Prove also that the corresponding array can always be constructed, and give one for $q_1 = 3$, $q_2 = q_3 = 6$.

2. A design for weighing p objects in n operations on a spring balance is defined by an $n \times p$ matrix A, whose rows refer to operations and columns to objects. If the jth object is included in the rth operation, then $a_{rj} = 1$; otherwise $a_{rj} = 0$. The *most efficient* design is the one which minimizes $|(A'A)^{-1}|$. Prove that when $n = p = 3$, the most efficient design is

$$X = \begin{bmatrix} 1 & 1 & 0 \\ 1 & 0 & 1 \\ 0 & 1 & 1 \end{bmatrix}.$$

When $n = 3t$ and $p = 3$, show that the most efficient design is obtained by repeating each row of X t times, and that the variance of each estimated weight is then $9\sigma^2/4n$, on the usual assumption that $\mathcal{D}y = \sigma^2 I$. (Mood, 1946.)

3. A complete factorial experiment for 3 factors, each at 2 levels, is replicated 3 times, and the treatment combinations are subdivided into the 6 blocks below.

abc	ab	abc	ab	abc	ab
a	bc	ac	bc	bc	ac
b	ca	b	a	a	b
c	1	1	c	1	c

Verify that ABC, AC, and BC can be estimated from comparisons within blocks, and show that the variance of the estimates is $1\frac{1}{2}$ times what it is for A, B, C, and AB. (Cochran and Cox, 1957.)

4. The treatment combinations of 5 factors, A, B, C, D, E, each at two levels, are arranged in an 8×8 square, each treatment combination appearing twice. Find an arrangement such that ABC, ADE, and $BCDE$ are confounded with the first four rows; ABD, BCE, and $ACDE$ with the second four rows; ACE, BCD, and $ABDE$ with the first four columns; and ACD, BDE, and $ABCE$ with the second four columns. (Yates, 1937.)

5. A Latin square is used to provide an experimental design for three factors, namely rows, columns, and treatments, each of which appears at q levels. The observation y_{uvw} on the treatment combination of the uth row, vth column, and wth treatment is missing. Distinguish by a prime the values of sums in which the missing observation is replaced by zero; for example, y_{u00} becomes y'_{u00}. Show that the sum of squared residuals can be calculated in the usual way provided that the missing observation is replaced by

$$\{q(y'_{u00} + y'_{0v0} + y'_{00w}) - 2y'_{000}\}/(q-1)(q-2).$$

Prove also that if the sum of squares for treatments is calculated using the fictitious observation on the same footing as the actual data, then the resulting value exceeds the correct sum of squares by

$$\{y'_{u00}+y'_{0v0}+y'_{00w}(q-1)-y'_{000}\}^2/(q-1)^2(q-2)^2.$$

6. For the orthogonal array $(n, k, q, 2t)$, show that an upper limit to k is given by

$$n \geqslant \sum_{j=0}^{t} \binom{k}{j}(q-1)^j;$$

and that the corresponding inequality for $(n, k, q, 2t+1)$ is

$$n \geqslant \sum_{j=0}^{t} \binom{k}{j}(q-1)^j+\binom{k-1}{t}(q-1)^{t+1}. \qquad \text{(Rao, 1947.)}$$

7. Show that a method of constructing the array $(2^r, 2^{r-1}, 2, 3)$ consists in labelling the rows by the factors $F_1, F_2, \ldots, F_r$ and by all the interactions of an odd number of factors. Prove that 2^{r-1} is the maximum possible number of rows. (Bose, 1947; Rao, 1947.)

8. Two columns of an orthogonal array are said to have i coincidences if there are exactly i rows where the symbols in the two columns are the same. Let n_i be the number of columns, other than the first, which have i coincidences with the first column. By considering the different possible sets of h rows of $(\lambda q^t, k, q, t)$ show that

$$\sum_{i=0}^{k} n_i\binom{i}{h} = \binom{k}{h}(\lambda q^{t-h}-1) \quad (1 \leqslant h \leqslant t).$$

$$\text{(Bose and Bush, 1952.)}$$

9. Show that every column of $O_2(q^s)$ contains $(q^{s-1}-1)/(q-1)$ zeros; and that every pair of columns has $(q^{s-1}-1)/(q-1)$ coincidences.

10. A factorial array is constructed by the following method. Using $x, v_1, v_2, \ldots, v_s$ to denote quantities which range independently over the marks of $GF(q)$, where $q > s$, the symbol

$$c(x) = v_1 x^{s-1}+v_2 x^{s-2}+\ldots+v_{s-1} x+v_s$$

is inserted in the row labelled x and the column labelled $(v_1, v_2, \ldots, v_s)$. This gives q rows and q^s columns. A $(q+1)$th row is added by assigning v_1 to those columns where $c(x)$ begins with $v_1 x^{s-1}$. Prove that the result is $(q^s, q+1, q, s)$.

When $s = 3$ and $q = 2^m$, prove that a $(q+2)$th row can be added by assigning v_2 to those columns where $c(x)$ contains the term $v_2 x$. (Bush, 1952.)

8.9. References

AITKEN, A. C. (1951). *Determinants and Matrices*, seventh edition. Edinburgh: Oliver and Boyd.

BOSE, R. C. (1938). On the application of the properties of Galois fields to the construction of hyper-Graeco-Latin squares. *Sankhyā*, **3**, 323–38.

—— (1947). Mathematical theory of the symmetrical factorial design. *Sankhyā*, **8**, 107–66.

BOSE, R. C., and BUSH, K. A. (1952). Orthogonal arrays of strength two and three. *Ann. Math. Statist.* **23**, 508–24.

—— and KISHEN, K. (1940). On the problem of confounding in the general symmetrical factorial design. *Sankhyā*, **5**, 21–36.

BUSH, K. A. (1952). Orthogonal arrays of index unity. *Ann. Math. Statist.* **23**, 426–34.

CARMICHAEL, R. D. (1937). *Introduction to the Theory of Groups of Finite Order.* Boston: Ginn.

COCHRAN, W. G., and COX, G. M. (1957). *Experimental Designs,* second edition New York: Wiley.

FINNEY, D. J. (1945). The fractional replication of factorial arrangements. *Ann. Eugen. Lond.* **12**, 291–301; (1950) Correction. ibid. **15**, 276.

FISHER, R. A. (1942). The theory of confounding in factorial experiments in relation to the theory of groups. *Ann. Eugen. Lond.* **11**, 341–53.

—— (1945). A system of confounding for factors with more than two alternatives, giving completely orthogonal cubes and higher powers. *Ann. Eugen. Lond.* **12**, 283–90.

—— (1951). *The Design of Experiments,* sixth edition. Edinburgh: Oliver and Boyd.

HOTELLING, H. (1944). Some improvements in weighing and other experimental techniques. *Ann. Math. Statist.* **15**, 297–306.

KEMPTHORNE, O. (1947). A simple approach to confounding and fractional replication in factorial experiments. *Biometrika,* **34**, 255–72.

MOOD, A. M. (1946). On Hotelling's weighing problem. *Ann. Math. Statist.* **17**, 432–46.

NATIONAL BUREAU OF STANDARDS (1957). *Fractional Factorial Experiment Designs for Factors at Two Levels.* Appl. Math. Ser. **48**: U.S. Govt. Printing Office.

PLACKETT, R. L. (1946). Some generalizations in the multifactorial design. *Biometrika,* **33**, 328–32.

—— and BURMAN, J. P. (1946). The design of optimum multifactorial experiments. *Biometrika,* **33**, 305–25.

RAO, C. R. (1946). Hypercubes of strength '*d*' leading to confounded designs in factorial experiments. *Bull. Calcutta Math. Soc.* **38**, 67–78.

—— (1947). Factorial experiments derivable from combinatorial arrangements of arrays. *Suppl. J. R. Statist. Soc.* **9**, 128–39.

STEVENS, W. L. (1939). The completely orthogonalized Latin square. *Ann. Eugen. Lond.* **9**, 82–93.

YATES, F. (1937). *The Design and Analysis of Factorial Experiments.* Imp. Bur. Soil Sci. Tech. Comm. **35**.

RANDOMIZATION

9.1. Introduction

MANY of the preceding Chapters are concerned with an experimental situation in which the observations have the same variance and are uncorrelated. These conditions, and particularly the second, may not be fulfilled in practice. They will fail to hold when observations are made successively in time and the error process is generated by a stochastic model of the form described in Chapter 7. They also fail to hold in agricultural experiments, where the observations consist of yields from plots of land, because the plots tend to be grouped in small blocks so as to diminish the effects of varying fertility, and the yields from neighbouring plots are correlated. The methods of Chapter 7, or two-dimensional generalizations of them, may be applicable to describe the correlation structure of plot yields, but in what follows we discuss another method of dealing with the difficulty. This takes account of the fact that the treatment combinations can usually be allocated to the plots in a large number of ways, and we proceed by choosing the actual allocation at random from a class of potential allocations. The technique is known as *randomization* and was introduced by Fisher (1925, 1926). We shall see that if it is suitably carried out then some of the most important features of the standard least-squares analysis are preserved. Since the applications are not confined to agricultural experiments, we shall subsequently refer to experimental units rather than plots.

9.2. Some permutable designs

Suppose that we wish to compare the effects of t different treatments. Possible methods of experimental procedure are as follows.

Completely randomized design. There are n experimental units. The first treatment is applied to n_1 units, the second to n_2 units,..., and the tth to n_t units, where $n_1+n_2+...+n_t = n$. Subject to this condition, treatments are allocated to units at random. The number of distinct arrangements is $n!/n_1! \, n_2! ... n_t!$

Randomized blocks. There are bt units, which are grouped in b

blocks, each containing t units. Each treatment appears once in each block, and the allocation of treatments to units is random within a block. The number of distinct arrangements is now $(t!)^b$.

Latin square. There are t^2 units, and they are arranged in a $t \times t$ square array. Designate the treatments by Latin letters. Each letter appears once in every row and once in every column of the square. A standard square is one where the letters in the first row and column are in alphabetical order, as in the 5×5 square below.

$$
\begin{matrix}
A & B & C & D & E \\
B & A & E & C & D \\
C & D & A & E & B \\
D & E & B & A & C \\
E & C & D & B & A
\end{matrix}
$$

The allocation of treatments to units can be made in several ways:

(i) Take a standard square and randomize all its rows, except the first, and all its columns, giving a total of $t!(t-1)!$ possible squares.

(ii) Take a standard square and randomize rows, columns, and letters. There are $(t!)^3$ possible squares, of which $t.t!$ are standard, but they are not necessarily all different.

(iii) Take a square at random from the class of all standard $t \times t$ squares and then proceed as in (i). This is possible only for $t \leqslant 7$, since no complete enumeration of squares has been made for higher values of t.

Latin squares are tabulated and discussed in detail by Fisher and Yates (1953).

In general, if C is a specified class of m acceptable designs, the actual design used is chosen from C by any method which satisfies the experimenter that all selections have the same probability.

9.3. Permutation distributions

Denote by d the experimental design actually chosen from the specified class of acceptable designs. When the observations resulting from d are available, let z be any quantity which compares the effects of different treatments.

Example 1. Suppose that the experimental units of a completely randomized design are arranged in some definite order. Let v_{ij} be the observation from the unit where treatment i appears for the jth time. A possible z is

$$\text{centre}\{v_{1j}\} - \text{centre}\{v_{2k}\},$$

where the centre of a sample is defined as half the sum of its largest and smallest members.

Example 2. Let v_{ij} be the observation from the ith treatment in the jth block of a randomized block experiment. A possible z is

$$\sum_i \left(\sum_j v_{ij}\right)^2 \Big/ b - \left(\sum_i \sum_j v_{ij}\right)^2 \Big/ bt,$$

i.e. the sum of squares between treatments.

If all treatments act alike, the observation on any unit would be the same whatever the treatment which is applied to that unit, and we can therefore compute from a given set of observations what value of z would have been obtained had we used another design d' instead of d. Let x be the vector whose elements $x_1, x_2, ..., x_n$ are the observations written in an order which depends on a fixed design d^*, in the same way that the order in the examples above depends on d. If we express the value of z corresponding to d^* as a function $z(x)$, then the value of z corresponding to d is $z(y)$, where the elements $y_1, y_2, ..., y_n$ of y form a permutation of $x_1, x_2, ..., x_n$. In our examples, the set of permutations carrying x into y forms a group, G, and is therefore independent of d^*, because a finite group is reproduced when all its elements are multiplied by the inverse of any one of them.

Denote the values of $z(y)$ corresponding to the m designs in C by $z_1, z_2, ..., z_m$—they are not necessarily all different. Since d is chosen at random, $z(y)$ is a random variable whose probability distribution, conditional on x and C, is defined by assigning a probability of $1/m$ to each of the values $z_1, z_2, ..., z_m$, or the appropriate multiple of $1/m$ when several values coincide. This *permutation distribution*, as it is called, can alternatively be regarded as the distribution of $z(gx)$, where g is selected at random from G and gx is the vector which results when the permutation g is applied to the vector x.

Permutation distributions were introduced by Fisher (1935 a). They can be generalized to the situation where treatment differences exist provided that we make some assumption about the structure of $y_1, y_2, ..., y_n$, as for example that the observation from the ith treatment on the kth unit takes the form $\theta_i + u_k$. The study of linear models which include, in addition, interactions between treatments and units, was initiated by Neyman *et al.* (1935) and has been pursued by Wilk and Kempthorne (e.g. 1957).

9.4. Properties of permutation distributions

When m is small, we can enumerate the values taken by a function $z(y)$ in its permutation distribution for given x and C; but m is usually very large, and enumeration is then impracticable. In such cases, we look for an approximate distribution, and the problem of supplying one has been approached by evaluating moments, and by experimental sampling.

As an illustration of the first approach, consider a randomized block experiment with two treatments. We shall find the mean and variance, over the class of all designs, of

$$W(y) = S/(R+S),$$

where S is the sum of squares between treatments and R the sum of squared residuals. W is simpler to handle than the variance-ratio, here $(b-1)W/(1-W)$, because its denominator is invariant under permutations of the observations within blocks. Each block provides two observations, and if the treatments act alike, then the observed difference h between the observation on treatment A and that on treatment B might with equal probability have been $-h$. Thus the set of possible differences can be generated by associating plus or minus signs at random with each of the b given differences $h_1, h_2, ..., h_b$. Under these conditions the jth difference a_j is a random variable which takes the values $\pm h_j$, each with probability $\frac{1}{2}$. Its characteristic function is

$$\mathcal{E} \exp(ita_j) = \tfrac{1}{2} \exp(ith_j) + \tfrac{1}{2} \exp(-ith_j) = \cos(th_j).$$

Hence the characteristic function of $\sum a_j$ is

$$\phi(t) = \prod_1^b \cos(th_j).$$

The odd moments of $\sum a_j$ vanish by symmetry. The even moments are obtained on expanding $\phi(t)$, which gives

$$\mu_2(\textstyle\sum a_j) = \sum h_j^2 \quad \text{and} \quad \mu_4(\textstyle\sum a_j) = -2\sum h_j^4 + 3(\sum h_j^2)^2.$$

Here
$$W = (\textstyle\sum a_j)^2 / b \sum h_j^2,$$

and we find that $\mathcal{E}_P W = 1/b$ and $\mathcal{V}_P W = 2\{1 - \sum h_j^4/(\sum h_j^2)^2\}/b^2$, where the suffix P indicates that these are permutation moments. On the other hand, when $a_1, a_2, ..., a_b$ have a normal distribution, W

is a $B\{\tfrac{1}{2}, \tfrac{1}{2}(b-1)\}$ variable with

$$\mathscr{E}_N W = 1/b \quad \text{and} \quad \mathscr{V}_N W = 2(b-1)/b^2(b+2),$$

where the suffix again refers to the parent distribution. Thus the permutation mean of W is the same as the normal mean. The permutation variance can range from 0 to $2(b-1)/b^3$; the lower limit is attained when all the $\{h_j\}$ are zero, except one, and the upper limit when all the $\{h_j\}$ are equal. These results were given by Bartlett (1935).

The corresponding generalization to t treatments was made by Welch (1937) and Pitman (1938). They showed that the permutation mean of W is the same as the normal mean, namely $1/b$; but that the permutation variance may range from 0 to $2(b-1)/b^3(t-1)$, whereas the normal variance is $2(b-1)/b^2(bt-b+2)$. Pitman also examined the third and fourth moments of W, and found that if the permutation distribution is approximated by a beta distribution having the same mean and variance, then the third and fourth moments of the two distributions agree well provided that the variance is not too small. Of course, the permutation distribution is discrete, and its representation by a continuous function can at best be approximate, but these results suggest that a beta distribution with the same mean and variance is likely to provide a reasonable fit. Further evidence on the nature of the permutation distribution in any given problem can be supplied by experimental sampling. An example is given by Eden and Yates (1933), whose data consisted of 256 height measurements of wheat. The data were arranged in 8 blocks of 4 values (each value being the sum of 8 measurements) and a sample of 1,000 arrangements was taken from the $(4!)^8$ possible arrangements. This sample of the permutation distribution conformed well with the predictions of normal theory, and in fact the permutation variance was $0 \cdot 0079$, close to the normal variance of $0 \cdot 0084$.

Suppose that x is a random vector variable. The distribution of $z(y)$ for given C is then obtained by integrating over all x its permutation distribution for given x and C. In particular, the mean and variance of $z(y)$ are

$$\mathscr{E}z(y) = \mathscr{E}\{\mathscr{E}_P z(y)\} \quad \text{and} \quad \mathscr{V}z(y) = \mathscr{E}\{\mathscr{V}_P z(y)\} + \mathscr{V}\{\mathscr{E}_P z(y)\}.$$

Thus, in a randomized block experiment with two treatments, $\mathscr{E}_P W = 1/b$ is independent of x and therefore

$$\mathscr{V}W = 2\{1 - \mathscr{E}[\textstyle\sum h_j^4/(\sum h_j^2)^2]\}/b^2.$$

Again, $z(x)$ is itself a random variable, defined over the set of possible results for a specified design in C. The probability distribution of $z(x)$ will generally differ from that of $z(y)$ but the two are identical if the probability distribution of x is invariant under the group of permutations on x induced by the experimental designs in C. This condition is satisfied, for example, when the observations are mutually independent, and have identical distributions. Under these circumstances, the moments of $W(y)$ are also those of $W(x)$; and the adequacy—for most values of x—of approximating to the conditional distribution of $W(y)$ by a beta distribution with the same mean and variance suggests that we can also apply this technique to the distribution of $W(x)$. Box and Andersen (1955) fitted a beta distribution to $W(x)$ when x is a random sample from a population of Edgeworth type; and their values for the probability of exceeding the nominal 5 per cent point are in good agreement with the results of Gayen (1950), who used the entirely different approach outlined in Section 5.3.

9.5. Validity of randomization schemes

Two criteria have been proposed, whereby the adequacy of any scheme of randomization can be assessed.

(1) We require that the expectations, under randomization, of the treatment and residual mean squares shall be equal. (Fisher, 1925.)

(2) Let c_1, c_2 be any pair of linear contrasts of treatment effects; they may be identical. On the assumption that the dispersion matrix of the observations is $\sigma^2 I$, the covariance of c_1 and c_2 is $b\sigma^2$; and, under randomization, their covariance is $b'\epsilon$, where ϵ is the expectation of the residual mean square. We require that $b = b'$. (Grundy and Healy, 1950.)

The second criterion implies the first, because the expectation of the treatment mean square is determined by the dispersion matrix of a set of independent linear contrasts; and since the reverse is not true, the second criterion is stronger.

We shall discuss the conditions under which criterion (2) is satisfied with particular reference to a randomized block experiment. First of all, let C be the class of all possible designs, with $(t!)^b$ members. In order to establish that (2) then holds, we note that both the treatment contrasts and the sum of squared residuals are built up from contrasts within blocks. In the jth block, let $y_1, y_2, ..., y_t$ be the observations on treatments $1, 2, ..., t$ respectively. Under randomization, all permutations of the observations $x_1, x_2, ..., x_t$, corresponding to d^*, are equally likely to be observed, so that each y_r has the same variance, say σ_j^2; and every pair (y_r, y_s) has the same correlation coefficient, say ρ_j. A complete set of contrasts within this block is Ly, where y is the vector of observations, and L is any $(t-1) \times t$ matrix, with rank $(t-1)$, such that $L1 = 0$. Under these conditions,

$$\mathscr{D}y = \sigma_j^2\{(1-\rho_j)I+\rho_j 11'\},$$

and hence

$$\mathscr{D}Ly = \sigma_j^2 L\{(1-\rho_j)I+\rho_j 11'\}L' = \sigma_j^2(1-\rho_j)LL'.$$

We can therefore proceed as if every observation in the jth block had a variance of $\sigma_j^2(1-\rho_j)$, and any two observations whatever were uncorrelated. On substituting these results in the usual formulae, we find that criterion (2) is satisfied with $\epsilon = \sum \sigma_j^2(1-\rho_j)/b$. We have already seen in the previous Section that (1) is satisfied.

When treatment differences exist, suppose that the result of applying the ith treatment to the kth unit is $\theta_i + u_k$. An adequate scheme of randomization then has the following consequences.

(3) The standard least-squares estimate θ^* of any treatment contrast θ is such that $\mathscr{E}_P \theta^* = \theta$.

(4) $\mathscr{E}_P S \geqslant (t-1)\epsilon$, with equality if and only if all treatments act alike.

In the case of randomized blocks, the arguments already given readily extend to prove these properties.

The adequacy of randomization over the class of $(t!)^b$ designs is seen to rest on the fact that a pair of positions in any block is equally likely to be occupied by each pair of treatments. This object can be achieved by selecting the design at random from any class C in which the set of permutations of the t treatments in each block forms a doubly-transitive group, i.e. one which contains all permutations sending any ordered pair of treatments into any other ordered pair. The set of all permutations on t treatments is doubly-transitive; and so is the set of even permutations, which contains $\frac{1}{2}t!$ members. Furthermore, if t is a prime number, the following construction is available for a doubly-transitive group of permutations having degree t and order $t(t-1)$, which is the minimum order possible (Carmichael, 1937, § 40). Denote the treatments by $0, 1, 2, ..., t-1$ and let the cyclic permutations J and K be defined by

$$J = (0, 1, 2, ..., t-1)$$

and
$$K = (1, \phi, \phi^2, ..., \phi^{t-2}),$$

where ϕ is any primitive root modulo t. Then the elements $J^r K^s$ $(r = 1, 2, ..., t; s = 1, 2, ..., t-1)$ form the group required. For example, take $t = 5$, in which case $\phi = 2$ is a primitive root because $2^0 = 1$, $2^1 = 2$, $2^2 = 4$, and $2^3 = 3$. We obtain the twenty permutations represented by the columns below.

```
0 0 0 0    4 3 1 2    3 1 2 4    2 4 3 1    1 2 4 3
1 2 4 3    0 0 0 0    4 3 1 2    3 1 2 4    2 4 3 1
2 4 3 1    1 2 4 3    0 0 0 0    4 3 1 2    3 1 2 4
3 1 2 4    2 4 3 1    1 2 4 3    0 0 0 0    4 3 1 2
4 3 1 2    3 1 2 4    2 4 3 1    1 2 4 3    0 0 0 0
```

When $t = 5$ and $b = 4$, we can therefore satisfy criterion (2) with a class of 160,000 designs in place of the 207,360,000 originally considered.

The choice of d is not usually restricted in a randomized block experiment, which was selected for a simple illustration of the theoretical principle involved. In more complex experiments, however, ordinary randomization may too often provide designs which are, in themselves, unsatisfactory arrangements (Yates, 1948; Grundy and Healy, 1950). Restricted randomization enables such designs to be excluded, although at the same time it necessarily excludes others which are perfectly admissible.

9.6. Permutation tests

Let w be a random vector variable of observations, which may result either from the use of a fixed design d^*, or from a random design d, both contained in the class C. Denote by T the assertion that all treatments act alike. We shall examine how far the value of w justifies T, which we do by embedding T in a statistical hypothesis $\mathfrak{h}$ and then testing $\mathfrak{h}$.

The customary procedure is to incorporate T in the hypothesis $\mathfrak{h}_N$, according to which the observations are normally and independently distributed with a common variance about means which are linear in parameters representing treatment effects. Thus, the joint density function of the observations on $\mathfrak{h}_N$ is

$$(2\pi\sigma^2)^{-\frac{1}{2}bt} \exp\left\{ -\sum_{i=1}^{t} \sum_{j=1}^{b} (v_{ij} - \beta_j)^2 / 2\sigma^2 \right\}$$

for a randomized block experiment with t treatments in each of b blocks, block effects being denoted by $\{\beta_j\}$.

Here, we incorporate T in the wider hypothesis $\mathfrak{h}_P$, according to which the probability distribution of w is invariant under the permutations in the group G, corresponding to the class C. If the design d^* is used, $\mathfrak{h}_P$ evidently covers a greater range of possible distributions than does $\mathfrak{h}_N$; and if d is used, then T implies $\mathfrak{h}_P$ whatever is the distribution of the observations before they are randomized.

We test $\mathfrak{h}_P$ by choosing a function $z(w)$ and referring its observed value to its permutation distribution for given w and C, large values of z being regarded as significant. The probability that the observed value is exceeded is taken into account in the usual intuitive way when assessing the evidence for or against $\mathfrak{h}_P$. Formally, let

$$z(w^1) \leqslant z(w^2) \leqslant \ldots \leqslant z(w^m)$$

be the m ordered values of $z(gw)$. If α is the chosen significance level, define
$$k = m - [m\alpha]$$

where $[m\alpha]$ is the largest integer less than or equal to $m\alpha$. Let $q(w)$ be the number of values of $z(gw)$ greater than $z(w^k)$; and $r(w)$ the number equal to $z(w^k)$. Define

$$a(w) = \{m\alpha - q(w)\}/r(w),$$

in which case $0 \leqslant a(w) < 1$. Denote by $\phi(w)$ the probability of rejecting $\mathfrak{h}_P$ when the observed vector is w, and define this function as follows:

$$\phi(w) = \begin{cases} 1 & \text{if } z(w) > z(w^k) \\ a(w) & \text{if } z(w) = z(w^k) \\ 0 & \text{if } z(w) < z(w^k). \end{cases}$$

For given w, the probability of rejecting $\mathfrak{h}_P$, when true, is the expectation of ϕ over the distribution of z, i.e.

$$\{q(w) + a(w)r(w)\}/m = \alpha.$$

When treatment differences are present, suppose that the distribution of w is specified by a probability density function $f(w)$, not invariant under the permutations of G. The power of a permutation test at this simple alternative to $\mathfrak{h}_P$ depends on the test function $z(w)$ which is employed, a point first made by Pearson (1937) in a sampling experiment. He took two rectangular distributions with different means, but the same spread, sampled both and formed permutation distributions for (a) the difference of sample means, (b) the difference of sample centres. When the process of sampling both distributions was repeated, the probability of exceeding the observed value of criterion (a) was invariably larger than the corresponding probability for criterion (b). This indicated the greater power of criterion (b) for the situation described.

In fact, a most powerful test of $\mathfrak{h}_P$ against f, at any assigned significance level, is obtained by taking $f(w)$ as the permutation test function. This result is due to Lehmann and Stein (1949) and an outline of their proof is as follows. Replace z by f throughout the formal definition of the test $\phi(w)$. The function $f(w^k)$ is invariant under the permutations of G, and is therefore proportional to a probability density function satisfying $\mathfrak{h}_P$. $\phi(w)$ is now seen to have the form of a likelihood-ratio test, and the proof is completed by using an adaptation of the fundamental lemma of Neyman and Pearson (Cramér, 1946, § 35.3). As an illustration, take a completely randomized design with two treatments, and suppose that the joint probability density function of the observations on the alternative to $\mathfrak{h}_P$ is given by

$$f(w) = (2\pi\sigma^2)^{-\frac{1}{2}n}\exp\Big\{-\sum_{j=1}^{n_1}(u_j-\theta)^2/2\sigma^2-\sum_{k=1}^{n_2}(v_k-\phi)^2/2\sigma^2\Big\},$$

where $\phi > \theta$. After a little manipulation,

$$f(w) = (2\pi\sigma^2)^{-\frac{1}{2}n}\exp[-\{\sum u_j^2+\sum v_k^2+n_1\theta^2+n_2\phi^2-$$
$$-2(\sum u_j+\sum v_k)(n_1\theta+n_2\phi)/(n_1+n_2)-$$
$$-2(\phi-\theta)(\bar{v}-\bar{u})(1/n_1+1/n_2)\}/2\sigma^2],$$

where $\bar{u}$, $\bar{v}$ are the sample means for treatments A and B respectively. Since $\sum u_j^2+\sum v_k^2$ and $\sum u_j+\sum v_k$ remain fixed when the observations are permuted, $f(w)$ is a strictly increasing function of $\bar{v}-\bar{u}$. Consequently, the criterion $z(w) = \bar{v}-\bar{u}$ defines the most powerful test of $\mathfrak{h}_P$ against f. This is also a valid test of the hypothesis $\mathfrak{h}_N$. The most powerful test of $\mathfrak{h}_N$ against f is the one-sided t-test, which is not, however, a valid test of $\mathfrak{h}_P$ and is, in fact, very sensitive to departures from normality, as noted in Section 5.2.

9.7. Exercises

1. Take a standard Latin square and randomize all its rows except the first. Show that every pair of units not in the same row or column receives like treatments with equal probability. If there are no differences between treatments, deduce that the treatment and residual mean squares have the same expectation. (Yates, 1933.)

2. When the following 5×5 Latin squares are superimposed on the same set of 25 observations, the sums of squares between treatments are respectively p, q, r, and s.

A	B	C	D	E		A	B	C	D	E		A	B	C	D	E		A	B	C	D	E

```
A B C D E     A B C D E     A B C D E     A B C D E
B C D E A     D E A B C     C D E A B     E A B C D
C D E A B     B C D E A     E A B C D     D E A B C
D E A B C     E A B C D     B C D E A     C D E A B
E A B C D     C D E A B     D E A B C     B C D E A
```

Prove that randomization of any square generates each sum of squares with probability $\frac{1}{4}$. If all treatments act alike, deduce that the treatment and residual mean squares both have expectation $(p+q+r+s)/16$. (Fisher, 1935 b.)

3. Show that ordinary randomization is valid for a Latin square with one row or one column or one treatment missing; or when a row and a column, a row and a treatment, or a column and a treatment, are missing. (Yates, 1936.)

4. In a completely randomized design with t treatments, denote the n observations by $x_1, x_2, ..., x_n$ and put
$$K_2 = \sum x_r^2/(n-1),$$
and
$$K_4 = \{n(n+1)\sum x_r^4 - 3(n-1)(\sum x_r^2)^2\}/(n-1)(n-2)(n-3).$$
Let $W = S/(R+S)$, where S is the sum of squares between treatments, and R the sum of squared residuals. Show that
$$\mathscr{E}_P W = (t-1)/(n-1),$$
and
$$\mathscr{V}_P W = \frac{2(t-1)(n-t)}{(n+1)(n-1)^2}\left\{1 - \frac{K_4}{nK_2^2}\right\} - \frac{K_4}{(n-1)^2 K_2^2}\left\{\frac{t^2}{n} - \sum \frac{1}{n_i}\right\}.$$
(Welch, 1938.)

5. In a randomized block experiment with two treatments, put
$$c_2 = (b+2)\{\sum h_j^4 - 3(\sum h_j^2)^2\}/(\sum h_j^2)^2.$$
Prove that

(i) $\mathscr{V}_P W = \mathscr{V}_N W\{1 - c_2/(b-1)\}$,

(ii) $c_2 = 0$ if $h_1 = h_2 = ... = h_{b-1} = h$ and
$$h_b^2 = h^2\{3 + \sqrt{(2b+4)}\}.$$

6. *Continuation.* Suppose that the observations are independent random variables with finite cumulants $\{\kappa_r\}$. Note that each h_j is the difference of two such observations, and expand the denominator of c_2 to show that
$$\mathscr{E}c_2 = \frac{1}{2}\gamma_2 - \frac{1}{4}(2\gamma_4 - 3\gamma_2^2 + 22\gamma_2)b^{-1} + O(b^{-2}),$$
where
$$\gamma_{r-2} = \kappa_r/(\kappa_2)^{\frac{1}{2}r}. \qquad \text{(Box and Andersen, 1955.)}$$

7. In this Exercise and the next, suppose that the result of applying the ith treatment to the kth unit is $\theta_i + u_k$; assume that $\sum \theta_i = \sum u_k = 0$; and put $T = \sum \theta_i^2$, $E = \sum u_k^2$. For a completely randomized design where t treatments each appear b times, show that
$$\mathscr{E}_P S = bT + (t-1)E/(bt-1)$$
and
$$\mathscr{E}_P R = t(b-1)E/(bt-1).$$

8. For a randomized block experiment with t treatments and b blocks, suppose in addition that M is the sum of squares of block totals, divided by t. Show that

$$\mathscr{E}_P S = bT + (E - M)/b$$

$$\mathscr{E}_P R = (b-1)(E - M)/b. \quad \text{(Cochran and Cox, 1957.)}$$

9. In a two-factor experiment, y_{ijk} is the kth observation on the treatment combination formed by the ith level of factor A, and the jth level of factor B. $(i = 1, 2,..., a; j = 1, 2,..., b; k = 1, 2,..., n.)$ Assume that

$$y_{ijk} = \mu + \alpha_i + \beta_j + \gamma_{ij} + e_{ijk},$$

where

$$\sum_i \alpha_i = \sum_j \beta_j = \sum_i \gamma_{ij} = \sum_j \gamma_{ij} = 0,$$

and the abn quantities $\{e_{ijk}\}$ are uncorrelated random variables with zero means and common variance σ^2. Put

$$\sigma_A^2 = \sum_i \alpha_i^2/(a-1),$$

$$\sigma_B^2 = \sum_j \beta_j^2/(b-1),$$

and

$$\sigma_{AB}^2 = \sum_i \sum_j \gamma_{ij}^2/(a-1)(b-1).$$

The analysis of variance is as follows, where a dot indicates an average over the suffix suppressed.

Hypothesis	Sum of squares	D.f.	Mean square
$\{\alpha_i\} = 0$	$S_A = bn \sum_i (y_{i..} - y_{...})^2$	$(a-1)$	MS_A
$\{\beta_j\} = 0$	$S_B = an \sum_j (y_{.j.} - y_{...})^2$	$(b-1)$	MS_B
$\{\gamma_{ij}\} = 0$	$S_{AB} = n \sum_i \sum_j (y_{ij.} - y_{i..} - y_{.j.} + y_{...})^2$	$(a-1)(b-1)$	MS_{AB}
	$R = \sum_i \sum_j \sum_k (y_{ijk} - y_{ij.})^2$	$ab(n-1)$	MR

Show that the expectations of the mean squares have the values given below.

Mean square	Expectation
MS_A	$bn\sigma_A^2 + \sigma^2$
MS_B	$an\sigma_B^2 + \sigma^2$
MS_{AB}	$n\sigma_{AB}^2 + \sigma^2$
MR	σ^2

(Scheffé, 1956.)

10. In a two-factor experiment the a levels of factor A are selected at random from $I = 1, 2,..., A$, and are denoted by $i = 1, 2,..., a$ in order of selection. Similarly, the b levels of factor B are selected at random from $J = 1, 2,..., B$, and are denoted by $j = 1, 2,..., b$. The treatment combination formed by the level of factor A corresponding to i, and the level of factor B corresponding to j, is replicated n times and the experimental units to which the abn treatment combinations are applied are selected at random from a population of U

experimental units. Assume that the observation on the kth replication of combination (i, j) is

$$y_{ijk} = \mu + \sum_I a_I^i \alpha_I + \sum_J b_J^j \beta_J + \sum_I \sum_J a_I^i b_J^j \gamma_{IJ} + \sum_K s_K^{ijk} \epsilon_K,$$

where the random variables a_I^i, b_J^j and s_K^{ijk} are such that $a_I^i = 1$ if i corresponds to I, $= 0$ otherwise; $b_J^j = 1$ if j corresponds to J, $= 0$ otherwise; and $s_K^{ijk} = 1$ if the kth replicate of combination (i, j) is applied to the Kth unit, $= 0$ otherwise; and the fixed constants satisfy

$$\sum_I \alpha_I = \sum_J \beta_J = \sum_I \gamma_{IJ} = \sum_J \gamma_{IJ} = \sum_K \epsilon_K = 0.$$

Put

$$\sigma_A^2 = \sum_I \alpha_I^2/(A-1),$$

$$\sigma_B^2 = \sum_J \beta_J^2/(B-1),$$

$$\sigma_{AB}^2 = \sum_I \sum_J \gamma_{IJ}^2/(A-1)(B-1),$$

and

$$\sigma^2 = \sum_K \epsilon_K^2/(U-1).$$

For the analysis of variance given in the previous Exercise, show that the expectations of mean squares have the following values.

Mean square	Expectation
MS_A	$bn\sigma_A^2 + (B-b)n\sigma_{AB}^2/B + \sigma^2$
MS_B	$an\sigma_A^2 + (A-a)n\sigma_{AB}^2/A + \sigma^2$
MS_{AB}	$n\sigma_{AB}^2 + \sigma^2$
MR	σ^2

(Wilk and Kempthorne, 1955.)

9.8. References

ANSCOMBE, F. J. (1948). The validity of comparative experiments. *J. R. Statist. Soc.* A, **111**, 181–200; discussion, 200–11.

BARTLETT, M. S. (1935). The effect of non-normality on the t-distribution. *Proc. Camb. Phil. Soc.* **31**, 223–31.

BOX, G. E. P., and ANDERSEN, S. L. (1955). Permutation theory in the derivation of robust criteria and the study of departures from assumption. *J. R. Statist. Soc.* B, **17**, 1–26; discussion, 26–34.

CARMICHAEL, R. G. (1937). *Introduction to the Theory of Groups of Finite Order.* Boston: Ginn.

COCHRAN, W. G., and COX, G. M. (1957). *Experimental Designs*, second edition. New York: Wiley.

CRAMÉR, H. (1946). *Mathematical Methods of Statistics.* Princeton University Press.

EDEN, T., and YATES, F. (1933). On the validity of Fisher's z-test when applied to an actual example of non-normal data. *J. Agric. Sci.* **23**, 6–17.

FISHER, R. A. (1925). *Statistical Methods for Research Workers.* Edinburgh: Oliver and Boyd.

—— (1926). The arrangement of field experiments. *J. Minist. Agric.* **33**, 503–13.

FISHER R. A, (1935 a). *The Design of Experiments*. Edinburgh: Oliver and Boyd.

—— (1935 b). Discussion following Neyman *et al.* (1935).

—— and YATES, F. (1953). *Statistical Tables for Biological, Agricultural and Medical Research*, fourth edition. Edinburgh: Oliver and Boyd.

GAYEN, A. K. (1950). The distribution of the variance ratio in random samples of any size drawn from non-normal universes. *Biometrika*, **37**, 236–55.

GRUNDY, P. M., and HEALY, M. J. R. (1950). Restricted randomization and quasi-Latin squares. *J. R. Statist. Soc.* B, **12**, 286–91.

LEHMANN, E. L., and STEIN, C. (1949). On the theory of some non-parametric hypotheses. *Ann. Math. Statist.* **20**, 28–45.

NEYMAN, J., with the co-operation of IWASZKIEWICZ, K., and KOLODZIEJCZYK, ST. (1935). Statistical problems in agricultural experimentation. *Suppl. J. R. Statist. Soc.* **2**, 107–54; discussion, 154–80.

PEARSON, E. S. (1937). Some aspects of the problem of randomization. *Biometrika*, **29**, 53–64.

PITMAN, E. J. G. (1938). Significance tests which may be applied to samples from any populations. III. The analysis of variance test. *Biometrika*, **29**, 322–35.

SCHEFFÉ, H. (1956). Alternative models for the analysis of variance. *Ann. Math. Statist.* **27**, 251–71.

WELCH, B. L. (1937). On the z-test in randomized blocks and Latin squares. *Biometrika*, **29**, 21–52.

—— (1938). On tests for homogeneity. *Biometrika*, **30**, 149–58.

WILK, M. B., and KEMPTHORNE, O. (1955). Fixed, mixed and random models. *J. Amer. Statist. Ass.* **50**, 1144–67.

—— —— (1957). Non-additivities in a Latin square design. *J. Amer. Statist. Ass.* **52**, 218–36.

YATES, F. (1933). The formation of Latin squares for use in field experiments. *Emp. J. Exp. Agric.* **1**, 235–44.

—— (1936). Incomplete Latin squares. *J. Agric. Sci.* **26**, 301–15.

—— (1948). Discussion following Anscombe (1948).

AUTHOR INDEX

A reference in the text or exercises precedes the semicolon; a reference to the source follows it.

SUBJECT INDEX

PRINTED IN GREAT BRITAIN
AT THE UNIVERSITY PRESS, OXFORD
BY VIVIAN RIDLER
PRINTER TO THE UNIVERSITY